Nuclear "aliment"

The Professor
and the
Prime Minister

The Professor
and the
Prime Minister

THE OFFICIAL LIFE OF
PROFESSOR F. A. LINDEMANN,
VISCOUNT CHERWELL

BY

The Earl of Birkenhead

The Riverside Press Cambridge
Houghton Mifflin Company Boston
1962

To Sir Winston Churchill,
my godfather and Prof's friend,
in admiration and affection

Preface and Acknowledgments

I HAVE written this book at the request of Lord Cherwell's brother, Brigadier Charles Lindemann, and my first thanks must be due to him not only for entrusting this work to me, but for his invaluable help throughout its writing. The two brothers were intimate and devoted to one another from childhood until they were separated by Lord Cherwell's death. It will therefore be obvious that Brigadier Lindemann has been able to provide me with information which could not have come from any other source, and I am deeply indebted to him for the kindness and understanding he has shown. Without his assistance it would have been impossible for me to write this book.

Lord Cherwell's character was not an easy one to estimate, and if I have succeeded in any degree in giving a true picture of the man and his achievement it will be due to the fact that I knew him intimately from my childhood onward and that he was for many years a constant visitor in our house. Indeed the last time I saw him there was only two days before his death.

As a lay man I have relied heavily upon the generous advice I have received from distinguished scientists, when referring to Lord Cherwell's scientific achievements. In particular I must thank Professor Derek Jackson for the magnificent contribution he has made to this work. Professor Jackson was an intimate friend of Lord Cherwell's from his Cambridge days, and afterward a member of the brilliant team assembled by him at the

vii

Clarendon Laboratory, Oxford. He has thus an unsurpassed knowledge of the subject, and his affection for Cherwell's memory has led him to devote immense pains and much time to the effort to keep it green.

I am also particularly grateful to Sir Thomas Merton, Professor R. V. Jones, Sir Robert Watson-Watt and Sir George Thomson. All these eminent and busy men have shown infinite patience and kindness in giving admirable answers to my repeated questions.

On the political and economic aspects of Lord Cherwell's life I owe particular thanks to Sir Donald MacDougall and Sir Roy Harrod. Sir Donald was Lord Cherwell's leading assistant in the Prime Minister's Statistical Section working at the heart of wartime administration, and I owe him a profound debt for the generosity with which he has placed his time and wide experience at my disposal amid his multifarious duties as Investment Bursar of Nuffield College, Oxford. Like Professor Jackson he has performed a labor of love for his old chief.

I am also under great debt to Mr. E. J. S. Clarke for his admirable contribution to the chapter describing Lord Cherwell's struggle for the independent Atomic Energy Authority. I also wish to thank Professor T. Wilson for his expert assistance in describing that part of Lord Cherwell's activities which concerned India.

To my secretary Miss Chloe Otto I owe grateful thanks for the courageous manner in which she tackled the great mass of material contained in the Cherwell archives, for typing and retyping the manuscript, and for the efficiency and loyalty she has shown throughout an arduous task.

In writing this book I have not once asked for help in vain, and in this respect must consider myself the most fortunate of authors. I hope that all those who have so kindly contributed will allow me to express my deep gratitude collectively.

I wish most sincerely to thank Lord Balfour of Inchrye, Mr. Douglas Bartrum, Lord Beaverbrook, Professor P. M. S. Blackett, Mr. Robert Blake, Mr. E. Bolton King, Professor Max Born, Sir Maurice Bowra, Colonel E. P. U. Brewer, Sir Norman Brook, Sir Frederick Brundrett, Mr. D. M. B. Butt, Mr. F. E. Cairns, Mrs. D. Carson-Roberts, Viscount Chandos, Sir Winston Churchill, Lady Churchill, Sir John Cockcroft, Mr. C. H. Collie, Mr. John Colville, Mr. R. Craig, Mrs. L. W. S. Cross, Sir Alwyn Crow, Captain C. N. E. Currey, Father Martin D'Arcy, S.J., Viscount De L'Isle, Mr. E. L. Delmar-Morgan, the Honorable Lady Egerton, Sir William Farren, Professor A. H. Gibson, Major F. M. Green, Dr. E. T. Hall, Sir Harold Hartley, Mr. James Harvey, Professor A. V. Hill, Miss Phyllis Hill, Sir Cyril Hinshelwood, Mr. P. V. Hoare, Mr. W. A. B. Hopkin, Lord Ismay, Mr. L. A. Jackets, Major General Sir Millis Jefferis, Sir Melvill Jones, Mr. T. C. Keeley, Mrs. Ian Kirkpatrick, Mr. Leslie Knight, Sir Ben Lockspeiser, Mr. H. L. Lucking, Colonel R. S. Macrae, Dr. D. C. Martin, Sir John Masterman, Mr. W. R. Merton, Mr. H. F. A. Nalson, Sir Edward Paris, Sir William Penney, Mr. R. J. Politzer, Squadron Leader C. A. Rea, Mr. A. P. Rowe, Dr. A. S. Russell, Mr. G. A. L. Rutledge, Mr. P. J. Searby, Mr. Anthony Shaw, Air Vice-Marshal H. N. Thornton, the late Sir Henry Tizard, Lady Townsend, Mr. H. Cobden Turner, Professor F. A. Vick, the Archdeacon of Cardigan (Mr. Richard Ward), Professor H. E. Watson, Sir Charles Webster, Air Commodore J. K. Wells, Mr. C. M. Wright, Professor E. M. Wright, Mr. R. C. Wright, Dr. Stuart Young, Sir Solly Zuckerman.

I would also like to express my appreciation to the following, for permission to quote from private correspondence: Lord Attlee, Mr. R. A. Butler, Professor Dee, Mr. Malcolm Macdonald, Lord Swinton, and Mr. Peter Tizard; for permission to quote from their published works: Sir Robert Watson-Watt (*Three Steps to Victory:* Odhams Press, London; retitled

The Pulse of Radar: Dial Press, New York), Sir Winston Churchill (*The Second World War,* Vols. II and IV: Cassell, London; Houghton Mifflin, Boston), Professor A. V. Hill (poem, "Air Defence," and *The Ethical Dilemma of Science,* Rockefeller Press), and Sir Roy Harrod (*The Prof:* Macmillan, London).

Contents

Illustrations

The Professor
and the
Prime Minister

1

An Arcadian Boyhood

THE CHARACTERS of great men are often conditioned by the experiences of their youth, and many are warped on the threshold of life. Blemishes of disposition, strange freaks of temperament, and aberrations of habit which some might attribute to original sin, may often be traced to a squalid background or a divided home. When a man reaches eminence in life yet appears to be different from others, his reticence more profound, his rancor more enduring, it is tempting to seek a psychological explanation.

No such excuse presents itself in the case of Frederick Lindemann. The good fairies who stood beside his cradle were in generous mood, and showered him with all the blessings that make life delightful: love of parents, ease of circumstance, and an intellectual brilliance that blossomed swiftly like a tropical garden which contained wayward self-sowing flowers. It was his fate in youth never to be brought into contact with the crude realities of life, or to gain insight into the way in which the great majority of people lived. Buttressed against all that was harsh and ungainly in the surrounding world, his scenes in youth were the green hills and lanes of Devonshire where he wandered as a boy, the Orangerie Garden in Darmstadt, the Tiergarten with its flowers and red squirrels in that bygone Berlin where his intellect gained sinew, Homburg, cool and shady with its avenue of lime trees, and Baden-Baden, where his mother took the cure, with its pellucid trout streams, and the Black Forest resinous in the sun.

In one who had spent such an arcadian boyhood, and had never known the melancholy of blighted youth, and who had been so utterly secluded from the spectacle of grief, such peculiarities of character as developed in later life were clearly innate.

The arrival in the world of Frederick Alexander Lindemann on April 5, 1886 at Baden-Baden, where his mother had rented a villa, provided him with a not unreasonable grievance against his parents. The fact that she knew her time was drawing near and yet chose to give birth to him on German territory was a source of lifelong annoyance to Lindemann, being, as he considered, unnecessary and inconsiderate, and for years entailing irritating difficulties over his passport, and even standing in his way when he wished to apply for a commission in 1916. His foreign birth was also to provide ammunition for those who sought to discredit him on the ground of his alien extraction. His birth was registered there by the English Vicar and also at the nearest British Consulate, and his godfather was Monsieur de Chauvin.

His family came from Alsace-Lorraine, and his father, A. F. Lindemann, was born at Langenburg in the Palatinate on May 13, 1846. His mother, Olga, was a forceful and handsome American woman, born in New London (Conn.) in 1851. Her British-born father, whose name was Noble, was a gifted and much-traveled engineer. This lady was a widow when she married Lindemann, with three children, two girls and a boy. By Lindemann she had four more children, three boys and a girl. The three Lindemann sons were highly gifted, although the youngest deviated so strongly from his brothers that he might have been the product of a different family. Charles, the eldest, was a physicist of a promise comparable in his early days to his brother F.A. The third son, James, whom they called Sepi, was a charming devil-may-care spendthrift who lived in a lovely little villa overlooking Villefranche Harbor, a boon companion whose arrival was eagerly awaited in Paris and Riviera nightclubs, a wonderful linguist and a sore trial to his brothers. The sister first married Noel Vickers, who was killed at Loos, and who had been liked by F.A. It was her second marriage to a Mr. Ian Kirkpatrick of whom he disapproved which led to a complete estrangement between him and his sister which lasted for forty years.

In this bleak episode may be clearly discerned one of the most notable aspects of Lindemann's character, the persistence with which he could nourish a grievance, real or imaginary. The ruthlessness with which he cut his younger brother and sister out of his life shows, too, another permanent weakness, an iron rigidity in his judgment of character. From the beginning a man to him was either black or white, and there were no intermediate colors. Those upon whom he frowned were as incapable in his eyes of a right action as those whom he loved were of wrong. To the latter he extended an affection and loyalty as unswerving as his enmity, splendidly invulnerable against worldly misfortune, thus dividing his acquaintances into two simple categories — those who were for him and those who were against him.

He was brought up in an atmosphere of wealth and ease. His father and mother had an income of about £20,000 a year, in those days a great sum. A. F. Lindemann built waterworks in two towns in Rhenish Bavaria in the Palatinate, Speyer and Pirmasens. A man of enterprise who was prevented from becoming an explorer only by an attack of typhoid, he was also concerned with the making and laying of early Atlantic cables. He came to England when a young man of about twenty, became naturalized, and remained there for the rest of his life.

F. A. Lindemann, both as a boy and a young man, enjoyed the immense advantage while his brilliant mind was maturing of a father who was a scientist himself, and an amateur astronomer of sufficient renown to have a minor planet named after him — No. 828 Lindemannia. With a deep love of his father, which remained steadfast until death, went a sincere respect for his scientific gifts, and it was their greatest mutual pleasure to discuss the problems with which he was grappling. His debt was indeed profound, but it also seemed to the father the fulfillment of all his wishes when he realized the turn his son's mind was taking. The father believed, in the arresting phrase of the Kaiser, that "mathematics and physical science have shown mankind how we may force the door of God's stupendous workshop," so that there was no fear that the son's ardent aspirations would like many others expire in the hiss of a cold douche.

The head of the family was A. F. Lindemann's uncle, Chrétien Philippe Adolphe, Comte et Baron de Lindemann, who settled in Paris, married the wealthy Mademoiselle Fabre of the shipping family, and was created Comte de Lindemann and also a Bavarian baron.

His son Charles was a notable swordsman and was A. F. Lindemann's first cousin. This Count Charles de Lindemann adopted F.A.'s brother Charles as *légataire universel,* and Charles inherited his fortune and properties when he died in 1929. The Count was a well-known figure in Paris, and for many years amateur champion at foils, and the Prix Lindemann is still contested annually by professional fencers. Charles spent most of his youth with him and passed his time most agreeably as the Count hunted in Leicestershire, shot in France and Scotland, kept a stable of steeplechasers and went to the theater nearly every evening when in Paris. The family tomb containing four Lindemanns is in Passy cemetery.

The father handed over to each of his sons two-thirds of the inheritance they would receive on his death. The elder brothers prudently invested their shares while Sepi, believing that money was there to be spent, quickly dissipated his on the Riviera. This droll creature, grossly spoiled by his mother as the baby of the family, exercised an irresistible charm on all who met him, except his brother F.A., to whom Sepi's extravagance, womanizing, and incorrigible idleness were an outrage, and who regarded him as a waster, a libertine, and a disgrace to the family.

Sepi's antics, which made everyone else laugh, he observed with contempt — such as the possession of two Rolls Royces, one white and driven by a Negro, and the other black, driven by an albino. In a long and intimate friendship with F. A. Lindemann I heard him make no single reference to his younger brother.

Many years later he was to have cause to regret this lofty attitude when he heard of Sepi's gallantry in the Second World War. Owing to his remarkable command of French he was credited with repeated visits to France for Intelligence purposes at the risk of his life. In the end he died of heart failure soon after the war, overexerting himself felling trees. When a contrite F.A. asked Charles why Sepi had never told him of his War service, Charles replied: "You should be the last person to ask that." With the sister and younger brother estranged, F.A. and Charles, with mutual respect and shared tastes, became and remained throughout life intimate and devoted.

At the age of ten, F.A. was entrusted to tutors. The first was a Swiss Socialist called Dessin, who was followed by Rosenstock from Oxford, an ornithologist and naturalist. He was next, at the age of thirteen, sent to a school in Scotland called Blair Lodge, his parents having a high opinion of the headmaster, Cooke-Gray. Mrs. Lindemann was inclined to take important decisions of this kind for personal reasons, and also to use her children as guinea pigs to test her theories in dietetic experiments to which she herself would have been the last to submit.

By the time he arrived at Blair Lodge his character had begun to form, and some of the traits which were afterwards so notable began to emerge. He was secretive and sensitive and felt a deep fear of others discovering anything about him that might make him ridiculous. He lived in constant dread that the pet name "Peach" by which his parents addressed him might be discovered and shame him. One of the worst of teases himself, he winced when teased by others, and his mother was particularly successful in probing for his most sensitive points, under the mistaken impression that it would do him good. He detested the kilt which was worn at Blair Lodge, and attempted to become a lance corporal in the cadets, which would have released him from wearing what he thought a humiliating and effeminate garment.

The school prepared cadets for Sandhurst and the army, and sometimes won the Spencer Cup at Bisley for rifle shooting, using the Lee-Metford rifle, and F.A. became a fair rifle shot. He and Charles made a series of toy brass cannon which they fired, using black powder fired, by a wax match in the touch hole and a hammer to strike the match. Afterwards a photographer of the highest class, he was already interested in the art, keeping his chemicals in a gin bottle from which the man who tidied the rooms once took an incautious swig. He learned golf at Blair Lodge, one of the solaces of his later life when forced to give up tennis, and he won several medals and was adroit in avoiding school by playing with the masters.

Peculiarities in his eyesight were already apparent. He was long-sighted in one eye and short-sighted in the other, sometimes wearing a monocle to be funny. It is remarkable that in spite of this strange optical condition he was later to play first-class tennis and to pass the medical examination in order to become a pilot. He obstinately refused to wear spectacles and preferred to rely on a magnifying glass. Spectacles excited his terror of the ridiculous, and he refused throughout his life to wear a wrist watch on the ground that it was effeminate.

He had already at Blair Lodge an incredible memory and facility for figures, being able to memorize a page of them, and up to 30 points of decimals, and his powers of lightning calculation were later to become legendary. As a boy he used this power of memory as a parlor game, reciting endless statistics about dull subjects, such as donations to cottage hospitals, published in the press, remembering every figure and pretending that he was mind reading.

That he was not unhappy at Blair Lodge and that his enthusiasms were those of an ordinary small boy can be seen in a letter he wrote to his parents at the time. The only significant difference between him and the others was that his mathematical genius and uncanny sense of figures were already precociously developed, and that he had already begun to use a slide rule, an instrument which remained a characteristic part of his everyday equipment to the end of his life.

DEAREST PAPA,

I am getting on pretty well with my work being top of my arithmetic, Algebra and Euclid forms. I ought easily to be top for the term if I can keep it up. The boy who used to be top of the arithmetic form hates me and is always trying to do me a mischief, but lately when there was a proper fight I seized him by the throat and flung him under the lockers and he has been quite decent since except when I can't hit him and am wrestling with other boys. My slide rule is the only one in the school and all the small boys wonder what it is, except the big boys who do not properly understand it. One of the masters wants me to lend it to him to show to his class. On Saturday there was a cricket match against the Edinburgh Academy. First Ellborough and Mitchel (cheery Mitchel is his nickname) went in and were in a good time till Mitchel was caught for 18 runs to him and 38 to Ellborough. Then Scott I but was bowled for 49 runs. Then a boy called Cheadle who made 13 not out. Ellborough's total was 113 not out. The Blair Lodge side retired and went out to field with a total of 203 runs. Mitchel I was put wickets and Thorburn I to bowl. However they could not do much till Ellborough went wickets and in a short time they were stumped and 3 caught for 109 runs.

I have got about 30 new stamps and the same number of post-cards for about 10 of my stamps. It will not be very long to the holidays now, only about 4½ weeks and the time passes very quickly here with so much to do. It will be fine to go to Schlangenbad first and as we have from July 27th to October 1 we might go to Blankenberge afterwards. With love from C.L. and myself I remain

Your affectionate son
F.A.L.

P.S. C.L. got the boy who hates me one time and has made his nose bleed and a good job too. He is always threatening to fight but it never comes off.[1]

He was given a severe dose of religion at Blair Lodge, being obliged to attend four Sunday services, and this excessive worship merely led him to eat chocolates when he was supposed to be praying. It is unlikely that he received much spiritual quickening from his parents, his father being a Roman Catholic of tepid enthusiasm, more interested in the constellations than the breviary, and his mother a non-proselytizing member of the Church of England.

Charles Lindemann denied that he and his brother were anticlerical, since as young men they "thought that Church was a good way to keep people in their proper place and a pillar of Conservatism."

This deplorable admission was an oversimplification of Lindemann's attitude, and his brother added:

I do, however, remember that as the physical conception of the universe became more complicated instead of more compre-

[1] Lindemann archives.

hensible, F.A. did sometimes say: "Well, when the going gets *too* hard we've always religion to fall back on, and divine intervention helps to explain the problems that are still insoluble." The Victorian scientists made such gigantic progress in such an incredibly short time that they became irritatingly cocksure of themselves. Conclusions that never lasted long were jumped at and propounded almost daily. Then he would say: "But just you try to explain how this and that and the other comes about. The nearer we get to fundamentals the farther we are from our problem. Sometimes I dream that I can see the entire basis of the universe in a perfectly simple and obvious form, but when I wake up I can only find it's vanished." This last observation struck me very much and I've never forgotten it. It's a pity he was so touchy about religion but it's quite explicable as our father, who came of a long line of devout Catholics, had married a Protestant and brought up his children as Anglicans to please our mother.

He was also known to have said that in spite of the persecution of scientists, such as Galileo, by the Inquisition, which retarded the advance of science for centuries, he admired the way the Catholic Church kept its members in order, made them toe the line, and did not allow "any Tom, Dick or Harry to invent a religion of his own."

When at Blair Lodge he discovered that he had a permanent high temperature, one degree above normal, and was fond of organizing epidemics by hanging upside down for ten minutes with other boys, after which they were all taken to the sanatorium with high temperatures. The dogged courage he always showed in later life was already apparent, and after much agonized vomiting on the Ostend boat in the holidays he was heard to mutter bravely: "Three more trips to the side will see me through."

His mother's interest in dietetic experiments caused her to do him a great disservice in boyhood which was to plague him for the rest of his life. There was at the time in fashion a cult of vegetarianism, and the Lindemann parents in an unfortunate moment decided to bring up the boys as vegetarians. This they found easy at home but an intolerable nuisance when traveling, and the parents decided to abandon the experiment. Charles readily turned to a normal diet, but F.A., both through obstinacy and because he had become repelled by the thought of eating animal flesh, refused to change, said that meat made him sick, and remained a vegetarian for the rest of his life.

What his food lacked in nutriment he compensated for by eating large quantities of eggs, butter and milk and relied heavily on olive oil for the mayonnaise sauces which were his great delight and which he poured in sickening profusion over his eggs. Hostesses were later irritated at periods of egg shortage by the fastidious manner in which he removed the yolk, presumably because it contained the germ of the chicken, and ate only the white, and some of the more astute defeated this habit by serving him the eggs scrambled.

In spite of this diet, his stamina was by no means impaired, at least in youth, and he was robust enough to stand a five-set tennis match in first-class company, but he was worried by the difficulties of dining out, when he had either to warn his friends and cause them unnecessary trouble, or eat nothing. These eccentricities were to present a real problem in the Second World War when eggs and olive oil were unprocurable and he was forced to live for long periods on a semistarvation diet. This malnutrition had a deplorable effect upon his health and may well have been a contributory cause of his death.

Two of Lindemann's indefensible prejudices appeared early: his abhorrence of Negroes and his aversion from Jews. Both tendencies, odious in the eyes of most people, were instinctively felt, but they were disastrous views to hold in the era in which he lived. His dislike of colored people was by far

the stronger of the two. They filled him with a physical re-
vulsion which he was unable to control, although his mother
was fond of them and told the children stories of her black
mammy from the South. He remembered that in childhood
he had been afraid of a Negro toy, and when his parents
teased him about his fears, he said: "I will sleep with lion,
sleep with tiger, sleep with bear, but not with little Negro."
The dreaded toy was a doll with a Negro's head. It was
dressed like the slaves of the plantations in the Southern states.
It carried a tray with fruits which opened to show a white
mouse, a couple waltzing, and a hideous monkey's head, an
object of terror to the child. He later told Charles that he
often thought that his distaste for Negroes began with that
toy. The phobia was in any case a strong one, and when his
parents thought of buying property in Jamaica he said there
were too many Negroes, and that it was not safe.

Lindemann's dislike of Jews and the sneers which he sometimes directed against the Jewish people led many to suppose
that he must be a Jew himself. How foolish he was to allow
himself to be accused of an unworthy prejudice which was
never more than skin-deep. In Berlin he had come into contact
with many brilliant Jews whom he had admired, and when the
Hitler persecution began he went to Germany and persuaded
some of the greatest Jewish physicists in Europe to join him
at the Clarendon Laboratory. With all these men, as we shall
see, he remained on terms of admiration and affection, and Professor Simon in particular became a lifelong friend.

That Lindemann was a Jew was, however, an opinion which
found wide acceptance among his enemies and was lent a certain plausibility by his name and his cast of feature. His
brother Charles was flabbergasted when he read in Sir Roy
Harrod's book[1] of the prevalence of such rumors and made a
spirited denial:

[1] Sir Roy Harrod, *The Prof*.

There is not a shred of foundation for the belief that F.A. was a Jew or had Jewish blood. I had never been so surprised as when I read this. I had no idea of any such rumour. I think it is unlikely that F.A. knew of it as I'm sure he'd have taken steps to put the record straight. Our Catholic family records go back to 1600 and there was not even a Protestant, let alone a Jew, in our family until our father married our Protestant American mother, who refused to give any undertaking about her children's faith. This caused a good deal of annoyance in the family, who considered we should all have been baptised in the Catholic faith instead of the Anglican. F.A. was certainly sensitive on this subject and wouldn't discuss it. Had there been any suspicion of Jewish blood I'd never have been allowed to marry into the de Lagotellerie family, but nobody in Paris could possibly entertain such an idea if of sound mind. F.A. was not agreeable to Jews when young, and our father was by no means enthusiastic about them; but when a lot of the best scientists were persecuted by Hitler F.A. was indignant about it and did all he could to help them.[1]

Did F.A. know of these suspicions? Certainly he did when he was an Oxford professor, as is shown by a letter he wrote to a member of the Oxford Union who had written with some boldness asking for confirmation of the fact that he had Jewish blood:

Oct. 30, 1936.

I thank you for your card of October 27. In reply to your question I can state categorically that I am not a Jew and do not number any Jews amongst my ancestors. I cannot understand how such a rumour was started; it may have been because I gave some eminent Jewish scientists, who had been compelled to leave Germany, an opportunity to continue their researches in my laboratory.

[1] Brigadier Lindemann to author.

He was not unhappy at Blair Lodge, but counted the days until he could go home to the place he loved. This was Sidholme, near Sidmouth in Devonshire, a large, opulent Victorian mansion which had belonged to the Earl of Buckinghamshire and been bought from him by Mrs. Lindemann's first husband, Davidson, afterwards becoming her property.

F.A. felt for Sidholme that deep affection which is the peculiar property of childhood experience. Sidmouth is still one of the least spoiled of English watering places with its uncrowded sunny esplanade, its cricket field and the same boardinghouses that existed in the days of his childhood, now a little shabby and down at heel like genteel people who have come down in the world.

At the end of the front by the little harbor where the fishing smacks lie, the river Sid ends its journey and flows into the sea. The country round Sidmouth which he came to know so well was that placid Devonshire mixture of rolling hills and downs, well wooded and the grass a lush emerald green, broken by patches of moorland suggesting Scotland or Yorkshire with their heather, and gorse brassy with color in the spring.

The seacoast, wild and desolate when the winter gales beat upon it, was in summer a place delightful and exciting to explore, with its long ebb and flow of the tide leaving strange creatures stranded in the sea pools, and its red crumbling cliffs which gave perilous footholds to the climber.

Sidholme, with its ugly luxury and wealth of heavy mahogany furniture, might well be taken as a symbol of Victorian prosperity. Downstairs in the Lindemanns' day was a grand living room, its walls lined with books, where their mother sat at her desk writing letters. Outside the living room she kept doves in a wired-in veranda, and, in another small room off the hall the walls were covered with peacocks' feathers. At the top of the stairs on the nursery floor was a gate to prevent the children falling downstairs. This F.A. would shake with rage and scream by the hour when imprisoned behind it when his nurse went downstairs for her tea.

Many memories of childhood came back to the eldest son when he made a sentimental journey to these scenes of his youth. In the great music room with its painted walls and ceiling and organ, built by the Earl of Buckinghamshire, after a quarrel with the vicar, with the intention of holding religious services there, he had remembered Paderewski, an old friend of the family, practicing. There was the back entrance to the house and the back stairs up which F.A. and Charles hauled the butler when he returned drunk from Torquay, after taking them to the regatta, F.A. carrying the butler's bowler hat.

Outside was the garden on which much loving care and expense were lavished, a large garden built on a gradient and straggling uphill with little paths winding among the rhododendron bushes to the old iron railings and hedge, beyond which lived a kindly doctor interested in the Lindemanns' science, a stalwart with whom the elder Lindemann had once swum three miles in a rough sea.

In this garden azaleas, hydrangeas and magnolias as well as rhododendrons blossomed in their seasons. There was a fine cedar, an old walnut tree now dying, and two linden trees planted to mark the births of Charles and his brother. Outside in the stableyard was the woodshed where they went ratting, earning twopence a rat, and hard by, their father's laboratory divided into a workshop and chemical and physical departments. The father had also built an observatory at the top of the garden, which he gave to Exeter University on leaving Sidholme after his wife's death in 1927. The laboratory was a mysterious and fascinating place to the two boys, and entry to it was a valued privilege, so that the father's threat to his sons was not that they could not ride, sail or fish, but that they could not go into the laboratory.

It was in this laboratory that F.A. who, contrary to general belief, was in his youth an admirable practical experimenter, later made the "Lindemann glass" in his early twenties. The glass was designed as a window on X-ray tubes; F.A. propounded the theory and he and Charles made the glass together. It was soon evident that he had hit upon a discovery of real commercial promise, and his father shrewdly advised them to sell the patents there and then before one of the big firms learned to make better glass.

They refused to consider this suggestion as they wished to keep their discovery to themselves, and argued that it would not be supplanted as their glass was transparent to X rays because it was made of the three elements, lithium, beryllium and boron, which come immediately after the gases in atomic weight. They afterwards bitterly regretted having rejected their father's advice when the General Electric Company discovered a way of producing X rays in such massive quantities that the transparency of the glass no longer mattered.

Other memories of bygone days came back to Charles Lindemann. He recalled their riding and tennis and golf, and, strange as it seemed afterwards, that F.A. was fond of horses and riding until he was eighteen. Other old landmarks revived memories of youth — the fortress home on the cliff of Captain Jemmett, their friend and hero, with "Jacob's ladder," the steps leading down to the sea. Their admiration for Captain Jemmett was unbounded, a splendid old sea dog with stories of the Seven Seas he had sailed, and lingering round him the romance of distant places. Dressed in sailor suits, they listened to the old man enthralled. "Don't hang about," he told them. "Get out. Go to sea." He rang the watches on a ship's bell on the roof of his house.

There was the recollection, when the tide was out and delicate shells lay on the beach and starfish were stranded in the pools, of fishing with hand nets on the rocks for prawns, which their mother loved, and sometimes a small lobster or a conger eel, and of scaling the red cliffs to the summit, a dangerous game on those treacherous slopes. There was the old stone bridge over the river Sid within sound of the weir, where they fished dry fly for trout in a stream elder-shaded and girt by willows, and speared eel for their tutor, F.A. attending for the ginger beer which accompanied the expedition, but so excited when his brother hooked two fish simultaneously that he leaped into the water.

How characteristic it was that when his self-consciousness had begun to exert its morbid grasp upon him he should pretend to forget this episode, saying: "You do exaggerate. I can't remember." It was his later irritating habit to be unable to see merit or skill in any pursuit which he did not himself enjoy.

But these inhibitions were of later growth; in his boyhood in Devonshire, apart from the laboratory, he led a country life, happy in the delights for which he was afterwards to express contempt — ratting, bolting rabbits with ferrets, trying to shoot wild pheasants with his friend Jack Tyrell on Peak Hill; walking all day on that superb sweep of open country from Muttersmoor to High Peak, and riding ponies on the moor and, when they became too big for them, hirelings; swimming great distances in the sea to the delight of his father and the anxiety of his mother.

His pleasure in the life of the country at this time is also shown by his relations with the large and delightful family of Bryces, who lived near Sidmouth. Old Bryce was an adventurous Englishman who had made a fortune in South America, married into the Candamo family and fathered a host of athletic children. His wife was a Peruvian lady of striking Latin beauty. A close but competitive friendship existed between the Bryce and Lindemann families, and there were often tennis matches between the boys watched anxiously by their parents, prolonged until twilight fell. The Lindemanns sent the Bryces a pair of peacocks as a token of friendship, which at once returned fifteen miles across country to their old home. Characteristic of his father's methods was the gift to Sepi of a motor car. Mr. Lindemann had it taken to pieces in the garage, and Sepi was told that he could have it if he put it together. They spent a whole holiday assembling the car and made it go.

Like many physicists, F.A. had a strong musical twist, and music played a great part in the life of the Lindemann family, the parents attending the opera and all the good concerts within reach. With more assiduous practice F.A. could have been a pianist in the first rank, and he must have been captivated by the genius of Paderewski.

By fostering his piano-playing the parents provided him with a wonderful solace for the tribulations of life, and in moments of bitterness and grief he would turn to the instrument he loved. They did him a great disservice by planting in his mind their own contempt for all forms of modern music.

This prejudice hardened as he grew older, until he came to the conclusion, invulnerable to argument, that no music of real consequence had been written since Bach. References to Stravinsky, de Falla, Prokofiev or Ravel drew contemptuous sneers. Debussy he regarded as the crowning joke of the century. He was later fond of relating how he had put a roll wound the wrong way round on the pianola at Blenheim Palace, and persuaded the audience that it was one of the master's less lucid pieces. It was useless to argue with him that these composers were no longer considered *avant garde*. His mind was closed. In music, apart from Bach, who appealed to his mathematical sense, and Wagner's easier operas such as *The Flying Dutchman, Tannhäuser* and *Lohengrin,* he liked melody, Offenbach's *Tales of Hoffmann,* Chopin, Mendelssohn and Johann Strauss.

When Mrs. Lindemann died, the property in Devonshire passed to her son by her first marriage, Gilbert Davidson, and that caused a family dispute about the house, as Davidson sold it with its contents after his mother's death. F.A. was deeply affronted and said: "I will never speak to any of them again," and he kept his word, showing once again the length of time for which he could sustain a grievance.

It is unlikely in any case that A. F. Lindemann would have wished to linger on at Sidholme. The place had become oppressive and charged with melancholy for him after his wife's death. She was buried nearby at Salcombe with her first husband. It was with relief that he decided to make a complete break with the past and to live at a house called The Heights at Marlow. There was a marsh between The Heights and Thames where a hundred and twenty bird species were said to have been counted, and where snipe drummed, observed by F.A. through binoculars. He constructed a piece of broomstick with two snipe feathers attached, which he whirled round in an effort to explain the snipe's "drumming," and which admirably reproduced this unique sound, and lent his ever-ready ingenuity to the making of fishing flies in order to delight and astonish his fisherman brother Charles.

2

A Continental Education

AFTER SPENDING three years at Blair Lodge Lindemann began his continental education in 1902, and it is interesting to speculate how he would have developed had he been given an English public school and Oxford upbringing. We may be sure that his brilliant impact on the scientific world would have been less impressive and his emergence longer delayed, since Germany was, at the beginning of the century, the center of scientific research, and any young man who was given access to her professors and laboratories started with a tremendous initial advantage.

The Lindemann parents were persuaded by an old friend in Darmstadt, an eminent chemist, to send their son to the Lyceum, or Real Gymnasium, an admirable school where, in addition to teaching of a high class, he found ample opportunities for tennis, which had by now become the passion of his leisure hours. It was in this school that he learned German, but found it difficult to master the German pronunciation of Latin. He was an adequate Latinist, and had won a prize for it at Blair Lodge, although he came afterward to ridicule the study of the classics, as he did anything else at which he did not excel.

He moved, at the age of eighteen, to the Scientific Polytechnical High School in Darmstadt, the Hochschule. His scientific insight and practical talent were at this point precociously evident in his search for a glassy material to be used for making windows which might be transparent to X rays. The fact that ordinary glass, made of soda and silica, was opaque to this novel kind of radiation was a serious difficulty in the design of X-ray equipment. Lindemann argued on theoretical grounds that a material made of the oxides of beryllium, boron and lithium should be more suitable. The development of this Lindemann glass, begun at Darmstadt, was successfully completed at his father's laboratory in Devonshire. It is typical of Lindemann's technical foresight that this glass has only recently become a standard component of commercial X-ray tubes.

At Darmstadt was the main residence of the Grand Duke Ernst Ludwig, whose sister married the Czar, and who was a grandson of Queen Victoria and son of Princess Alice. He took a benevolent interest in the Lindemann boys and encouraged their tennis, and it was gratifying for the young men to find themselves playing with the Kaiser and the Czar on the courts of the Grand Duke's beautiful castle, Wolfsgarten, near Darmstadt. In those days, and long after, there were no tennis coaches, but in spite of this handicap they were soon playing in tournaments, F.A. developing a strong forehand drive, a fine overhead game and uncanny anticipation at the net.

Proof of his courage and quick temper was the fact that he and his brother challenged a man to a duel. He was not seeking a student duel, which is governed by elaborate rules, but a fight to the death. It was to have been a contest with pistols, and seconds had already been appointed. He was spoiling for a fight, being angered by the tendency of Germans to pick quarrels with foreigners while relying on their own immunity from the risk of a duel. When the author of the insult discovered that the other side meant business, he sent an unqualified letter of apology, thus closing an episode which might have had tragic consequences.

After distinguishing himself at the Hochschule F.A. pro-

ceeded to Berlin where he was accepted by the renowned physicist, Nernst, into his Physikalisch Chemisches Institut and took
his Ph.D. in 1910. His name was already known to Nernst,
a friend of A. F. Lindemann, who had spoken highly to him
of his son's abilities. He was accompanied to Berlin University
by Charles.

By that time Berlin had grown to be one of the world's great
centers of physical science. It was the city in which Max
Planck had put forward his doctrine of the Quantum Theory
in 1900, and to which Einstein had migrated after his historic
work on the "Brownian motion," the theory of light and the
special theory of relativity. Nernst's work was in many ways
an essential complement to those more widely known developments. This succession of great discoveries gave a characteristic flavor to the scientific work of Berlin at the beginning of
the century, and its influence is plainly to be seen in Lindemann's personal contribution to science.

The atmosphere was one of great excitement. By 1910 it had
seemed that the inconsistencies and contradictions in physical
science which had become painfully apparent at the end of
the nineteenth century were now quickly to be resolved.
Planck's Quantum Theory, for instance, had shown that energy, like matter, had a kind of atomic structure. Thus he had
shown that when hot bodies rid themselves of some of their
energy by radiation this is done not by the continuous loss of
energy but by the flinging off of discrete packets of energy —
the entities which Planck called "quanta." The other side of
this coin, as Planck and his colleagues were quick to recognize,
was that when objects are made hotter by some process, this
represents the accumulation in them of similarly discrete packets of energy or quanta. Thus Planck had done more than
merely explain the pattern of radiation of heat from hot objects, which had been his original goal. He had also prepared
the way for the revision of the Newtonian concepts of mechan-

ics and of matter which have been the preoccupation of physicists ever since.

The work of Nernst's laboratory was a part of this picture
because it centered on a detailed and systematic study of the
way in which heat could be stored in ordinary materials in just
those circumstances where the atomistic character of energy
was evident. In practical terms this entailed a study of the
"specific heat" of different materials at very low temperatures.
For the specific heat of material, which is the amount of heat
needed to increase the temperature by a very small fixed
quantity, is a guide to the capacity of the material for storing
energy. Low temperatures were important because, from
Planck's point of view, only small numbers of quanta of energy should be present in materials so that the individuality of
separate quanta should be more readily apparent.

Nernst himself, from conservations of chemical equilibrium
in the gaseous and solid states, had been led to the formulation in 1906 of his Heat Theorem, the "Third Law of Thermodynamics," his most important contribution to science. This
postulated that at absolute zero of temperature all substances
would reach a state of complete order, without any of the
chance variations due to molecular motion which occur at ordinary temperatures, or, as would now be expressed, at absolute
zero all substances would have zero "entropy." These postu-
lates were closely tied up with other properties, such as specific
heat, and Nernst's laboratory was actively engaged in intense
research in these directions at the lowest temperatures available. It followed also as a consequence of the Third Law that
no practical device for lowering the temperature of a material
could ever cool it quite to the absolute zero of temperature,
however close to this it were possible to go.

Unlike the work of Planck and Einstein, Nernst's law was
quickly and openly disputed and its truth was not eventually
confirmed until the thirties. In the event Planck and his stu-

dents were almost exclusively engaged on the collection of whatever information could be made to bear on the validity or otherwise of the Third Law of Thermodynamics, and the predominant task here was the measurement of the specific heat of a wide variety of materials. Sir George Thomson has recalled[1] how Lindemann in later life expressed his admiration for the way in which "Nernst swung the whole effort of his co-workers on this when it began to show striking results, abandoning some quite promising experiments."

The atmosphere of scientific Berlin at the beginning of the century, its excitement and expectation, the sense of long-accepted principles about to die, and of new fundamental theories being born to replace them is vividly caught in the words of Mr. C. H. Collie to the author:

1900 Berlin had become one of the great centres of physical science. In particular it nourished the small groups who realised that the foundations of physics were crumbling. This not very welcome belief was based not on the spectacular discoveries in which the times abounded, but on a series of small discrepancies in the rather humdrum data of classical physics. Each discrepancy in isolation could be disregarded as an exception for which a special explanation could be found. Viewed as a whole they pointed inexorably to the downfall of the whole intellectual system which had been built up on Newton's work.

The architects of this intellectual revolution were Planck, the Professor of Theoretical Physics in Berlin, and Einstein, an obscure outsider holding no academic position who earned his living in the Swiss patent office. Nernst, the distinguished Professor of Physical Chemistry, was in sympathy with the impending revolution, having reached similar conclusions from general considerations of chemical equilibrium.

The most immediate crucial test of the new views lay in increasing the heat capacity of the elements of low temperature.

[1] Biographical Memoirs of Fellows of The Royal Society.

It is difficult now to realise what an act of faith was required to embark on these very difficult measurements. It had all the appearance of a completely retrograde step; a return to studying matter at very low energies when all the new exciting discoveries (x-rays, radioactivity, relativity) were being made by going to higher and higher energies. Worse still, the measurement of heat capacity was the most humdrum of measurements, well known and despised by every schoolboy. Yet to carry out these simple measurements at low temperatures was a matter which required outstanding technical ability and considerable resources.

Of all the pundits aware of the great importance of the issue only Nernst, head of a great and real experimental institute, had the means at his disposal, and in Lindemann he found a man with the technical skill and courage and singlemindedness to make use of these means.

In the years between 1910 and the outbreak of the war the whole foundations of scientific thought were transformed. The experimental work, without which bold speculation cannot survive in science, was carried out in the main by Nernst and Lindemann in Berlin and Rutherford in Manchester.

The events in Berlin developed Lindemann's character. To form an opinion from a selection of the facts, decide upon a course of action and then to devote the whole of one's resources to carrying it out even if one has to battle against the stream of contemporary opinion became second nature to him.

Charles Lindemann still retains warm recollections of the character and genius of Nernst, then, with his colleague Planck, the propounder of the Quantum Theory, at his prime:

He was very fond of F.A., and I should say he was his outstanding pupil. He liked me because I helped to prove experimentally some of his theories, as well as some of my brother's, in low temperature down to 20 absolute.

Nernst was one of the greatest experimental physicists who

ever lived, in the van of the problems of the universe. He was a considerable fundamentalist, but proud of the fact that his father had baptised one of his chief assistants' father, a Dr. Politzer. F.A. and I sometimes wondered about Nernst's beliefs, as he came of an old and devout Protestant family. I need hardly say that we had not the impudence to touch upon the subject with him.[1]

F.A.'s half-sister, now Mrs. Carson-Roberts, remembers Nernst saying that he had had hundreds of able young men through his hands, but that Lindemann was in a class by himself and that he regarded his mind as Newtonian. Nernst was imperturbable in the face of dangerous crises in the laboratory. He "was engaged in a race with Kamerlingh-Onnes of Leiden to liquify helium gas, which was difficult and expensive to procure. He managed to obtain 80 litres through Siemens, whose son was working in the lab, and we had produced a pump with mercury pistons which circulated the gas under pressure and was supposed to be infallible. There was, however, a low spot in the pipes which kept freezing up, and a lab boy was told to keep it warm. Whilst listening to Nernst's account of how he had shot a wild boar over the weekend, the idiot boy got the pipe too hot and the soldered joint blew out. Nernst merely said: 'Gentlemen, all breathe as fast as you can; twenty thousand marks' worth of helium is in the air.' "[2]

A number of able men were also studying at this time under Nernst, men who were to rise to the high rank later and become Dr. A. S. Russell, Professor Max Born, Professor Gibson, Professor Watson and Sir Henry Tizard. The great Einstein himself was also working in Berlin. Nernst was at first irritated by Einstein's Theory of Relativity and said in mock annoyance: "Why, Planck and I engaged him just as you take on a butler, and now look at the mess he's made of physics;

[1] Brigadier Lindemann to author.
[2] Idem.

one can't turn one's back for a minute." This was, of course, before the conclusive eclipse evidence of the Relativity Theory.

Observing this shy genius at close quarters, Lindemann formed an opinion of Einstein's character which he never revised. He saw there the towering intellect which made him for Lindemann the greatest genius of the century, but he saw also a pathetic naïveté in the ordinary affairs of life. Einstein appeared to him to be living in a universe of his own creation, and almost to need protection when he touched the mundane sphere. In all matters of politics he was a guileless child and would lend his great name to worthless causes which he did not understand, signing any ridiculous political or other manifestoes put before him by designing people.

"He would in fact," said Charles, "sign pretty well anything, and it got him into all sorts of scrapes. F.A. liked and admired his scientific achievements a great deal, but had the utmost contempt for him as a navigator through life."

From his Berlin days onward Lindemann had a low opinion of scientists in any activities except their own, and it is possible that this view was based on his experiences with Einstein at Berlin. Nothing angered him more than the assumption that the scientist, on account of his superior knowledge, was the proper person to heal the woes of mankind.

His opinion, strongly held, was that scientists should concentrate on their own work, which they understood and to which they had devoted all their mental powers, and that their incursions into politics were usually ignorant and dangerous. He believed that the art of statesmanship was one that demanded ripe experience and a long novitiate. It was to him axiomatic that a scientist who had spent his youth and maturity at the experimental bench could not at will turn to the problems of government with any hope of offering a coherent opinion, and for the megalomania of certain Marxian scientists holding these views, he felt an icy disdain. It was ironical that he himself was destined to become both a politician and an economist.

What sort of man was the F. A. Lindemann who was now entering Berlin University? He remained clear in the memory of his fellow student, A. S. Russell:

> I worked in Professor Nernst's laboratory in the Bunsenstrasse there from April 1910 till August 1911. During that time Lindemann was there working before and after his Ph.D. He was recognised then as the most distinguished of the researchers working for that degree. He had good ideas in physics; he was a good mathematician as well as a good experimenter. He had also a flair for designing instruments.
>
> We all started work like good little boys at 9 A.M. Lindemann rarely appeared before noon, and rarely stayed after four, but he was known to be a great night-worker. He was always well dressed, often in morning coat. No one ever saw him with his coat off, working, so to speak, at the bench; he directed others in his research. He was then very thin, a tall maypole of a man with dark shiny hair. He spoke German softly in a thin voice with an English accent. Most of us lived in cheap "digs" in Charlottenburg, two miles away. Lindemann lived in one or other of the hotels in Unter den Linden, less than a quarter of a mile away. His staying at the Adlon Hotel there impressed the German element in the laboratory enormously.
>
> He kept aloof from the English and American group in the laboratory as well as from the German but without giving offence. He was always pleasant and helpful when approached but never joined in any extra-laboratory activity.[1]

This account is not entirely borne out by Charles Lindemann. There can at least be no doubt that F.A., then as always, set a high store by his creature comforts. He would say with deep sincerity that danger must be accepted, but that squalor

[1] Dr. A. S. Russell to author.

was horrible and degrading. For this reason, he said, he would always choose the air in time of war, knowing that if he survived he would at least sleep in his own bed. He had been brought up in an atmosphere of wealth and comfortable living, and he shunned the meaner side of life with far more intensity than most men. It was in keeping with his character that he should have chosen the Adlon Hotel even when a student, and his extravagance in doing so was less than would appear as he lived there on an allowance of £600 per annum, which in those days was possible, particularly as he spent so little on food and drink.

Charles Lindemann does not agree with Dr. Russell's description of the indolence of F.A.'s Berlin mornings or his faultless wardrobe: "He had to be in the lab at 8 like any other student. He never wore a morning coat except on formal occasions."

One can only remark that if he regularly began work at 8 A.M. in Berlin it must have been the only period in his life when he did, for he shared with Descartes a distaste for the dawn and a strong appreciation of the comforts of bed in the morning. It is possible that during the Blair Lodge and Darmstadt periods the compulsion to rise at 7 A.M. produced a condition which he never overcame, and which he attempted to neutralize in the holidays by sleeping until lunchtime.

Henry Tizard, later Sir Henry Tizard and a leading scientist, was also one of Lindemann's fellow students. Their intimate friendship at the time is of particular interest in view of their bitter quarrel in later years. The feud between these two unyielding men was, as we shall see, to divide the scientific world and poison their old friendship for ever. It reflects little credit on either party, and the rancorous and wounding remarks made by each about the other are in melancholy contrast with their early friendship.

Nothing but affection is apparent at that time in Lindemann's attitude toward his able colleague. He called him by his initials "H.T.," and was in turn sometimes called "Lindy" by Tizard. They played tennis together, corresponded when apart, and so close were they that Lindemann afterwards stood godfather to Tizard's son. There can be little doubt also that Tizard was instrumental in obtaining for his friend the longed-for Chair of Experimental Philosophy (physics) at Oxford.

Tizard first met F.A. in 1909. He would dine with the Lindemann family at Claridge's when they came to London, remembering the father as a patriarchal figure and the mother as an American woman of great attractions and a strong personality, whose visits to Berlin were a godsend to Tizard, who then knew no German. He recalled with a shudder the dinner parties at Nernst's, beginning between five and six o'clock. At this gruesome hour full evening dress with white ties and tails was obligatory, with the ladies *en grande tenue,* and the sessions were enlivened by cumbersome badinage by the German guests at the expense of the English.

Tizard was irritated on one of these occasions by a German claiming that the English, compared with them, were grossly ignorant of the works of their own poet Shakespeare. Lindemann replied that for that matter the Germans knew little of Goethe and recited a couplet in German, adding, "Come to that, we know more about Goethe than you do." He told Tizard afterward that he had made up the lines on the spur of the moment.

It is possible that certain seeds of doubt about some aspects of Lindemann's character had been planted in Tizard's receptive mind as early as their Berlin University days. Tizard was in the habit of taking exercise in the local gymnasium with an ex-lightweight boxing champion. F.A. had heard about this and went to the gymnasium to watch. At one point he said: "We had better box each other." Tizard, being far more experienced, was able to toy with his opponent, and Lindemann lost his temper, and began lashing out wildly, until the man in charge of the gymnasium intervened.

"This," said Tizard, "gave me my first insight into the other side of Lindemann's character at that age." But in spite of this they remained friends, and when Lindemann was dead and the sands were running out for Tizard himself, and the terrible feud had become an episode of the past, Tizard was to pay a fine tribute to the dead enemy and sometime friend: "He was one of the cleverest men I ever met," he said, "as clever as Rutherford." [1]

We become aware of his first impressions of Berlin in his letters to his father, and it was indeed fortunate for him that he could write about his scientific progress and difficulties to a parent who was technically equipped to understand him.

Berlin, N.W.
Nov. 4, 1908

My dear Papa,

I have started work at the University properly now so I can tell you something about it. The arrangements in the way of "Hörsale," instruments and so on are not nearly as good as Darmstadt, but the professors seem much better. They all strike one as being remarkably young, Planck and Rubens only seem about 45. The "Institute" are all a long way from the University, Physics and Physical Chemistry, Rubens and Nernst down by the Reichstag, Chemistry and Mineralogy, Fischer and Liebisch, out by the Stettiner Bahnhof. Mathematics are in the University itself Unter den Linden up nearly opposite the Schloss . . . "Integralrechnung" is not very amusing but very necessary and well taught once a week the whole hour examples and Prof Landau also gives examples which one can do in the evening, give him next day, and he returns the books corrected next lesson. He is a typical little Jew, about thirty, but is very jolly and amusing and seems to be a very good mathematician. Nernst is very "unscheinbar," small with a big head, bald, with a moustache and a little napoleon. At present his physical chemistry is also very elementary.

I am afraid it was a mistake going in for Fischer's Chemic

[1] Sir Henry Tizard to author.

and Rubens' Physik. You know Emil Fischer of course. I thought his lectures would be more advanced. They are excellent in their way . . . but the lectures are absolutely elementary, the constitution of H_2O and so on, actually for people who know nothing whatever about chemistry. Rubens' physics are the same; he is the best lecturer of any of them, perhaps I should say the best teacher. I find his static electricity quite interesting although of course it is all well known things.

It is generally agreed that the first part of Lindemann's research in the physical science was also the most important, and this is Sir George Thomson's view. It is also borne out by the fact that the pieces of research with which Lindemann's name is still associated date from the first years in Nernst's laboratory.

There, in Berlin, Lindemann first started to work for the degree of Ph.D. His task was to measure the discrepancies between the actual specific heats of materials, especially solids, and the predictions of the classical rule for calculating these usually known as the Law of Dulong and Petit. Instances of specific heats which were lower than those predicted had been known for some time, and in the milieu of Planck, Einstein and Nernst it was recognized that these were probably to be explained in terms of the atomistic character of energy.

Lindemann's success as a graduate student turned at first on his skill as a designer of equipment. During this period he developed a version of an apparatus known as a "calorimeter," which was well designed for measuring small quantities of heat with great accuracy and was particularly suitable for work at very low temperatures, using a very high vacuum as a means of reducing the loss of heat, and using electricity as a means of supplying extremely small and accurately measurable amounts of heat to whatever specimen might be placed inside the calorimeter.

One of Lindemann's fellow students, now Professor Watson,

was struck by the craftsmanship which accompanied this originality in the development of instruments.

> What I remember best, however, was his skill as a glass-blower: we were both very surprised to find that the reputation of Germans for ability in this art applied only to professionals, and the University students never thought of making their own apparatus. Lindemann would often sit down to a blowpipe and at once became the centre of an admiring crowd. His favourite demonstration was making very small vacuum vessels, a comparatively simple but very delicate operation.[1]

The outcome of the examination for the Ph.D. degree does not seem to have been the great distinction which it would have been reasonable to expect. Thus Dr. A. S. Russell, after recalling that Planck and Nernst both recognized Lindemann as a "young man with a great future in physics," goes on to say:

> Oddly enough Lindemann did not get the highest honours when he took his Ph.D. . . . The four classifications are Summa cum laude, Magna cum laude, Cum laude and Rite. There were no written papers for the Ph.D., a viva and the printed thesis. At the viva Lindemann said he often had to answer: "Dass weiss ich nicht," merely because he had been questioned on some part of the wide subject of physics in which he was uninterested. Unless he was vilifying himself, he couldn't have got more than a Cum laude.

The usual story about Lindemann's Ph.D. examination is that most of the professors had one or two standard questions of extreme difficulty which they put to the candidate as a matter of form. These were well known to the average Berlin student and acceptable stock answers were passed on as student

---

[1] Professor H. E. Watson to author.

gossip. Lindemann was in the dark about this side of student life, took questions seriously and replied, *"Dass weiss ich nicht,"* a candid answer which did not impress the examining board.

However this may have been, the research which had gone into the preparation of the Ph.D degree was published, jointly with Nernst, as the first of nearly a score of scientific papers to appear between then and 1924. The bearing of this work on the understanding of how the thermal properties of materials were to be understood in terms of the Quantum Theory was both direct and important.

Most immediately it provided an effective test of the theory which Einstein had developed for describing how the amount of energy stored in a solid would increase with increasing temperature. The starting point for this work had been the assumption that the thermal energy of a solid, which is embodied physically in the mechanical vibrations of its individual atoms, could only be increased by the addition of small quanta of energy as in Planck's Quantum Theory. The actual size of this quantum was supposed to be characteristic of the material. From these considerations Einstein had in 1907 reached the conclusion that the specific heats of solids should become zero at absolute zero.

This prediction was not taken seriously at the time, but in 1911 Nernst and Lindemann working together showed that the Einstein formula was substantially correct, but that there were systematic deviations. They gave a new formula which was the sum of two Einstein frequencies, one double the other. At the same time Lindemann was able to point out that the size of his energy quantum should be related to certain optical properties of the material — yet another example of the way in which the young researchers in Berlin were able to demonstrate the essential unity of physical phenomena.

In his assessment of this work Sir George Thomson has pointed out that the somewhat arbitrary nature of Lindemann's alteration of the assumptions of Einstein's theory was permissible "at a time when the Quantum Theory was still fluid." In the event, however, the Lindemann-Nernst theory was overtaken by a more intricate elaboration of the same principles due to the physicist Debye. It is interesting to note that subsequent refinements of the Debye theory by Blackman have to some extent vindicated the Lindemann-Nernst idea of two characteristic frequencies.

The second important part of Lindemann's work in Berlin was concerned with the relationship between the melting temperature of a solid and certain other of its thermal properties. This again was an attempt to exploit to the full the consequences of the Quantum Theory.

Here Lindemann's starting point was his recognition that the melting of a solid might be set in train when the vibration of its atoms was great enough in its amplitude to cover the gap normally present between neighboring atoms. For then, the argument might have gone, one atom might displace its neighbors from their positions and so break up the ordered arrangement of atoms which is an essential characteristic of solid materials.

But the vibrations of the atoms in a solid are the embodiment of the thermal energy stored in it. Indeed, for simple solids at least, the theory which Einstein had put forward, and which Nernst and Lindemann had modified, made the assumption that all these vibrations took place with the same frequency and that the size of the frequency was related to the size of the quantum of energy characteristic of the solid. On the other hand, the amplitude of these vibrations would increase with the accumulation of energy quanta, and hence with an increase of temperature. Thus it was that Lindemann was able to relate the melting temperature of a solid to the way in which it would accumulate heat with rising temperature and thus to the variation of its specific heat at very low temperatures.

This linking together of thermal properties belonging to relatively high and relatively low temperatures was a dramatic feature of the theory. It is fair to say that the relationships which it expresses are still of some rough practical value as a means of predicting the melting points of solids. However, with the growth of support for Debye's theory, Lindemann's arguments were robbed of much of their intellectual force, while eventually it became apparent that the phenomenon of melting was in any case much more intricate than he had supposed.

Though these two lines of inquiry were outstanding among Lindemann's contributions to science before the first war, they were accompanied by a number of other ideas which foreshadowed future developments of great importance. For example, Lindemann made an attempt to account for the then puzzling fact that the electrons free to move about within metal made no apparent contribution to the specific heat of the whole. He appears to have been one of the first to draw attention to the fact that the mechanical strength of solid materials was not nearly as great as theoretical calculation would suggest it should be. He also devoted some of his attention to the motion of electrons within atoms, and considered some of the problems which Bohr later solved to discover the modification of the Newtonian laws of mechanics demanded by the Quantum Theory.

There are some scientific men who interpret Lindemann's life as divided into two parts: a period of brilliant promise and achievement in Berlin, and, during the First World War, at the Royal Aircraft Establishment, Farnborough, in which his best work was accomplished; and a somewhat desultory and slow decline as Professor of Experimental Philosophy at Oxford, when he was distracted by other new-found interests, social and political, which, combined with a natural indolence, conspired thenceforth against original research.

This view of his work at Oxford is completely false and lamentably belittles his great contribution to Oxford physics. One cannot, however, escape the conclusion that his finest work was done during the first period, and that its brilliant dawn was in Berlin.

After the war, according to Professor Jackson,

> . . . Lindemann did little experimental work himself, although he designed experiments for the research workers in the Clarendon Laboratory, and the younger generation were apt to regard him as more of a theoretical physicist devoid of experimental ability.[1]

The last judgment is, ironically, belied by the fact that the most enduring of Lindemann's contributions to experimental science dates from the period immediately after the war when, in a paper written with his father in 1919, he described the first form of the electrometer for measuring electrical charges and voltages which was developed into a finished instrumental technique in the early twenties. During this period Lindemann was also concerned with a number of astronomical questions, and investigated for the first time the question of how photo-electric cells might be used to improve the performance, and particularly the speed, of astronomical telescopes. This technique is only now, some forty years later, finding its natural place in astronomical research.

Throughout this period Lindemann's scientific work is plainly stamped with his versatility. The same quality determined his more personal influence in physics. On this question, which is clearly of great importance, Professor Jackson writes of the early period:

> Lindemann's enthusiastic acceptance of Planck's quantum theory, and the lucidity with which he was able to explain its success in predicting and explaining phenomena far removed

[1] Professor Derek Jackson, F.R.S., to author.

from the distribution of energy in the continuance spectrum at the most important conferences of physicists at this time, played a large role in the general acceptance of the quantum theory.

Indeed his success in conference was one of his more important achievements, a fact which cannot be realised by studying his published papers. Consequently a generation of physicists, who neither attended these conferences nor had the chance of talking with the leading physicists of that time (Einstein, Planck, Sommerfeld, Born, Rutherford, von Laue, Poincaré, Wien, Jeans, Eddington) have no means of understanding the importance of Lindemann's contribution to physics, and, judging only from his published papers, they are apt to wonder why his reputation as a physicist stood so high among the greatest physicists of the first quarter of the century.

Sir George Thomson found in Lindemann a rare and stimulating mind, and one of astonishing versatility:

It was typical of Lindemann's mind to bring together ideas in this way from different branches of physics, in an order-of-magnitude calculation. His mind was unusually lively, and he also had an unusually wide knowledge of physics and what is now called geophysics, even if he sometimes went too far in ignoring the aspects of secondary importance. He was a most stimulating conversationalist on matters of physics, and one went away from a session with him feeling that one had rearranged all one's mental furniture, and added one or two rather bizarre objects to the room.[1]

It should not be thought from this account of Lindemann's scientific achievements in Berlin that he had no time for amusement. He played tennis in the summer, arriving with the prizes he had collected in Darmstadt and adding greatly to

[1] Sir George Thomson, Obituary notice of F.A.L. in *Proceedings of The Royal Society.*

them. Tennis had, by then, become the strongest interest in his life outside his parents and his work, and he and Charles combined so well in doubles that they became known as "the German Dohertys." So seriously did he take the game that he gave up golf, as the opinion of the day held that it was bad for tennis. He became a player in the first class, winning many open tournaments in Germany and becoming at one time champion of Sweden.

It was his habit to play strenuous tennis in a shirt buttoned to the neck, with long sleeves fastened at the wrists, thick, black, ribbed socks and white boots, thus avoiding the revelation of any unnecessary part of his anatomy. A stickler for orthodoxy, he was disgusted when players at last abandoned the constraint of trousers for the freedom of shorts. Arguments that tennis had become a game of great speed and force, and that one would expect a wing three-quarter or a sprinter to be seriously hampered by long trousers, were brushed aside. His passion for the game increased as he improved, and Nernst complained that he got little work out of Lindemann in the tennis season. He was a tactician of the highest order, and in mixed doubles an astute psychologist, his normal chivalry to women being notably absent on the courts.

With his brother he took part in University dances, at home in the stiff ceremonial and heel-clickings, and, no ascetic in youth, was far from ignoring the other sex. His life in Berlin was full of flirtations, and the later accusations of frigidity are in no way borne out by the evidence of this period. Like most of Nernst's protégés, the brothers considered themselves creatures apart from the other students and had little to do with them. Their membership of the Red White and Blue White tennis clubs ensured that they had many agreeable friends who made a point of hospitality to strangers, however snobbish they may have been in electing their own compatriots. These clubs were beautifully equipped both for tennis and for social purposes, and were used as agreeable meeting places even by those who did not play the game. Although the clubs were particular in their choice of members, anti-Semitism as it developed under the Nazis was then unknown, and, besides some Jews, the Red White Club included at least one West Indian Negro in its membership. These were exceptions, and the club consisted largely of court circles and officers. Here the Lindemann brothers played their tennis and discussed international affairs with the Corps Diplomatique.

Then, as later, F.A. was fastidious in indulging his taste in food, and the fashionable restaurants of Unter den Linden took great trouble with *omelette aux truffes,* pancakes, mayonnaise and hollandaise. It was his peculiarity that for months on end he would eat identical meals daily, and it gave his orderly mind pleasure to see waiters at the Esplanade or the Adlon automatically bring his meal day after day. He ate enormous quantities of sweets, having a particular fondness for chocolates filled with brandy and other liqueurs.

It is curious, in view of his terror of the little Negro toy and his strong physical aversion from colored people, that his favorite doubles partner at tennis was a charming West Indian from Barbados, O'Hara Murray. With him he played in many northern tournaments, winning particular distinction in Sweden. In Bonn he played a losing game against the great German player Froitzheim, and Charles heard him muttering urgently: "Buck up. Buck up. This fellow is damned good."

He made up for these long absences from the laboratory by hard work and an amazing assimilative faculty. "He believed," said Charles, "that what we call intelligence was the development of only two faculties which could be used as coordinates; one is memory, the other the associative faculty, without which the former is not much use. A man with only an extreme memory becomes a freak. The one whom everything reminds of something else ends up on the music hall stage as a comic. But when you get someone who has both faculties equally developed you get a Kelvin, a really great intellect."

When the brothers first came to Berlin from Darmstadt they brought with them a housekeeper and maid called Kätchen Weber, whose home was between Darmstadt and Heidelberg on the Bergstrasse. She had studied F.A.'s taste in food and made him delicious dishes — pancakes, egg dishes of all sorts, fried, sautéed and Lyonnaise potatoes, *pain perdu,* omelettes, and salads of lentil, potato and lettuce. Before moving into the Adlon they lived in a comfortable flat in happy bachelor disorder, and were in the habit of bringing back their girls from skating, tennis, and the theater.

"It was not unusual," said Charles, "for them to stay the night. F.A. was usually courting some girl or other. When we moved to the Adlon to be near our work, of course we had to give up this charming promiscuity. I think that, in the continental manner, it never occurred to F.A. that girls were not intended for sleeping purposes."

Why then his notable shyness of intimacy with women at Oxford and his fear of commitment? In his brother's opinion: "When he got to Oxford he was very different. Just as careful to keep any casual affairs dark as he was to conceal his nickname 'Peach.' He used to say: 'Don't joke about it — it would make a terribly bad impression here. In fact, the only grounds a professor can get sacked for are "gross immorality." ' But he was greatly attracted to the opposite sex, though not what I would call a very enterprising suitor. He had a terror of being turned down, and I've always thought that the girls he liked best came more than halfway."

On at least two occasions he wished to marry. At the beginning of his Oxford life he fell in love with the daughter of a family well known in industry whom he greatly admired and whose parents had an estate in Scotland to which he was a frequent visitor. It was there that he was first observed wearing a bowler hat upon the moors. He was frustrated in this courtship by his fatal inhibition, and when Charles asked him if he had definitely proposed, he could only answer weakly: "Well, I gave her to understand . . ." Later, at some time in the early twenties at Oxford, he actually brought himself to propose, in the house of a friend, to a lady who was afterward to become prominent in public life. He was refused. The friends in whose house the proposal took place were distressed to see how stricken he was and what a deep laceration this failure had made in his emotions, for the wound was abiding. It is easy to imagine the struggle with diffidence, like a man screwing up his courage to jump off the Eiffel Tower, that preceded his action. Terrible for him, too, after all this emotional expenditure, must have been the mortification of refusal. It was the kind of effort that can be made once, and once only, by such a man as he, and it is not unreasonable to attribute to it his long avoidance of matrimony. Psychological probings into other causes of this condition are fruitless, and can only amount to speculation. Suggestions that he might have had a latent homosexual strain are to those who knew him wholly without foundation. That long period of celibacy which many found so unnatural and even repellent, did not in his brother's opinion exist. This reputation for frigidity was due to the secrecy with which he surrounded this aspect of his private life. But his desire for marriage had been destroyed, and it may be that he derived from the companionship of the Senior Common Room and the warmth of his friends some emotional coefficient of the relationship he had been too timid to grasp.

In 1911 a notable honor was paid to him when he was invited with his lifelong friend, the scientist Duc de Broglie, to act as co-secretary to the Solvay Conference at Brussels. No greater tribute could have been paid to the brilliant achievements of a young physicist, and it is doubtful whether in the history of science so much genius had been contained within the four walls of a single room.

The young Lindemann sat with Jeans and Rutherford, Nernst, Planck, Einstein, Rubens, Sommerfeld, Wien and Warburg. From Paris came Madame Curie, Poincaré and Langevin. Also taking part in the conference, although not present at its sessions, was Lord Rayleigh. Throughout the conference Lindemann impressed these eminent people, the scientific leaders of the world, with his brilliant ability. As always after an unusual achievement, his reticence permitted no outward sign of elation. We find him writing to his father on November 4, 1911, describing how the conference was set up and his impressions of some of those who took part in it:

Nov. 4 1911.

MY DEAR PAPA,

Many thanks for your dear letter also Mamma for hers. I have been here since Sunday but so busy that I could not write. The enclosed list will tell you who was here. The Council was invited by Mr. Solvay, the inventor of the Solvay sodax process, at the instance of Nernst. Mond worked his English patents for him, and as Solvay and his affiliated companies is supposed to make 9/10 of all the soda in the world he must be "very rich." He is a very nice man unfortunately though with rather liberal views. He did us all very well. I had a nice bedroom and bathroom, and there were two large rooms for the séances. Everyone got a thousand francs handed to them for expenses, and when I protested they said that as secretary I would have a lot to do and must take them. As all the others took it as a matter of course, and as I was the youngest of the lot I could not say very much. . . .

The discussions were most interesting but the result is that we seem to be getting deeper and deeper into the mire than ever. On every side there seem to be contradictions. My melting point formula and my calculation of the photo-effect were about the only things that were not contradicted. When I come over I will bring all the reports with me so that you can look through them. I got on very well with all the people here even with Mme Curie who is quite a good sort when one knows her. I got on very well with Einstein who made the most impression on me except perhaps Lorentz. He looks rather like Fritz Fleischer en mal, but has not got a Jewish nose. He asked me to come and stay with him if I came to Prague and I nearly asked him to come and see us at Sidholme . . . He says he knows very little mathematics, but he seems to have had a great success with them. Lorentz is a wonderful all round man with extraordinarily quick comprehension and also a sense of humour. Sommerfeld seems generally to be considered the best *mathematical* physicist in Germany. I got on very well with him, and promised to visit him when I go to Munich. . . .

With tons of love to Mamma and yourself

Your affectionate son

PEACH

In February 1913 F.A. received an invitation from the American physicist Professor Robert A. Millikan, to lecture on any subject he chose to the University of Chicago in the summer quarter. It was suggested that he should offer a graduate lecture course, four or five hours a week for a fee of five hundred dollars.

Professor Millikan realized that this sum would scarcely defray his visitor's expenses, and in itself could hold no attraction for a wealthy man, but it is possible that he suspected that Lindemann had still no other appointment in view after his studies in Berlin had ended, and hoped to attract him like other gifted Europeans to America.

I realise [he wrote] that there is nothing particularly attractive about this offer itself, but I should hope you might find interesting acquaintances here with some of our American scientific men, and if you are still uncertain as to where your future work may lie, you might be somewhat interested in the acquaintanceships and the connections which might possibly be established in this country.

F.A. decided to accept the invitation. It is probable that he was partly attracted by the fascinating prospect of exploring a new continent, but it may well be that, uncommitted as he was with no immediate post in view, he was also alive to the possible advantages of working in America where he might expect well-endowed laboratories and the latest instruments. Tizard sped him on his way with a breezy, facetious letter:

So you are going to give the Chicago lads a chinwag. Don't you let them jolly you or step on your neck in any way. Give them the glad eye straight away and take your glad rags and a boiled shirt or two with you. (I suppose it wouldn't be really decent to take more than one as a matter of fact.) Also write and tell me how you get on as it ought to be rather amusing. I've half a mind to come out and hear you.[1]

Equipped with a course of lectures on kinetic theories, he set sail in the *Olympic*. A miserable sailor, he was not likely to have been reassured by a telegram from the Duc and Duchesse de Broglie: "*Une pensée des amis de France pour le voyageur. Voeux et sage estomac.*" Their anxiety was unnecessary, for the *Olympic* had a splendid passage. F.A., who in his quiet way had enjoyed shipboard life on the great vessel with its strange cross-section of human beings and its peaceful progress across the ocean, wrote to his father from the ship soon after she had docked in New York:

[1] Cherwell archives.

On board R.M.S. "Olympic"
June 10, 1913

MY DEAR PAPA,

Just a line to tell you I have arrived safely after an excellent passage. There is really no news to give you as the voyage was absolutely uneventful. We passed an iceberg at five one morning but of course no one except the sailors and officers saw it. We are off Nantucket Island at the moment, get to the quarantine section tonight and land tomorrow morning. There is a very mixed crowd on the boat. At our table a motor manufacturer and his wife, and a so-called wholesale grocer evidently in a large way, a leather man from Boston and a mining engineer from British Columbia who has been floating in Europe a gold mine in Alaska which he claims will yield £80,000 a year. He is really a most amusing little man a typical sort of Dawson City man I should think. There is also of course one of the usual kind of card-sharpers on board who managed to take £65 off an inoffensive old American before the latter knew they were playing for money. He is to be introduced to the detective this evening but does not know it yet.

Mrs. Lindemann had from childhood onward a strong influence upon F.A., and her vitality and gaiety had made considerable inroads into his abnormally reserved character. Noticing with distaste his tendency to tease others, she attempted to correct this by unmerciful raillery at his expense. In this endeavor she unfortunately failed, but there can be no doubt that his mother, whom at first he loved and of whose sharp tongue he was in awe, was until the age of about sixteen a great humanizing influence in his life. He was also keenly alive to feminine beauty as well as brains, and in his mother he saw a combination of both. A letter written by her to F.A. at the University of Chicago gives us an impression of this woman's personality, and under the banter indicates the deep pride which she felt in her remarkable son.

Sidholme,
Sidmouth
June 17, 1913

Can't let this go dear love without a line enclosed from "Pordle" or "Mimi" or whatever you call me. We were very glad of your nice long wire — dollars evidently plentiful . . . We are now longing for a nice long letter and get considering the work you have before you. Poor boy it seems hardly fair to expect you to write *any*thing but just what you must for the lectures! Why don't they ask ME to lecture to them? Firstly I should love to, and secondly I believe I would tell them (in 40 lectures bien entendu) a great deal more useful stuff than you will, and they could laugh freely at my remarks and enjoy themselves, whereas their brows will ache from excessive knitting of them all the time *you* are lecturing and they won't have understood at the end as they would me. However there is no accounting for tastes and fancies. . . . So glad you saw Niagara — it is lovelier in winter but a good sight always. . . . in my mind's eye it is there as a glorious vision.

Although he and his mother felt for one another in his childhood a strong mutual devotion, it did not survive into early manhood. Ruptures between them were rendered inevitable by the mother's uncontrollable wish to dominate, and her failure to understand that her sons were no longer children but men. They had one or two bad quarrels, notably when Mrs. Lindemann sent him straight back to London from the station in Devonshire because he had not asked permission to visit his own home. Charles shared his brother's resentment at being treated like a child:

For two years F.A. refused to come to Sidholme. In our early youth our mother was extremely amusing and openhanded, handing out tips and presents right and left. But she liked to boss everybody and could never realise that we had grown up. She continued to interfere and to order us about in quite an absurd way. This was of course the worst possible way to handle F.A., who was just beginning to resent the foreign birthplace and the choice of a Scottish school of no particular standing.

He was, on the other hand, extremely fond of his father, who rarely uttered a cross word and who closely shared his scientific interests and guided him in his early career. If he approved of a scientific plan unlimited cash was forthcoming, and he was very good-natured about our continual absence at tennis tournaments. F.A. and his father published a few papers together, and a lot of developments took place in his laboratory at Sidmouth and at Marlow in the way of instruments for astronomical purposes. The Lindemann electrometer was a joint father and son effort.

We have another indication in a letter written by F.A. to his father toward the end of November 1913 not only of the friendly relations existing at that time between him and Tizard, but also of the fact that he had already, at this early date, the Chair of Experimental Philosophy in mind, and was well aware of the importance of Tizard's good offices:

Tizard would like to come down early in January. Can I invite him definitely? The professorship in question is for physics, the Clarendon Lab. The present "encumbrance" is Clifton. He has been there since about 1870. They chose him in preference to Helmholtz who wanted to come. Tizard thinks I might get it. I can hardly believe it. Townsend who is the other physicist there is very nice. I lunched with him today. He is one of Carson's Ulstermen. Clifton says he is going to retire next September.

The consciousness of ever-growing powers and the prospect of a brilliant career were clouded by a gigantic shadow. There was going to be a war. He felt it in his bones. He had already winded the Prussian menace seeping like the smell of a sewer across the North Sea, and he had warned his father of it in his letters from Berlin. Of the extent of the disaster to come he had no idea. He must have been amazed by the naïveté of even intelligent men about the coldly premeditated German assault. He might well have shrugged his shoulders at his friend Jack Egerton, whom he had known when working with Nernst in Berlin, when he described how he went to the *Times* office "to try and prevent the stupid anti-German articles and leaders that were being published and to show them how fairly the Germans appeared to be behaving, considering the massing of the Russian troops on their frontier."

As war approached, Egerton, by arrangement with Lindemann, sent an application for service to the War Office, which his adjutant forgot to forward, and which shows how uncertain F.A. was of his role in the coming war.

O.T.C. Headquarters
August 8, 1914

Lieut. A. C. Egerton . . . University of London O.T.C. and F. A. Lindemann esq. D.Sc. would be glad to hear whether the War Office would accept their services in the following capacity:

They would be willing to drive and be responsible for a motor car (any type of small fast car would be suitable) and equip it either with (a) apparatus for generating electricity for X ray purposes etc. (b) or with water pumping and purifying apparatus, whichever may be most useful.

Lieut. Egerton knows German and some French, and can drive and look after the motor car. He has also acted as a company commander in the University of London O.T.C. two years ago. Mr. Lindemann knows German and French perfectly (like a native) and is expert in electrical matters, especially in X ray work.

We have made this offer in view of the fact that the Royal Flying Corps require motor cars and those who speak French and German are also required . . . They could therefore act as interpreters.[1]

Even had the adjutant not mislaid the application, it is improbable that this lonely cry would have met with sympathy in a harassed War Office.

Instead F.A. turned to a young institution in which he was to give invaluable and dangerous service throughout the war, the Royal Aircraft Factory, Farnborough, later to become the Royal Aircraft Establishment. Here scientists and leading engineers labored in the hothouse atmosphere of war to rationalize and improve the rudimentary fighting aircraft of the day, and to study for the first time for practical purposes the science of aerodynamics.

In August 1914, F.A. was playing tennis in the European championship at Zoppol, a port on the Baltic, which he did not wish to leave as he was likely to win the tournament, and it was with foreboding that he went down to the pier with his friends the Egertons and watched the Kaiser land from his yacht after the Sarajevo crisis.

On March 28, 1915, after producing satisfactory references, he was asked by Superintendent Mervyn O'Gorman to report for duty at the Royal Aircraft Factory, Farnborough, on the following day, as a temporary technical assistant at the agreed salary of £3 a week, and thither we must follow him.

[1] Cherwell archives.

3

Farnborough

THE ROYAL AIRCRAFT FACTORY at Farnborough was a peculiar and fascinating institution which perfectly suited Lindemann. There was something challenging in being one of those who assisted the process of rapid change in the forcing house of war. The routine of this place was irregular and its discipline of the mildest. The colleagues with whom he worked were scientists and engineers, men of his own turn of mind and easy companions. As an institution, it offered, compared with the armed forces, an atmosphere as civilized and stimulating as that of a university compared to a public school. In it he was not only to study problems of aerodynamics and precision instruments largely of his own choice, but was to show a cold-blooded physical courage and indifference to death which amazed others but was held of little account by himself.

The Royal Aircraft Factory, when he arrived there, was addressing itself, among other things, under the pressure of war to the study of this new science of aerodynamics. Flight had up to then been considered more as an art than a science, and the military authorities had been slow and skeptical of the mighty latent power of this prodigious infant, and slow to perceive the complete transformation of warfare which was to come from these ungainly heavier-than-air contraptions.

Farnborough was undoubtedly the perfect place for the most useful display of Lindemann's gifts. He was to take calculated risks as great as those of any combative soldier, but he was spared the squalor of their lives and, what would have been to such a temperament as his, the terrors of propinquity and institutional life. The discipline, the compulsion of rank, the constant association with strangers, the bawdy talk and the lack of privacy — all these would have played havoc with his nervous system. At Farnborough orders were not given, but desires conveyed, and there, at ease and on an intellectual equality with his fellow boffins, he was able to grope his way by trial and error through the new problems and make a positive contribution to the winning of the war under a superintendent, Mervyn O'Gorman, whose coming inaugurated the use of scientific methods in aeronautical development. Such an unconventional establishment could not have been given a more receptive or a bolder superintendent than Mervyn O'Gorman, whose prescient mind grasped the vital part that aviation was to play in warfare, and who was a pioneer in enlisting scientists to join his professional staff, and to explore the new terra incognita of aerodynamics. He was both loved and revered by the brilliant young men he gathered round him. Lindemann came also to feel a strong *esprit de corps* with others in this friendly and unconventional establishment, and to experience the thrilling sense that they were leaders and explorers in a vital new field of science and engineering.

It was intriguing for him to find that his new telegraphic address was "Ballooning, Farnborough," a relic of the establishment's foundation when a Balloon Equipment Store was opened by the War Office at Woolwich in 1878. Later the pioneers of airplanes joined the balloonists, and the first primitive machines began to stagger into the air. The family tree had divided in 1909, one branch remaining at Farnborough and growing up through H.M. Balloon Factory successively into the Army Aircraft Factory, the Royal Aircraft Factory, and the Royal Aircraft Establishment.

It was called a factory because, in those early days, to design, build and fly an airplane, although perhaps an art and certainly a hazardous adventure, was not yet a science.

> . . . when the war came and with it the stunning fact that war itself could grow wings, the pioneers had to be very quickly organised and expanded. The brave and brilliant group of Farnborough men who got the B.E.2c and its successors into the air and coaxed them to stay there were aeroplane fanciers. It was natural and right that Farnborough should build what they fancied. But they had to reckon with the aircraft industry, a turbulent infant howling for its sustenance, and they lost their battle.
>
> In 1916 it was decided that the men of Farnborough would have quite enough to do in amassing knowledge on how aeroplanes should be designed and flown; others would in future build them.[1]

The Royal Aircraft Factory under O'Gorman's leadership and in collaboration with the new Advisory Committee for Aeronautics and the National Physical Laboratory, became the chief center of experimental aviation in England. O'Gorman was joined by F. M. Green from Daimler as "engineer in charge of design," responsible for airships and airplanes and testing, and by Godfrey de Havilland who brought with him the DH-2.

With the coming of war the languid interest of the military authorities in aviation was sharply aroused and gave way to an intense effort to create the first fighter aircraft. The scene of this struggle was Farnborough, and its driving force O'Gorman. Convinced in his own mind of the scientific problems involved in a swift development of aviation, he cast his net wide for recruits. He engaged men whose lives were already committed to aviation, but he also scoured the universities, achieving a mixed bag of brilliant young men — mathemati-

[1] *Fifty Years at Farnborough*, H.M.S.O., 1955.

cians, physicists, biologists, as well as professional and amateur pilots.

By a process of improvisation that has since become legendary, they were to invent airplanes capable of remaining in the air for a few hours, and devise the instruments by which they were navigated and controlled. O'Gorman's reign was an epic struggle to break through the mysteries of flight at the grim tempo of war, and well deserved Sir Roy Fedden's tribute:

> There is no doubt that history has shown that this was an unique place, and you could hardly turn anywhere in British aviation without finding that the good things that were done on aircraft between the two wars stem almost entirely from engineers who had been at this remarkable place and who were inspired by an outstanding leader.

It is strange that Lindemann was not at first contented in employment that so obviously suited him, among colleagues with whom he felt at ease. His initial restlessness is shown in despondent letters to his father about abortive attempts to find employment at the Admiralty. There is depression in the words: "My job here is about all I am fit for and I think I had better stick to it."

Again he had reason to curse his mother's lack of consideration for his future by giving birth to him in Germany instead of in England, for there were those at Farnborough who were amazed at his employment in such secret work, and it was a doubt that affected not only his equals but even the mechanics. He was deeply concerned by the possible effect of his unfortunate German birth upon his application for a commission, and the concern emerges clearly from a revealing self-exculpatory letter to O'Gorman in November 1915.

Nov. 24, 1915

DEAR MR. O'GORMAN,

In spite of the fact that a number of other technical assistants at the Royal Aircraft Factory have applied for commissions in the Hampshire Territorial Aircraft Park now being formed, I am taking this opportunity of asking whether I may consider myself eligible. I must admit that my training has been almost exclusively scientific, and beyond belonging to the school (Blair Lodge) Cadet Corps, I cannot lay claim to any previous military experience. On the other hand my thorough knowledge of French and German may perhaps count in my favour.

The point which may well arouse misgivings is the enemy origin suggested by my name. As a matter of fact our family which originated in Alsace is altogether cosmopolitan. Thus the head of the family my cousin the Comte de Lindemann is French as my great uncle established himself in Paris when the Duchy of Deux Ponts where our family owned property was given to Bavaria in 1815. My grandfather on the other hand remained on the estates and my father was born on what is now the German Empire. He emigrated to England some 45 years ago and has become a naturalised British subject. Unfortunately I also appear to count only as a naturalised Englishman as my parents were taking the cure at Baden-Baden at the time of my birth. I never was German however, not even technically, for my father had lost his German nationality long before the time of my birth (1886) and as he was not domiciled in Germany at the time.

In view of these facts I venture to hope that my name will not debar me from obtaining a commission.

His desire for a commission was common to a generation not yet disillusioned by experience, who regarded the First World War as a crusade against evil. It persisted until the beginning of 1916 after which he appears to have abandoned hope. O'Gorman, who recognized a good scientist when he saw one, had probably no intention of losing him, and contented himself with keeping him in suspense.

Another reason for abandoning hope of a commission was that a new interest had entered his life at Farnborough in 1916.

A strong feeling had by then grown among some of the scientists and engineers that they should learn to fly as pilots, partly in order to gain firsthand experience of the behavior of an airplane in flight and thus buttress theory by practical experience, and partly in order to be able to conduct experiments on the aircraft and to discover what instruments it required. Further reasons for his belief in the research worker learning to fly appear in a letter to his father at the beginning of 1917 in which he refers to the accidents of others which might have been avoided:

June 28, 1917

My dear Papa,

Many thanks for your dear letters . . . We went to a lecture at the Aeronautical Society on Wednesday. The lecture was very good but the discussion was absolutely puerile. Everybody who spoke disagreed with the lecturer in the matter of instruments. They all said the pilot ought not to use them as they might go wrong. A lot of people get killed by not using them. Evans is an example; he flew much too slowly and stalled on the turn. Having done this he seems to have lost his head and failed to recover himself. Our head pilot got killed today. Nobody can make out quite what happened; probably he tried to loop too quickly and broke the machine. It is very bad luck but he has been a good deal safer and certainly a lot more comfortable than the officers in the trenches.

He was foremost in pressing for this change. He did so, not because he had any particular interest in learning to fly but because he felt that experiments divorced from practical experience in the air lost much of their validity. He certainly felt no romantic excitement in mastering the art of flight. For him it was simply a means to a scientific end, worthy of no credit in itself. Any fool, in his opinion, could learn to fly. Courage, in which he was to show himself pre-eminent, was a second-rate virtue shared by millions of others, and for the rest of his life he shrank in genuine embarrassment from eulogies of his feats in the air.

His first efforts to obtain permission to fly were unsuccessful, and his colleague at Farnborough, William Farren,[1] wrote:

> Mervyn O'Gorman, who was then the head of the Factory, was not impressed by our arguments. Moreover, he thought that if we were to fly as pilots, the position of the professional pilots, whether civilian or R.F.C., might be weakened. They were the recognised experts in flying and critics of aircraft and everything connected with them.

O'Gorman did not believe that the War Office, who were then in control of military aviation, would agree to scientists flying. After O'Gorman's retirement in the middle of 1916, his deputy, Major S. Heckstall Smith, was persuaded by Lindemann to send a letter to the War Office which he had drafted, and to the general surprise the permission was given. It was mainly owing to his pressure that five or six scientists were chosen to attend courses at the Central Flying Schools at Netheravon and Uphaven. At the latter school Lindemann, flying Maurice Foreman Longhorns and Shorthorns, Avro 504's and BE-2c's, successfully passed and was awarded a Flying Certificate dated October 23, 1916. His freak memory allowed him to bluff his way through the medical eye-test, and his method of doing so amazed his colleague William Farren:

> The sight in one of his eyes was so poor that it was hardly an exaggeration to say that from the point of view of a test it was blind.[2] It certainly hindered his flying afterwards, particularly in landing, since his stereoscopic vision was seri-

---

[1] Afterward Sir William Farren, F.R.S.
[2] In fact, his eye was only good at short range for reading books.

ously impaired. When he came out from the test, naturally triumphant, I asked him how he had done it. His wonderful memory . . . was the clue, and he said: "I took a fifty-fifty chance," and when I asked him what he meant he explained: "I went in and he sat me in the chair, and whilst we were chatting I used my good eye to memorise the letters on the side of the card I could see. When he started the test I knew that he would either leave it that way round or turn it over, so I shut my bad eye and read the new side without any difficulty. He then turned it the other way round and I looked at it with my bad eye and read out the letters from memory. Of course he might have insisted on which eye I used first, but I had to risk that." [1]

It is the generally accepted opinion that Lindemann first flew in September 1916 and became a certified pilot in October. There has, however, been propounded a plausible argument that he in fact flew before that time after a rushed tuition arranged by O'Gorman, who allowed him to be the first to put his theories on spinning to practical experiment in actual flight, and this theory will be considered when discussing his experiments in spinning.

When we consider Lindemann's social life during his time at Farnborough, we realize how fortunate he was that a commission had been denied him. He lived in a house which came to be called the Chudleigh Mess, and the company there was indeed different from that among which he would have been thrown in the army. Those who lived at Chudleigh in a happy state of bachelordom and intellectual argument were men of the highest mental caliber, and caused the president of this unofficial mess, F. M. Green, the engineer, to write later:

I thought then that my mess-mates were rather a bright lot, but I never imagined that among them were three future

[1] Copy of note sent to Sir George Thomson by Sir William Farren.

peers, five knights, three Nobel prize-winners and Professors
and Fellows of the Royal Society galore.

The house was on the Fleet Road. Green had found it un-
furnished but took beds and bedding from store, and furnished the living rooms by installment purchases. One remains
amazed at the perspicacity of O'Gorman in choosing such a
body of men. Among them were the brilliant Glauert, who was
later made a F.R.S. for his work in aeronautics and who was
killed in an unnecessary explosion; Frank Aston, who afterward
won the Nobel Prize, William Farren, and two other Nobel
prize-winners, George Thomson, later F.R.S. and Master of
Corpus Christi College, Cambridge, and Edgar Douglas Adrian,
afterward Lord Adrian, F.R.S. and Vice-Chancellor of Cambridge University. Melvill Jones, the future Professor of Aeronautics at Cambridge, was an early member of the mess. To
these were added Geoffrey Taylor with his bubbling vivacity,
now a world-famous physicist, and Southwell, who was to become Sir Richard Southwell, Professor of Engineering at Oxford.

There was little fear of embarrassment for Lindemann in such
company. The atmosphere was that of a somewhat rowdy Senior
Common Room in which violent disputes on abstruse subjects
and hearty undergraduate banter were frequent, the youth of
the members preventing a too solemn parade of knowledge.
Aston came to the mess indignant that he had been forced to
shut down a diffusion apparatus intended to separate the then
undiscovered isotopes of neon, but Lindemann persuaded
him that the apparatus would not have worked in any case.

He also engaged in many heated arguments with Geoffrey
Taylor, and "they delighted the mess by differing on the question of the closest packing of spheres as instanced by a dish of
oranges. One said there was only one possible way, and the
other, I forget which, said that there were two. They were

cheered on by the rest of the mess. I can still hear Taylor say-ing: 'but don't you see stoopid,' to the delight of the rest of us, who settled the argument by throwing the oranges at the ar-guers."[1] When Lindemann first entered the mess in 1915 he was seen to be a tall, dark young man with a good figure. He was reserved and inclined to be sarcastic, and it was noticed that he did not suffer fools gladly. F. M. Green felt from the first that he was somehow different from the other members of the mess, and it is likely that his acute self-consciousness and continental training contributed to this impression. As he be-came accustomed to his surroundings and grew to know his colleagues, he lost his shyness and joined freely in their argu-ments, often using his dialectical skill in a perverse defense of the indefensible. As his shyness thawed, he entered into the prevailing spirit of banter, even flying to Cambridge and drop-ping a boot by parachute over the church when Farren and his wife emerged from their wedding service.

Whether or not they were brought to his attention, there were rumors at Farnborough that he was a German. H. L. Lucking, who had studied at Heidelberg where he noticed Lindemann's skill at tennis and remembered that he and Charles had been locally known as "the German Doherties," and had often gossiped to them in cafés in German, was introduced to him in the Chudleigh Mess in the breezy words: "Do you know Lindy?"

I was tongue-tied and astounded that the Royal Aircraft Factory should be employing a man I thought to be a German in a highly important task. I voiced my fears confidentially to Aston who soon put me wise as to the true state of affairs and subsequently I had plenty of opportunity of appreciating the valuable and dangerous work that F.A.L. was doing. The wings of his special plane were coated in every kind and

[1] F. M. Green, *The Chudleigh Mess*, January 1958.

colour of material, including gold paint. He was a man of gadgets and had a specially built massive undercarriage as, I was told, good as he was in the air he would write off any normal undercarriage on landing.

Professor Gibson,[1] who was conducting engine research at Farnborough, registered impressions of Lindemann which remained fresh after fifty years:

> We used to attend meetings of the R.A.F. in London together, and I vividly remember one meeting when a member of the National Physical Laboratory had criticised a paper of his, and on his way up from the station at Farnborough to the R.A.F. he burst forth — "The man is nothing but a d-dirty l-little Jew." It was the only unkind word I ever heard him say.

Gibson observed with astonishment another strange characteristic in Lindemann. His terror of appearing conspicuous or unusual led to a strong dislike of being seen in his flying kit.

> He had one queer idiosyncracy. He had to fly to Martlesham quite often from Farnborough. He would arrive at the airfield in bowler hat, long Melton Mowbray coat with velvet collar, and a rolled umbrella. Before boarding his plane which he piloted himself he carefully rolled up his coat, umbrella etc., packed it under the seat and got into his flying kit. Before getting out of the plane at Martlesham he would reverse the process and would step out fully dressed in bowler hat, overcoat and umbrella. Of course the Martlesham pilots thought he was partially non-compos-mentis.

Gibson was also aware of the racial suspicions which vexed the unhappy physicist owing to his mother's fondness for Baden-Baden:

[1] Professor of Engineering, Manchester University, S.Sc., LL.D., M.Inst.C.E., M.I.Mech.E.

The workshop staff at Farnborough firmly believed that he was a German and that he was never allowed enough petrol to carry him across the channel.

The boisterous but learned companionship at Chudleigh did much to draw him out, and he became a popular and happy member of the mess. He began to feel one of the company, and joined freely in the ribaldry, particularly endearing himself to Farren, who was impressed by his poise and knowledge of the world:

> Having had the pleasure of living in the same house as Lindemann at Farnborough for some eighteen months, I had come to know him very well, but I think the experience of learning to fly in his company was something unique. In the first place it showed me what a great man he was, not that I had any doubt about it. He was six years older than I was in years but many more in experience, both of the world and of science. But I doubt whether anything about him impressed me quite so much as his indifference to the difficulties of arriving at an R.F.C. Station in a bowler hat and carrying an umbrella. Lucas and I were in khaki, and therefore relatively inconspicuous for which we were thankful. Lindemann was unperturbed, and to our surprise, so was the R.F.C.

There is here a hint, too, of the lordly Lindemann of the Adlon Hotel, who strolled into the lab at noon, and was seldom seen at the bench, in the fact that Farren and Lucas, on account of their uniform, were forced to drill like soldiers, and attend parades from which F.A. was exempted.

His health was severely tested by his regime at Farnborough, where he took little exercise and subsisted on an unrelieved dietary of tinned apricots. He refused to join Farren and Lucas in their long walks on Salisbury Plain. He continued to conceal his accomplishments with the morbid secrecy of a schoolboy attempting to protect an unusual Christian name. There was a piano in the mess, and although his skill on the keys was suspected by the others, he was too diffident to play, excusing himself on the grounds that he preferred the pianola because it could not strike false notes.

Haunted by that inbred terror of being seen as a figure of fun, he was extremely reluctant to do anything in public which he did not do perfectly. His friends were surprised when after much persuasion he allowed himself to be taken skating by Aston. They went to Fleet Pond where, supported by Aston, he tottered to the middle amid derisive cheers. Once there, to Farren's astonishment, "he proceeded to show how figure skating should really be done. I am sure one of his reasons for this particular joke was the unholy delight we all took in ragging Aston, much as we loved him."

Lindemann's courage in conducting spinning experiments on those early machines when a spin usually meant death for the aviator became a legend from which his own self-effacing character particularly recoiled. These spins, which were carried out in June and July 1917, provided a scientific analysis of the behavior of a machine in a spin, with the result that its extrication from such a spin became a recognized maneuver, instead of a lucky fluke the reasons for which the pilot only dimly understood. To Lindemann his own cold-blooded courage meant nothing, and he winced from the publicity he received for what was to him an ordinary part of the day's work.

Sir Roy Harrod has propounded an ingenious theory that Lindemann in fact, relying on his own calculations, put an airplane into a spin both clockwise and anticlockwise in June or July 1916, a month or two before the test pilot, Goodden, performed the same feat in an FE-8, one of the factory machines which had acquired a bad reputation for spinning. Goodden had used the technique of pushing the stick forward, which was accepted at the time as the best that could be done, and which had been discovered accidentally and the reasons for which were little understood. F.A.'s priority over Goodden in spinning is disputed by both Farren and Thomson, but it must be examined, for, if true, it would clearly ensure for him an even greater degree of credit for skill and courage than he has already received.

It is not claimed that he was the first man to survive a spiral spin. The feat had been performed by E. G. Hawker in a Sopwith plane, and one of the earliest analyzed cases of a pilot extricating himself from a spin was that of Parke in 1912, which took place over Salisbury Plain.[1] Orville Wright is also credited with a similar feat in America in 1916.

The proposition depends almost exclusively on the evidence of O'Gorman as given to Harrod, both verbal and written. Verbally O'Gorman stated that Lindemann, when working on the ground at Farnborough, evolved a theory of the correct course of action for a pilot to take when in a spin; that it was clearly impossible for him to ask a pilot to put a machine into a spin, push the joy stick forward and straighten the rudder in reliance on Lindemann's calculations alone. O'Gorman stated that Lindemann told him that if he would allow him to learn to fly, he would perform the experiment himself. To this O'Gorman agreed, and "with immense misgiving" entrusted him with a plane.

Harrod relates that O'Gorman described to him "with the utmost vividness" how he watched the airplane ascend to a great height and go into a spin. He admitted that "his heart sank into his heels." Having extricated himself from a clockwise spin Lindemann ascended again, and to O'Gorman's consternation performed a second spin anticlockwise. Lindemann, to whom compliments and gratitude were always embarrassing emotions, avoided O'Gorman by taking leave on the same day and immediately leaving Farnborough on landing his machine. It is claimed that he took further precautions by send-

[1] *Flight*, August 31, 1912.

ing O'Gorman a full report through the office messenger on his return. O'Gorman's written evidence takes the form of a letter to Harrod on November 2, 1949:

> I was eye-witness of the incident* and well remember the hesitancy with which I entrusted to him a B.E.2 aeroplane for the risky experiment . . .
>
> Yours sincerely,
MERVYN O'GORMAN
>
> * in company with my Assistant Superintendent Mr. Heckstall Smith who will no doubt vouch for it also.

Footnote. When auto-rotation was little understood and when an aeroplane seen to be spinning was regarded as doomed, Lindemann then at work at the Royal Aircraft Establishment ("Factory") worked out theoretically the proper actions for a pilot to take, asked leave to learn flying so as to test his theory and within three weeks put a B.E.2 aeroplane into a spin at 14,000 feet and brought it safely out — repeating the action first right, then left. This was good work, useful to the war effort, and shows the courage of his conviction.

M. O'GORMAN

The argument continues that this account could not have referred to the series of spins by Lindemann in June and July 1917 as O'Gorman had left Farnborough nearly a year before, and that splendid as those experiments were they had been conducted at a time when spinning was already a recognized maneuver, whereas the earlier 1916 spins had been performed at a time when spinning was generally fatal.

Sir George Thomson displayed skepticism about these earlier experiments, observing, among other things, that if Lindemann performed the 1916 spins, his fellow scientists at Farnborough, and particularly himself and Farren who actually belonged to the same mess as Lindemann, must have heard about them. He also objected that it would have been impossible for Lindemann to have performed the experiments in June or July 1916 as he had not then a test pilot's certificate, and that it was inconceivable that O'Gorman would have given him permission to do so. In reply to this objection Harrod quoted Air Ministry Folder A.H. 176/2 in which a report by O'Gorman at the end of the First World War contains these passages:

> Latterly (1916) the discovery has been made by Mr. Lindemann that spinning is an evolution which all aeroplanes may perform, that the rate of rotation during a spin is the chief difference between one spin and another, and that the ease with which a pilot can get out of a spin is partly physiological and in some measure determined by the degree of longitudinal stability which the aeroplane possesses.
>
> The concurrence of a spin was equivalent to a crash. When Mr. Lindemann analysed the movements of a spin, made instrumental observations during a spin voluntarily started in the air, he by great personal courage gave aeronautics a new military manoeuvre.

Harrod invites us to consider how much we must disbelieve if we wish to discredit O'Gorman's story — that he was persuaded by Lindemann to let him learn to fly, that he entrusted him with an airplane "With trepidation," that he watched the flight, and that Lindemann left Farnborough to avoid his congratulations. He reminds us that O'Gorman's Air Ministry report was written only two years after the event when he was still quite young, and in which he cites Heckstall Smith as witness. The latter could not have seen the 1917 spins as he had by then left Farnborough. Harrod attempts to explain the fact that neither Thomson nor Farren heard anything of the 1916 spins by saying that Lindemann himself would have been the last person to boast of it. He believes that it is unlikely that O'Gorman would have told these two young scientists recently graduated from Cambridge, each only twenty-four years old, before the test pilot had confirmed the tests by experiment, and that in view of the irregularity of the whole proceedings it is likely that Lindemann was asked to remain quiet.

Thomson maintains that Lindemann could not have done spins in June or July 1916 as he only learned to fly in the autumn of that year at Netheravon, but Harrod's theory rests on the fact that O'Gorman's written account implies that he performed the spins before he had full and proper instruction in flying, after three weeks' tuition. Thomson is emphatic that it is inconceivable that O'Gorman would have authorized a man who had no certificate to attempt a highly dangerous experiment in the air, and it is the heart of Harrod's argument that this was, in fact, what he did.

Thomson further raises the question of why no one saw these alleged spins, and this objection meets the answer that O'Gorman and Lindemann may have arranged that they took place far from the aerodrome above some particular field agreed on the map. It is also evident that if the theory is correct Lindemann must have been pretending to be a complete novice when he underwent instruction at Netheravon in the autumn of 1916, and deluded his friends and instructors into believing that this was the case.

After adducing various other reasons Harrod concludes tnat Lindemann carried out his spins in June or July 1916; Goodden his on August 23, and that after this the "spin lost much of its terror," and became a recognized military maneuver.

Harrod alleges that Thomson and Farren made an "11th hour" suggestion that Lindemann might have persuaded O'Gorman to have the flights done, and taken part in them in O'Gorman's time, but as a passenger, and claims that this admission disposes of their original agreement that the flight could not have happened because they had never heard of it, or because it was not in the logbook. If he flew as a passenger, who was the pilot? If it was Goodden, why was Goodden's first spin recorded as on August 23 after O'Gorman's departure from Farnborough?

Harrod also cites a letter from Charles Lindemann in support of his case:

> When I asked F.A. about this he said that obviously he could not let anyone else try to prove his theory as if he got smashed up everyone would say: "Why didn't he try it himself first?"

When Harrod showed Lindemann a footnote about his spin appearing somewhat incongruously in the biography of Keynes, he received an angry rebuke, but he tells us that when pressed as to whether O'Gorman's account was true "he muttered his assent."

> We may be quite sure [said Harrod] that had he detected any errors in my narrative, he would have pointed them out. We were very old and intimate friends, and F.A. had never hesitated to convict me of error when he had the chance.

He admits that O'Gorman did not supply him with the dates of the spins, and he relics on the fact that the experiment was "done when an aeroplane seen to be spinning was regarded as doomed." He concludes his argument with the reminder that in Sir Walter Raleigh's history of the Royal Flying Corps, *War in the Air*, the author gives sole credit to Lindemann for supplying the correct theoretical answer to tne problem of spin, and for courageously testing his theory in practice. He reasons that as this was an official war history it must have been approved by experts in the Air Ministry, many of whom must have been familiar with the problem, and that if the passages giving sole credit to Lindemann were incorrect they must surely have been challenged and altered. The following is the passage from *War in the Air* referred to by Harrod:

> The spin at the outbreak of war was regarded as a fault in an aeroplane, due chiefly to bad construction; later Dr. F. A. Lindemann, by his research and courageous experiments at the Royal Aircraft Factory, proved that any aeroplane could spin, and that any pilot who understands the spin can get out of it if there is height to spare. During the war the spin was freely used by pilots to break off a flight, to simulate defeat, or to descend in a vertical path.

Harrod has described at length the suppositions we are obliged to make if we reject O'Gorman's story. An equally formidable set of assumptions must be made if we are to accept it.

The theory, admirably argued, is constructed entirely on the evidence of one man, now dead. We are asked to believe that neither Farren nor Thomson, who lived in the same mess as Lindemann and knew him intimately, had any inkling that he had performed these feats. We are invited to agree that O'Gorman, who was strongly against the scientists learning to fly at all on the ground that it would upset the professional pilots, allowed him to go up and perform a maneuver which had almost always ended in death, without a test pilot's certificate, and after a mere three weeks' clandestine instruction. Is it possible that he was taught to fly in such secrecy by an unnamed instructor that even his closest friends knew nothing of it? Is it likely that the instructor never mentioned this irregular episode to anyone?

We are asked to believe that these historic tests were carried out with no one noticing them except O'Gorman and Heckstall Smith, and that in order to ensure secrecy they may have been carried out over some distant field marked X on the map.

Where did he receive his three weeks' instruction? If it was at Farnborough, it is surely inconceivable that it did not become public property. The Harrod theory then would have us believe that, having performed this feat, he learned to fly as an absolute novice at Netheravon, simulating ignorance of the aircraft, without either his colleagues or his instructors realizing that he had flown an airplane before. It would also mean that he carried out his tests before Goodden, and that his vital report to O'Gorman was allowed to lie uncirculated in a filing cabinet.

Anyone who knew Lindemann intimately would agree that so serene was his courage and so strong his confidence in his own calculations that he would have been perfectly willing to put them to the hazard in this way, but that he did so in June or July 1916 [1] cannot be considered proven. In the absence of hard proof, which is now unlikely to be forthcoming, we shall do better to pay homage to Lindemann for the achievement which is fully attested — his immortal and perilous contributions to the scientific solution of spinning in June and July 1917.

It must be remembered that airplanes are not all the same and that a maneuver which might be successful with one type of machine would not necessarily work for another, so that a great deal of mystery remained until the publication of Lindemann's work.

It is possible but improbable that he made a spinning flight in November 1916, on his return from learning to fly at Netheravon, but there is no evidence that he did so. Nor is it

[1] Since the above was written Sir Roy Harrod has informed me that Lindemann's sister recalls Lindemann taking her husband for a flight just before her child was born on April 6, 1916. She has not felt able to confirm this statement to me, and maintains that she has no cast-iron evidence that her brother was a pilot at this period of 1916.

likely that Goodden carried out his spin in reliance on Lindemann's calculations. In Thomson's words:

> Goodden and the other pilots were something between jealous and scornful of the scientific staff, and I doubt if he would have been influenced by Lindeman's theoretical ideas. I am not sure indeed if Lindemann had thought the matter out to this extent. It must be remembered, however, that until Lindemann's work in 1917 spinning was a mystery. You got out of it at best by an unnatural operation, and there was no saying whether a particular machine would get out, or if it did straighten up whether it would not go into a spin the other way round.
>
> Lindemann cleared the whole matter up and provided a frame-work on which all experiments of spinning could be based. It became possible to make model tests to see whether an aeroplane was likely to spin badly or not. There is considerable variety from one machine to another, and particularly with the type of wing section, and, of course, power of the controls also comes in. It may be doubtful if even now every machine could be got out of a prolonged spin, but Lindemann gave the basic theory into which experimental results, model or otherwise, could be fitted. This is the real claim, and an important one.[1]

Let Lindemann describe in his own modest words his stupendous achievement, remembering as we read the primitive machine, the deadly task and the prodigious feat of memory as his airplane plunged earthward. We should also have before our minds the loneliness of the pilot in the sky, and his exposed position; the constant anxiety with which his ear listened for any change in the rhythm of his engine which might spell disaster, and perhaps a slight sickness from the altitude. About him was the deafening roar of the engine and the wind scream-

---

[1] Sir George Thomson to author.

ing through the struts, and his movements, in thick flying clothes, were hampered in the tiny cockpit. Then it was necessary to make a supreme and unnatural effort of the will to throw the plane into that terrifying spinning rush toward earth, turning and turning as it fell, and during this giddy descent, relying for survival on his own calculations, to observe and memorize eight readings on his instruments. Nothing in Lindemann's life was more characteristic than the flat and unemotional manner in which he recorded this wonderful feat of cold-blooded scientific investigation.

In 1916 many pilots were killed flying our recently designed R.E.8s by spinning into the ground. Although various people had succeeded in getting out of a spin, nobody quite knew how, nor indeed how or why aircraft spun at all. Anyone watching a spinning plane could see that the rate of turn did not increase on the way down. I concluded therefore that the lift on both wings must be equal; and this could only be true — since the outer wing is beating against the air whereas the inner is not — if its effective angle of incidence was on the high side of the angle of maximum lift, whereas for the inner wing it was the other way round. This being so, if the speed were increased the aeroplane would no longer spin. Experiments proved that this idea was correct and the whole theory was worked out by Glauert and myself. . . . therefore the pilots were taught to push the stick forward — the very opposite of the instinctive reaction of pulling it back in order to get the nose up — and to straighten out the rudder and then pull out of the dive in the ordinary way.

The only merit I can claim in carrying out these experiments is that (unlike the professional pilot, who had usually not got a very good head for figures) I was able to remember the readings of the air speed indicator, the bubble, the angle of incidence on the two wings (measured by tapes on the struts), the height of the beginning and ending of the spin, the time taken and the number of turns, and to write them down in my notebook when I had straightened out the plane again. I am glad to have this opportunity to correct some of the absurdly dramatic stories which have appeared about this investigation.[1]

I accept Sir George Thomson's summing-up of the matter:

> To sum up, the main flights were certainly those of June/July 1917. There could have been an unrecorded flight at the end of 1916 when Cherwell returned, but I do not think so. Where O'Gorman got his story from is the real mystery. I think it is probably a complex derived from what he was told about the flights of Goodden in 1916 and of Cherwell in 1917 which fused together in his mind and produced the effect that he had seen them himself.
>
> One difficulty is that we were all very fond of O'Gorman and no one likes to say that he was spinning a story. I am perfectly sure that he believed every word he said.[2]

Lindemann was also one of the first men in aviation to design and test stabilized bombsights. He had observed the immense lateral error in bombing without such a device: "If the sighting wire indicated that one was aiming, say, to the right of the target and one turned left, the bank of the aeroplane made it look as if one were deviating to the right; hence one had to flatten out carefully and then look again before correcting; there was seldom much time for this."

He fixed two mirrors in front of the pilot which reflected the horizon on left and right and made it easy to see when the airplane was horizontal. In this position a free gyro carrying a light bombsight was released, and he found that it was possible to fly on exactly the right line, keeping the sighting wire on the target, and from 10,000 feet to obtain an average

[1] *Fifty Years at Farnborough.*
[2] Sir George Thomson to author.

accuracy of 60 yards, although helped by flying upwind in a slow machine and being undisturbed by gunfire.

> Bombing experiments [he recalled] in the early days were carried out at Oxford, a sort of sub-station of the R.A.E. I well remember how, early one morning, I dropped my stop-watch, required for calculating one's ground speed, and despite all my efforts to reach it, saw it disappear through the floor past the joy stick . . . In the meanwhile my colleague stationed on the ground to plot the fall of the bombs, concluded that I had abandoned the test and went for a swim. As I had to jettison the bombs before landing and they unhappily straddled him in the sea, he took the whole performance somewhat amiss although they were only 20 pounders.

Further evidence of Lindemann's early experiments in bombing is provided by Group Captain Wells:

> Lindemann was attached to Orfordness from Farnborough where he was director of the Physical Laboratory and also experimental pilot, and Rea and I were detached from the R.N.A.S. station Grain to carry out tests with two types of bombsight of special design. Both these bombsights embodied gyro control to stabilise the "Line of Sight" in a vertical plane. The sight used by Lindemann was one of his own design, and the one use by Rea and myself was the Service Course Setting Sight (designed by H. E. Wimperis) stabilised by a gyro device invented by a Professor Gray.
>
> All the trials were carried out at a height of 15,000 feet which at that time was considered to be a high altitude for bomb dropping. The aircraft of the "pusher type" designed by Farnborough and was known as the N.E. (night experimental).
>
> The trials were in the nature of a competition, Lindemann flying solo and acting as both pilot and bomb aimer. These trials on the part of Lindemann were a very stout effort as he

had both to steer and control the aircraft, aim and drop the bombs.

These initial trials with the stabilised sights gave invaluable information regarding the accuracy which could be achieved with high altitude bombing. . . . I cannot but think that the early pioneer work carried out by the R.N.A.S. with the valuable help of the scientists, of whom Lindemann was one, played a large part in developing the bombsight to the state of perfection attained in the second war.[1]

At the end of the war Lindemann could look back with satisfaction on his work at Farnborough. His foreign education ended, the love of England which had been nourished in boyhood by the hills and lanes of Devonshire, and which was to burn with so fierce a flame for the rest of his life, now possessed him, becoming the focus of his loyalty and devotion. The intense patriotism had found a worthy outlet, and he had taken his life in his hands in exhibitions of cold-blooded courage equal to those of any professional test pilot, and carried out experiments which have since found an honored and permanent place in the history of aviation.

[1] Group Captain J. K. Wells, A.F.C., to author.

4

The Interwar Years I:
The Clarendon Laboratory

F. A. LINDEMANN was elected Dr. Lee's Professor of Experimental Philosophy on April 23, 1919. He had distinguished sponsors — Lord Rayleigh, O.M., Sir Ernest Rutherford F.R.S., the Duc de Broglie and Professor Langevin. The Electoral Board consisted of the Vice-Chancellor of Oxford, Dr. Blakiston, President of Trinity College, Sir Joseph Larmor, F.R.S., Professor A. Schuster, F.R.S., of Manchester, Mr. R. E. Baynes, Dr. Lee's Reader of Christ Chuch, Professor W. H. Perkin, F.R.S., and the Warden of Wadham, Dr. Joseph Wells.

The study of physics in Oxford, or experimental philosophy as it is still officially called there, began in 1749, when a readership with a stipend of £30 a year, and originally attached to the Professorship of Astronomy, was founded as a part of Lord Crewe's benefaction. The honorarium was raised to £100 a year by the Prince Regent, and financial responsibility taken over by the University in 1885. In the meantime, in 1860, the status of the post had been raised to that of a professorship, the first holder being Robert Walker, a Fellow of Wadham College, who had been Reader since 1839. He was succeeded in 1865 by Robert Bellamy Clifton, also ex officio a Fellow of Wadham College, who held the Chair until 1915, being succeeded, after the war in 1919, by F. A. Lindemann.

The Chair was still attached to Wadham College, but after the Royal Commission of 1921, as a result of a financial rearrangement of endowment, its title became "Dr. Lee's Profes-

sorship of Experimental Philosophy." Dr. Lee was a benefactor
of Christ Church, and that college, in agreement with Wadham, elected Lindemann to a studentship, not on the Governing Body, but allowing him to have rooms in Christ Church
more spacious than were possible in the smaller college, and
thither, in due course, he moved. This is the explanation of
the fact which puzzled many people, that he was a Fellow
and a member of the Governing Body of Wadham, and simultaneously a student of Christ Church without the latter
privilege.

Before transferring to Christ Church he was offered rooms
in Wadham, and here he at once found his plans obstructed
by a series of petty restrictions. Oxford has always regarded
with watchful mistrust any private attempts to introduce bath-
rooms and other forms of essential modern sanitation, approaching the subject with some of the abhorrence of the medieval
Church for the licentious baths of declining Rome. Indeed it
is said that when a progressively minded don asked permission
to install a bath in his rooms an older colleague observed: "I
can't think what all the fuss is about. After all, the term only
lasts eight weeks." Lindemann's request to the Warden of
Wadham to incorporate a bath and a lavatory in his rooms at his
own expense as necessary adjuncts to civilized living encountered the same bleak reception, and he wrote irritably to his
father in July 1919:

> I have just had a letter from the Warden of Wadham which
> annoys me very much, in which he says I cannot put a W.C.
> in my rooms. He says the feeling in Oxford has always been
> against doing this sort of thing. He offers me other rooms
> with conveniences near at hand but as they look out on a dark
> and noisy street I do not think I shall take these. The real
> objection is that the man who does all their plumbing asked
> £115 for putting in the bath. I then got another contractor

to estimate who asked £40. The first was much enraged at someone estimating against him and said he would see the Bursar. He evidently frightened the Bursar who is an inefficient old dodderer by saying the building would have to be pulled about, and this I suppose caused all the trouble.

Lindemann, always obstinate in a crisis, continued to fight for the bathroom and the lavatory, and the harassed Warden was forced to bring up reinforcements, even enlisting in his hour of need the formidable aid of Professor Dicey, the great jurist, and the oriental scholar Stenning:

> The Bursar has mentioned to me the suggestion that we should have a W.C. put into the rooms on No. II. Both Stenning and he are strongly opposed to this, and I agree with them. It would be very difficult in an old building, and the feeling has always been in Oxford that such an arrangement is most undesirable.

Thus defeated, and always susceptible to colds, he was forced out of a warm room when hot after exercise for his bath. He did this resentfully, believing that all intimate details of the toilet should be performed in the strictest privacy, and his dislike of being seen otherwise than conventionally dressed made the walk to the bath in a dressing gown in the full public gaze a severe ordeal. The Warden, Dr. Wells, was not a man against whom it was possible to sustain rancor, and Lindemann reserved for Stenning his long memory for a slight. Perhaps there were recollections in his mind of the bath that was not when, many years after, he said to Stenning, who had asked him to see a judas tree he had just planted in his garden: "Well, if you can't make it flourish, nobody can." It should be added in fairness to Wadham College that they did not keep up this stubborn resistance for long, and the bathroom was eventually installed.

Lindemann remained a Fellow of Wadham College, which he left for Christ Church in 1922, until his death. It was a small Governing Body compared with Christ Church, consisting of seven or eight members, and his vote was important. He attended all meetings. In early days, in Sir Maurice Bowra's memory, Lindemann was nearly always right. He was bent on getting more science and mathematics scholars, and, since the Royal Society was founded at Wadham, that college became the pioneer in this endeavor, obtaining two science scholarships a year, which have now risen to between six and eight, so that as a result of his foresight Wadham became a leading scientific College.

On college issues he was a good and sensible member of the Governing Body, but Bowra, like Harrod, found him tiresome and talkative about subjects he did not understand.

> In spite of his tendency to tell dubious stories, he was extremely puritanical, and wished to give no mercy to any moral lapses on the part of the undergraduates. On this subject he was brutal.[1]

Keeley remembers, however, one occasion when, after such a moral lapse on the part of a scholar, the question of the deprivation of his scholarship arose. Lindemann strongly supported this but at the same time offered to make up his emoluments privately for the rest of his time so that his career should not be ruined. In the end the young man was allowed to retain his scholarship.

Lindemann enjoyed talking to Bowra about certain aspects of Greek history, becoming in the end absorbed in this interest, and procuring for Bowra information on smelting bronze. He also became fascinated, when at Wadham, in the discovery of Mycenaean relics, and of those in Pylos, Crete

---

[1] Sir Maurice Bowra to author.

and the Peloponnese, and in the writings telling of the end of a world that existed five hundred years before Homer, who had probably only heard of that world in legend. He was later to be fascinated, too, by Ventry's genius which succeeded in the modern age in deciphering them, and thus turning back a curtain of the incredible past. The story appealed to his love of unraveling things, of solving problems, and to his instinct for the dramatic.

Bowra felt none of the "Great Man" worship felt by some in Lindemann's presence. He saw in him an able business partner with whom he could do a deal, and their characters were too disparate to permit an intimate friendship. Bowra disliked what he regarded as Lindemann's philistinism, his sneering references to the classics, and his inability to feel poetic beauty or to understand any form of art. He felt somewhat repelled also by the pharisiaism which led him, a supposed atheist, to be in favor of the Church of England for what Bowra considered political reasons, but we shall see that in fact this supposed atheism was far from certain.

What was the contribution that Lindemann made to science after the assumption of his Chair? He had many enemies, a large number of his own making. Those who disliked him maintained that he was a once great physicist who had fallen a victim to the blandishments of the English aristocracy. It was thought by many that he had become a worldling and a snob, who had deserted the profession in which he had been trained, and for which he was so eminently gifted. In spite of this, his high scientific reputation was recognized when, in October 1919, Professor Jeans wrote to tell him that a number of Fellows had spoken to him of the suitability of Lindemann as a candidate for Fellowship of the Royal Society, but added: "You probably know that a candidate's chance of election at his first time of standing is slight." Lindemann gratefully accepted the suggestion, and eventu-

ally, in spite of the hazards of a first standing, he was elected
F.R.S. in March 1920 at the early age of thirty-three, a clear
tribute to his brilliant record.[1]

Before attempting to explain his work in recreating the
Clarendon Laboratory, which he achieved from miserable
beginnings, until it began to approach in fame the Cavendish at
Cambridge, we should notice what his own desires and ambitions were in his new post. Two letters explain them perfectly, and they should be considered together. One is addressed to the American physicist Robert A. Millikan, and
the other to Mr. Vickers of the firm of Armstrong Vickers.
These letters give us a true indication of the state of
Lindemann's mind at the outset of his Oxford career. The letter
to Millikan also shows that he was seriously considering offers
of scientific work in America, should his application for the
Oxford Chair fail:

> The main desideratum however is to my mind that there
> should be ample opportunity for research and not too much
> time lost in teaching. By research I mean pure research,
> unfettered by considerations of industrial application, and
> by opportunity I imply the power to get good men to work
> on the problems in which one is interested, rather than the
> possession of elaborate apparatus in magnificent buildings.
> Another point of the greatest importance to my mind is the
> opportunity of frequent and unofficial meetings with workers
> in the same or allied subjects, for the law of mass action holds
> in physics as well as in chemistry.
> At Oxford, for instance, one is within a few hours journey
> of all the English universities and observatories and one has
> long holidays in which one can visit the continental labora-
> tories. One need not lecture for more than a few hours a
> week and should be able to inspire a dozen or so students

[1] Cherwell archives.

to research along those lines which one believes to be promising. On the other hand, the pay and yearly grant for keeping
up the laboratory are comparatively meagre. In America one
cannot hope for such a high concentration of science per unit
area, but the facilities in the way of apparatus may be greater.
In view of the social unrest likely to prevail over here and to
disturb scientific work I should be much inclined to go to
America provided I could find a post which offered sufficient
remuneration and leisure to allow me to keep in close touch
with the American and European physicists and first and foremost provided that I could reckon upon adequate facilities
for building up a research school. I fear you will think I am
looking for Utopia.

His election as Professor ended any plans for settling in
America, but we find him on November 8, 1919, writing a letter from the Clarendon Laboratory appealing for financial
aid to Mr. Vickers. In it he renews his claims on behalf of pure
research, and explains the financial plight of physics at Oxford.

His own words are largely a justification for his actions —
the poverty of Oxford science, the patronizing contempt in
which he felt it was held by humanists, the proud need to
equate it with the older schools of learning. He had convinced
himself with some justice that scientists were regarded by the
leaders of these as scruffy, barely accepted additions to an
ancient seat of learning, and that it was his duty in every way to
forward their cause. To do this he sought to establish the vital
importance of pure as well as applied physics, and to make perfectly clear that pure research was the quarry which mere in-
ventors excavated:

> When we speak of inventions we mean generally the applica-
> tion of some well known scientific principle to produce some-
> thing that will be of use in everyday life. It is the stage
> between the discovery of the fundamental scientific principle

and the industrial production and distribution of the article in question. Thus the inventor need not be a great scientist; indeed he seldom is. For a great scientist is a man who hews new pathways through the jungle of our ignorance, who discovers new phenomena and new theories to interpret them. The inventor is the man who realises that such pathways lead to delectable places and paves and drains them.

To Vickers he wrote with evident sincerity and a sense of real urgency when describing the plight of Oxford science:

The University of Oxford, as you no doubt know, is poor, and even the Colleges, which were comparatively well-off before the war, are now suffering like everybody else in consequence of the depreciation in the value of the sovereign. Under the circumstances it is therefore impossible to expect sufficient grants from the usual sources to carry out research on an adequate scale.

It will I think be generally conceded that the progress and standing of a nation will be measured by the amount it contributes to the advancement of knowledge. I need only instance the difference in the France of 1860 and 1880 or the Germany of 1860 and 1910. Though apparently purely academic, every addition to our knowledge re-acts upon industrial problems and either suggests improvements in technical processes or at any rate prevents the waste of time entailed in attempting impossibilities. It is not too much to say, therefore, that the neglect of pure science, as opposed to applied science, would be fatal to our prospects.

To use a simple analogy, an applied scientist would, no doubt, have improved the old semaphore telegraph, but the electric telegraph could only be produced as the result of apparently purely academic researches in a laboratory on the interaction between electricity and a magnet. It is precisely in this type of research I hope to interest you, not that I can promise or hold out hopes of any immediate technical results, but because I am convinced that all progress is ultimately made in this way. . . . Any research involving appreciable expense is almost impossible.

The amount required is not very large since no important capital expenditure for building or the like is contemplated. What is wanted is an annual grant if possible of £1,000 to £1,500 which is earmarked solely for research purposes. . . . If you think there is any chance of private benefactors subscribing some such annual amount I should be most grateful if you would put the matter before them. It would be desirable of course if they could be persuaded to commit themselves to a period of say three or better five years.

Unless one can promise a continuance of laboratory facilities for some such period it will be difficult to attract good men. At the end of such time however I am confident that the Oxford physics school will have established itself, thanks to this assistance, in such a commanding position, that the University will continue the grant if the private benefactors withdraw. Unless our success is sufficient to ensure this I shall have to confess that I have failed.

He was not, however, to fail, and his immense administrative labors were to bring European fame to the Clarendon Laboratory, which is a monument to the exertions of one man. The old laboratory was indeed a sorry legacy to receive, and the only advantage it offered was that he was able to create a new establishment from nothing. It had been built for Professor Clifton in 1872, and by 1900 the subject had become so much extended in scope that a second professorship was established to cover the advancing science of electricity and magnetism. In 1901 the new Wykeham Chair of Experimental Physics was founded with Professor J. E. Townsend as the first occupant. Until his new electrical laboratory adjoining the Clarendon was built with the endowments of the Drapers Company in 1910, his work was carried out in rooms in the University Museum in the Observatory. Mr. Keeley thus describes the origins of this now great institution:

The original Clarendon Laboratory, which now in modified and enlarged form houses the Department of Geology, was built in 1872 for Professor Clifton, being financed from the proceeds of the sale of the Earl of Clarendon's "History of the Great Rebellion." Dr. Madan, a former Bodley's Librarian, writes as follows: "Henry, Lord Cornbury, grandson of the historian, the first Earl of Clarendon, left many of the first earl's papers to trustees, with the direction that the money from the sale or publication of his papers should be the nucleus of a fund for an academy for riding or other exercises at Oxford. This was in 1751. But he died before his father. However, a sister carried out his intention, but the money was left to accumulate. In 1860 his trustees found they had £ 10,000, but as the University did not need a riding school, but did badly want a laboratory for physical science, his trustees, by that wisdom which belongs only to lawyers and trustees, promptly erected the Clarendon Laboratory which Professor Clifton was the first to administer in 1872. . . ."

When Lindemann came in 1919 the Clarendon Laboratory was in much the same state as when it was built, and, apart from the teaching of some dozen undergraduates, the responsibility of a single University demonstrator, little work had been done for many years. There was an inadequate water supply, lighting was entirely by gas (fishtail burners) and the only electricity was generated by a small private plant. For demonstration purposes a small gas engine driving a dynamo could be started up. There was a workshop with a treadle lathe and a few tools, the mechanic in charge of which was also responsible for the general maintenance of the laboratory and its apparatus. Modern equipment, both mechanical and scientific, was almost entirely absent, and the annual budget of some £ 2000, a great deal of which was earmarked for routine expenditure, was pathetically inadequate for what should have been an up-to-date progressive department. The Clarendon in 1919 in fact reflected great discredit on Lindemann's predecessor. Professor Clifton, who had held the Chair for about forty years, had been entirely opposed to research. The building which housed the physics department was fairly large, with a number of rooms in which research could have been conducted, although far from ideal for the purpose. It was built in the Gothic style and had a remarkable construction in which no metal was allowed to be used, since this would adversely affect measurements of the earth's magnetic field.

When Lindemann assumed this depressing inheritance he found scarcely any apparatus suitable for carrying out research, no facilities for electric power and, above all, no staff of research physicists. In fact, as regards physics, Oxford was moribund, while Cambridge, at, or approaching, its greatest, was the leading university for physics in Great Britain, and probably in the world.

When considering the charges so often brought against Lindemann by his enemies that he was a once fine research physicist who had fallen by the wayside drawn by the lure of great houses and names, and by a growing absorption in politics, we shall find the truth of the matter in the words of Professor Derek Jackson, F.R.S., who, writing of the old Clarendon, said:

It was the Prof's ambition to change all this, to make Oxford physics worthy of Oxford. He had a threefold task: to get the buildings made more suitable for research; to get funds for buying the apparatus necessary for research; and to get the research workers, and funds for paying them. This vast task obviously made it almost impossible for the Prof to carry out research himself; research is very much a whole time job, and the expense of time and energy in which the Prof was involved left him little possibility of doing research personally. In spite of this, he was able to produce an entirely new form of electrometer, constructed from minute fuzed quartz fibres, which was not only much more sensitive than any earlier form of electrometer, but was also compact and stable so that, with the appropriate simple electric circuit, it proved an effective means of measuring the minute currents emitted when a photoelectric cell is illuminated with a very feeble light.[1]

His tendency to throw out brilliant ideas to his young men for research, which he seldom followed to their conclusion himself in the laboratory, was a positive advantage to Oxford science, as it released him from routine and left him free for general supervision and important outside contacts. Indeed, it can be argued that the Clarendon would never have reached its commanding position under a Professor more devoted to personal research. But it is not true to say that Lindemann never conducted research in the laboratory. From 1919 to 1928 he worked there with the men he had appointed — Keeley, Bolton King and R. d'E. Atkinson. It was in any case necessary for him to do so, for at that time physics was at a low ebb in England, and the Cavendish at Cambridge enjoyed an absolutely dominating position. At the beginning his laboratory was somewhat amateur in character, and it was only later that he formed a plan for combining nuclear physics and low-temperature research. The advantage of this example was that when a research student protested, "I can't," Lindemann could reply, "I can."

The work of a new vigorous hand was quickly visible in the transformation of the old laboratory. Clearly a completely new installation of electricity, gas and water had to be provided as a first requirement, and the University, realizing the disgraceful obsolescence of the existing services, undertook the work at once.

- Professor Derek Jackson, F.R.S., to author.

The build-up of staff, academic and technical, was a far more serious problem, and it was eventually solved by Lindemann's energy in his first years at Oxford, by the charm and persuasiveness which he could command when he wished, and by his quietly passionate determination to raise the defunct Clarendon Laboratory to the glories of the Cavendish at Cambridge.

In those early days he consumed much of his energy in putting his case for a continually increasing annual grant for more research and teaching staff and more mechanics. Between 1919 and 1939 the research and academic staff had increased from two to twenty, and the technical staff from one to five, and the intake of undergraduates from six to twenty-five. In his efforts to obtain financial support from the University, Lindemann was ably seconded by Mr. I. O. Griffith, Fellow of Brasenose, a member of Hebdomenal Council and of most of the relevant committees, and a powerful ally.

In spite of this, the University could not provide all that was necessary for the transformation of the Clarendon, and it was by his tapping of rich outside sources that Lindemann proved his immense administrative value. Already, as a result of his contacts at Farnborough, he numbered many industrialists among his friends. His persistence in approaching these people was unflagging, and his tact was perfect. He never allowed himself to degenerate into the role of scientific mendicant. Always at his lucid best on paper, his letters to them were admirably written, and full of modest persuasiveness. Frightened of importunity, he made careful preliminary drafts of these letters. Such skill did he show in these approaches that he enlisted the sympathy of many leading companies in the needs of his department, and received from them large contributions.

The electrical supply laid on in 1919 was 100 volts D.C., and there was no supply of alternating current, which can easily be transformed to other voltages, and which is essential in a scientific laboratory. Through one of their directors, Mr. Fairbairn, the English Electric Company presented a motor-generator to Lindemann which supplied the department with A.C. for many years, until, long after the rest of Oxford, the mains supply to the science area was converted to A.C.

In a similar way the electrolytic plant producing hydrogen for liquefaction and oxygen for glass-blowing was provided through Mr. A. Edgar Knowles by the International Electrolytic Plant Company, Ltd., Chester. Lindemann owed much, too, to the co-operation of the Associated Electrical Industries group of companies, particularly Metropolitan Vickers and the British Thomson-Houston Company, the latter presenting and installing one of the first betatrons built in this country. The growing importance of the laboratory was recognized by the Department of Scientific and Industrial Research (D.S.I.R.), which made numerous grants for research of "especial timeliness and promise." All these additions to the equipment of the laboratory were directly due to his personal initiative.

Perhaps his most successful negotiation was twenty-five years later with Lord Nuffield. They were personal friends, and Lindemann often stopped on his way back from London in the summer to play a round of golf at Huntercombe with Nuffield. He had for long attempted without success to interest the manufacturer in science, but he had found, as others before him, that Nuffield, although generous to a fault in his benefactions to medicine, found it difficult to understand the importance of pure and indeed even of applied physics.

At last Lindemann persuaded him to support his application to the Trustees of the Nuffield Foundation, as a result of which the University was offered and accepted a sum of £8000 per annum for eight years from 1946, which was later extended by a total of £20,000 over the five years 1954 –58. This grant was exceptionally useful as it gave a great deal of discretion in its allotment, being available both for research workers and workshop staff.

There was, between the two Oxford departments of physics, the Clarendon Laboratory and the Electrical Laboratory, a dichotomy by statute on the teaching side, the Clarendon being limited to instruction in heat, light and sound, while electricity and magnetism were taught in the Electrical Laboratory.

No such limitation was laid down for research, but although the two professors eventually became firm friends, after bitter rivalry between their two departments, there was an almost complete absence of liaison between them. This was due largely to Townsend's rejection of the Theory of Relativity, of which Lindemann was one of the foremost exponents, and a consequent difference of interpretation of their work.

This separation of function had long fretted Lindemann's orderly mind, and on Townsend's retirement, his Chair, in accordance with Lindemann's ideas and largely on his initiative, was converted to theoretical physics; the two laboratories were joined administratively and, when a small extension was built a short time later, structurally. The new professor and his staff are still housed in this department, thus meeting Lindemann's often expressed ideal that there should be the most intimate relations between the two sides of the subject.[1]

From the beginning of his appointment at Oxford his work was to be mainly concerned with directing the research of young workers, choosing men of outstanding ability, and raising funds to pay them, and to pay for the apparatus they required. One of his most brilliant pupils, now Professor Derek Jackson, F.R.S., pointed out that for these tasks his personal charm was an enormous asset, and that many successful physicists owe their careers to him. His success in choosing the right

[1] T. C. Keeley to author.

research workers is apparent in the list of Fellows of the Royal Society whose research was carried out at the Clarendon Laboratory.

The first research workers to join him at Oxford were men whom he had met at Farnborough during the Great War. One of these, G. B. M. Dobson, has become a leading meteorologist, discovering the presence of ozone in the upper atmosphere and its effect in raising the temperature in that region. For Dobson, who came from Cambridge and the Royal Aircraft Establishment, Lindemann persuaded the University to create a new post, and later a college to provide a new fellowship. Dobson collaborated with him in his research on meteors and the upper atmosphere. By a combination of simple physical ideas and elegantly direct mathematics, Lindemann and Dobson were the first to explain meteoric flashes, their heights of appearance and disappearance and the distribution of light along the trails. They showed that there must be a region of high temperature in the middle atmosphere — an important and striking new conclusion. This work is of permanent value, and is probably the most important scientific research done by Lindemann at Oxford.

Of T. R. Merton,[1] his predecessor in spectroscopy at the Clarendon Laboratory, from Lindemann's arrival there until 1926, Jackson observes:

At that time the concept of isotopes (atoms having the same nuclear charge or atomic number, and thus identically the same chemical properties, but with different atomic weights or mass numbers) was relatively new. Merton was able to show that the wavelengths of the lines of two different isotopes of the element lead, one ordinary lead, and the other lead formed as a result of radioactive decay of radium, were measurably different, a most interesting discovery, in that it showed that it was possible by spectroscopic methods to distinguish

[1] Now Sir Thomas Merton, F.R.S.

between two isotopes. In recent years this has become an important effect in nuclear physics.[1]

A. C. G. Egerton, whom we have already met at Farnborough, was another of the earlier research workers whom Lindemann attracted to Oxford, a brilliant scientist and an intimate friend. He made measurements of vapor pressures of metals, tracing the change in vapor pressure with the change in temperature, and showing that it conformed precisely with the predictions of thermodynamics. He was an expert on combustion and on the relative merits of various fuels, and became a member of the Scientific Advisory Committee to the War Cabinet and Chairman of the Scientific Advisory Committee to the Ministry of Fuel and Power.

These three men whom Lindemann had chosen, Dobson, Merton and Egerton, were all elected Fellows of the Royal Society, and the last two were knighted. Merton served as Treasurer of the Royal Society and Egerton as Secretary. Merton combined with a gift for physics a passion for salmon fishing, and acquired a fine collection of pictures, being one of the few private collectors in the world to possess two Botticellis. On leaving Oxford he continued spectroscopic research in a private laboratory attached to his house in Herefordshire. His place was taken by Jackson who, apart from Keeley, Bosanquet, Bolton King and de Selincourt, was the next chronologically to join Lindemann's team.

Keeley might well be called Lindemann's alter ego in the Clarendon story, and he became a fundamental part of his life. So highly did Lindemann think of him that he released emoluments from Wadham to which he was entitled in order to pay for Keeley's fellowship, and his great indebtedness to him is shown by the fact that he was responsible for the laboratory throughout the war and from 1951 to 1953.

[1] Professor Derek Jackson, F.R.S., to author.

Jackson's impressions of Lindemann as a superior are fresh and firsthand:

> So I got to know the Prof and his ways in physics in this post First War period. He had in common with other great physicists the gift of inspiring enthusiasm and confidence in their work in the men working in his laboratory. Research in physics, then as now, can be very discouraging; weeks and months may pass full of hard work but producing no tangible results or even no progress towards the solution of a problem; and it was in these bad times that the personality of the Prof came to the rescue. Regularly he visited in their laboratories all the men working in his Clarendon Laboratory; and, even if the technique was rather far removed from that which he had acquired in experimental and theoretical physics so that he could not give any exact advice as to how some particular difficulty could be overcome, his sympathetic encouragement enabled the research worker to persevere and find the solution himself.

Jackson, like others, noted and approved Lindemann's aptitude for finding methods that were simple both mathematically and experimentally, but was forced to admit that his enthusiasm for rapidly obtaining, and by simple means, an approximate result, could be dangerous, as it might result in missing a discovery of the highest importance.

Although an able mathematician, Lindemann was rightly adverse to using a problem in theoretical physics as a peg on which to hang an extensive mathematical development, which, though interesting to mathematicians, would achieve very little toward the solution of the problem in physics. His ability to make lightning mental calculations was extraordinary and became almost a legend in the scientific world. He would use it with devastating effect to confound wild generalizations, and in science was adept at producing in a minute the numerical answer to a long and cumbersome formula.

He occasionally consulted a little slide rule which he always carried with him, and had two other aids to his work in the laboratory which were always at hand — a miniature Galilean telescope, sufficiently powerful to enable him to read the smallest writing on the blackboard in spite of his defective eyesight, and a small pocket flash lamp shaped like a fountain pen, which he used for reading the indication of the various meters in the laboratories of the research workers he was visiting — meters which often had to be so feebly illuminated that several minutes of accommodation were needed before they could be read without additional light. The appearance of this large fountain-pen-like object which he carried everywhere amused his nonscientific friends, and came to be accepted as one of the eccentricities of his personal attire. Always a man of gadgets, he was later to refresh himself in the House of Lords in hot weather with an electric pocket fan, to the amusement and the envy of his fellow peers.

We are afforded another glimpse of Lindemann at Oxford through the eyes of an accomplished later pupil, now Professor R. V. Jones of Aberdeen University. He first met Lindemann in 1930 when he was an undergraduate at Wadham and attended his lectures. Partly from Lindemann's inbred diffidence, and partly through a complete ignorance of the art of elocution his lectures were almost inaudible and in consequence sparsely attended, although the matter was admirable. This fatal weakness was to dog him through life, and went far to ruin his speeches later in the House of Lords. His most successful lectures were to come later, after the war, on the relations between physics and philosophy and were well attended by men from both faculties.

It was Lindemann's habit each term to set an examination instead of the usual College Collections,[1] including a few of his own intelligence questions. Jones did not realize that these

[1] Examination papers set at the beginning of each term on work done in the vacation.

questions had been set personally by Lindemann, and left himself no time to answer any of the others. This happy miscalculation delighted Lindemann, who at once began to take a personal interest in Jones. The undergraduate found that when following up an idea of Lindemann's about heat radiation his Professor's mind was always ranging far ahead of his own — "a super-speed and superb mind of imagination," which was continually throwing out ideas for investigation.

He thought that Lindemann was often unwilling to justify the exploration of a theory, and that it was because he was so enamored of theory that he was prone to ignore fact. Lindemann did not take kindly to opposition in any form, and was capable of taking a spiteful and petty revenge. He was angry when Jones changed a certain plan of research, because he thought that Lindemann was proceeding upon a false premise, and prohibited him from having the use of the workshops for several months. "You depend too much on mechanics," he said.

His resentment at opposition carried him to the length of deducting from the pay of one of the mechanics five shillings a week, then a considerable sum, because the man had said that certain work could not be done. In the first case Lindemann was not even right, and Jones, continuing work out of hours, proved his contention which concerned the instruments for detecting infrared radiation.

Professor Max Born, an eminent physicist and friend of Lindemann, like R. V. Jones, also mused over the reasons why Lindemann's ideas at this time seldom advanced beyond general abstract ideas.

I have pondered what feature of his character prohibited this versatile mind from producing a great new concept of physics, comparable with the quantum of action. Planck stuck to classical concepts as long as possible; but when he had convinced himself that the facts of observation could not be explained in the frame of classical theory he was just as decided to develop new and strange ideas. He was a revolutionary not by character but through his willingness to acknowledge the power of evidence. Lindemann, though conservative in many respects, had a natural revolutionary strain which found its outlet in physical theory. He had little respect for traditional thinking and as soon as some new facts appeared not to fit in with current theory he jumped to conclusions about fundamental assumptions without analysing the evidence in detail. His occupation with other things, the administration of his laboratory, University affairs and politics, allowed him little time for following up his ideas and for looking in the physical literature for confirmation.[1]

Lindemann at this time seldom spoke of science to his friends unless asked a direct question, to which he would always give a lucid and sometimes dramatic reply, but it was evident that he gave it deep and continuous thought. This fact appears from one of his interesting forms of recreation, the study of the theory of numbers which, with social activity, tennis and piano playing, helped to pass his considerable leisure hours. It is yet another indication that his interest in mathematics did not wither away after his appointment to his Chair.

Professor E. M. Wright was much impressed by Lindemann's experiments in the theory of numbers, which were to him the same relaxation as a game of bridge would be to an ordinary man.

The Prof published three papers on the Theory of Numbers . . . all in the Quarterly Journal of Mathematics. The first (1933) gave a very simple and elegant proof of the Fundamental Theorem of Arithmetic (that the factorisation of an integer into primes is unique). The second paper (1946) on the frequency of prime-pairs, triplets etc. was the most charac-

[1] Professor Max Born to author.

teristic. He found formulae in connection with Goldbach's Theorem and others for the frequency of occurrence of any pattern (e.g. p, p + 2, p + 6 all primes) by simple heuristic arguments confirmed by experiment (i.e. counting). He was unaware that Stäckel (1916–18), and Hardy and Littlewood (1923) had found the same formulae, the former by very lengthy probability arguments and the latter by elaborate analytic methods using an improved hypothesis. The formulae are clearly right, but no rigorous proof had yet been found. The Prof's arguments are much the simplest and most direct and illuminating of the three. This paper was sent to the Quarterly and referred by G. H. Hardy.[1] He reported favourably but said that it should be sent to me to recommend amendment. . . . The Prof and I had some correspondence and I contributed a brief note on the work done by Stäckel and Hardy and Littlewood.

I could not understand one particular step in his argument and asked him to explain it. The explanation was simple and it was stupid of me not to have understood it. But the fact that so simple a step was not obvious led the Prof to consider what else could be deduced from the principle involved. This led eventually to a joint paper "Mean Values of Arithmetical Functions" with F. V. Atkinson, now Professor at Canberra but then a lecturer at Christ Church. . . .

The Prof's main interest, however, lay in the possibility of obtaining proofs by the methods of probability of the prime number theorem (i.e. the approximate formula for the number of primes less than a large integer) and of his tentative results about prime-patterns. There are, of course, several well-known proofs of the Prime Number Theorem; but none is simple or at all transparent, and he was not alone in feeling that it ought to be possible to produce a proof which is more obviously the "right" one. If one applies probability arguments in the most straightforward way, one gets the wrong result. Obviously this difficulty has to be cleared up before one can begin

[1] One of the greatest pure mathematicians of the day.

on the much more difficult problem of making this kind of proof rigorous. After much discussion and correspondence, the Prof eventually obtained an explanation of where the probability arguments go wrong.

We had a prolonged correspondence about the Goldbach and "prime-patterns" problems. As a result I drafted two heuristic "proofs" of the formulae, which were short and made it clear where the gap still occurred. The Prof felt that we could go further on these lines and obtain a complete proof. I was more pessimistic since many mathematicians of outstanding ability had seriously tackled this problem and the real difficulties they had encountered were precisely those that we were up against.[1]

Lindemann's work on the theory of numbers is convincing proof of his remarkable ability to have interesting ideas even in a field in which he was an amateur, and in equal association with such a great pure mathematician as G. H. Hardy.

Perhaps his most notable contribution to Oxford physics was his introduction of Jewish scientists from the spring of 1933 onward, when the Nazi persecution made it dangerous for them to continue working in Germany. He was one of the first to realize that these brilliant men, owing to the folly and brutality of Hitler, were now available for research work at the highest level abroad. He wasted no time, went at once to Germany to visit them with a view to inviting some of them to continue their research work in his Clarendon Laboratory; there was, he thought, room for at least six of them to continue their work at Oxford and to assist in the development of his laboratory.

For the funds to pay their salaries he relied on his own powers of persuasion, which he proposed to exercise on such corporations as Imperial Chemical Industries, or upon Oxford Colleges or private individuals with sufficient resources.

[1] Professor E. M. Wright to author.

In approaching such people he had the immense advantage over the ordinary professor of being on close personal terms with many of the leaders of industry, such as Melchett and Mc-Gowan of Imperial Chemical Industries, and Nuffield of Morris Motors.

Another advantage was that by his habit of taking motoring holidays abroad he had remained in touch with the continental laboratories, and he had a good general idea of the men who worked in them. His methods of enlisting these scientists were described by one of the first to be approached, Professor Max Born:

In the spring of 1933 I was compelled to leave Germany as a consequence of Hitler's accession to power. We spent the summer in Selva, Val Gardena, South Tyrol, and there Lindemann appeared with his car and chauffeur, to discuss the political situation with me, in particular the fate of the numerous scientists who had lost their position in Germany. He explained to me his plan to improve the situation of science in Oxford by inviting refugee physicists to the Clarendon Laboratory. I was not available for this project as Cambridge had offered me a post. But I was deeply impressed by Lindemann's idea which was not only generous to the homeless scientists but clever and farsighted in regard to the future of Oxford.

Lindemann was convinced that science would dominate the fate of the civilised world. He regarded the expulsion of so many excellent brains, even of a genius like Einstein, not only as a foul misdeed, but an indescribable stupidity of the Nazi regime, and he decided to make good use of the error by collecting a group of eminent men in his laboratory.

He did not shrink from travelling far and wide through Europe to achieve this aim, and thus he found me in Selva. . . . It is known how he made the Clarendon one of the centres of physics in Great Britain by inviting Simon and his group, Kurti, Mendelssohn, Kühn and others, providing them with decent positions, excellent working conditions, and — last not least — of encouraging them through a deep understanding of their projects . . . although he practically gave up physical research he was always amazingly up to date not only about the work done in the Clarendon, but everywhere in the world.[1]

His action in securing the German scientists was sometimes wrongly attributed to a selfish desire to increase the prestige of Oxford science and his own Clarendon Laboratory in particular. In fact, he did excellent work in placing distinguished German Jewish scientists in other English universities besides Oxford, and in obtaining grants for them. To this end he worked mainly with the Academic Assistance Council, whose Chairman was Lord Rutherford, and I.C.I. (Imperial Chemical Industries), whose chairman at that time was Sir Harry McGowan.

The only difference of emphasis between them was that, whereas the object of the Academic Assistance Council was to help all displaced German scholars to find work and to obtain temporary maintenance grants in any country, the avowed intention of Lindemann and I.C.I. was to take action so that science should not be deprived of the services of its most important exponents. He insisted more than once that the object was not philanthropy but to promote scientific progress in England. He wrote to Einstein on May 4, 1933, saying that the present circumstances in Germany might provide an opportunity to get one or two good theoretical physicists to Oxford for two or three years. No doubt, as things became worse, the concept widened, and though his first thought may have been the cause of science in Oxford in particular and in England generally, it is certain that his sympathy and gen-

[1] Professor Max Born to author.

erosity were aroused by the misfortunes of these men, some of whom were old friends and colleagues.

Admirable as his selection of the German scientists was, one discordant element must be noted. One of them behaved with deplorable intellectual arrogance, and was refused an I.C.I. grant. A brilliant physicist, he had been engaged on atomic research in his own laboratory in Berlin. Lindemann offered him a position at Oxford which he did not want. His father had asked Sir Hugo Hirst to help his son, and other scientists had written to Lindemann supporting him and extolling his brilliance. After much insolent behavior toward those who were trying to help him, he was dropped, and did not come to England, causing Lindemann to make the acid comment:

> As to his own ability, I have no doubts whatever. His methods of dealing with people, however, seem very extraordinary. Let us hope that he is such a great genius that he need not fall into line with the usages customary amongst lesser mortals.[1]

Thus physics in Oxford was immensely strengthened, and its future prestige assured, but there is another matter involved which is indicative of Lindemann's character. His kindness to these Jewish *émigrés* and the fact that he became a close personal friend to several of them show clearly that his hostile attitude toward Jews was never a deep one and was probably, with much else, casually absorbed in youth. It would be cynical to assume, as some have done, that his kindness to the German Jews was merely a matter of self-interest in the cause of Oxford physics. His fondness for these men, particularly Simon, and his deep pride in their achievements exclude any such suggestion.

An important consequence of their arrival was that the Clarendon became the most advanced low-temperature lab-

[1] Cherwell archives.

oratory in England, and probably in the world, and Lindemann was able to return to the subject that had fascinated him as a student in Berlin, low-temperature physics.

Professor Simon was the senior member of the group of physicists who helped Lindemann to establish the school of low-temperature research at Oxford. He was already famous for the work he had accomplished in Berlin and Breslau in this field, which had established him as one of the world's leading low-temperature physicists. He was an expert both in experimental research and in the peculiar thermodynamic properties at very low temperatures. In spite of Simon's great distinction and European fame, he "relied," says Jackson, "exclusively on Lindemann's advice; and depended entirely on him in the matter of administration, Lindemann having to persuade the University, the D.S.I.R. and Imperial Chemical Industries to give the funds necessary for the personnel and apparatus needed for the work. Moreover, the Prof had already started low temperature in the Clarendon Laboratory, having constructed and successfully operated a hydrogen liquefier."[1] This instrument was built in Simon's workshop in Berlin and re-erected in Oxford.

The other scientists brought to Oxford were Nicholas Kurti, who had worked with Simon in Breslau, the brothers Franz and Heinz London, Kurt Mendelssohn, Simon's cousin, and Heinrich Kühn. Franz London was a theoretical physicist and Heinrich Kühn a spectroscopist. Each of these men was a first-class research worker, a clear proof of Lindemann's remarkable ability in picking the right man.

Simon's experimental work at Oxford was done in collaboration with a group of younger research workers, among whom were N. Kurti, who had accompanied him from Germany, B. V. Rollin, A. H. Cooke, G. L. Pickard and B. Bleaney. The last three were all Oxford students, and their excellent

[1] Professor Derek Jackson, F.R.S., to author.

work is yet another proof of how successful Lindemann was in attracting able undergraduates who had decided to make physics their career. There is no doubt that before his arrival at Oxford and his work of rehabilitation at the Clarendon, undergraduates of this caliber would inevitably have been found at Cambridge in view of the pathetic condition of Oxford physics.

As an example of the sort of contribution made by the Jewish physicists, Simon's work in connection with liquid helium was regarded as outstanding. This gas had the advantage over liquid hydrogen that far lower temperatures could be achieved by its use in low-temperature research. Simon had developed in Breslau, just before he came to Oxford, an ultrasimple method of making liquid helium. This he achieved by cooling helium, compressed to a pressure of 150 atmospheres, by means of liquid hydrogen, and then allowing it to expand to atmospheric pressure, when the work it did in expanding resulted in such a strong cooling effect that 80 per cent of the gas liquefied. In order to do this he required only a simple apparatus, and Lindemann had already got working the liquefier for producing the liquid hydrogen.

By collaborating with Simon when he was still at Breslau, and with Simon's cousin K. Mendelssohn, Lindemann was able to produce liquid helium in Oxford by Simon's expansion method in 1933. It was a strange coincidence that the issue of *Nature* in which Lindemann announced the discovery contained a similar note from Kapitza, who had reached the same result at Cambridge. Thus it came about that Oxford and Cambridge became simultaneously the only universities in the world, apart from Leiden, Berlin and Toronto, in which liquid helium was produced, and the importance of having it available cannot be overestimated.

The fundamental advantage of Simon's method of producing liquid helium was that it required a much less elaborate and expensive apparatus. It was not necessary to rely on a large staff of engineers, which would have been needed if an independent installation were used to supply all the liquid helium required in the low-temperature laboratory, as was the practice in Leiden and Toronto.

J. G. Daunt and K. Mendelssohn worked together as a team in the Clarendon Laboratory in low-temperature physics. They worked under the direct supervision of Lindemann, and independently of Simon. Their first work was the complete investigation of the properties of creeping films of liquid helium. Mendelssohn and H. London also did important work in the field of superconductivity. All these experiments were completed before the war, which put an abrupt stop to research.

Important work was also conducted at this time by one of Lindemann's favorite protégés, Derek Jackson. He stands out from all his colleagues by virtue of the extraordinary versatility of his accomplishments. Never before can one man have been a leading spectroscopist, a millionaire, a director of the Sunday newspaper with the largest circulation in the world, a gentleman rider who twice rode in the Grand National, and a night fighter pilot who won the D.F.C., A.F.C. and O.B.E. We may leave this gifted man to describe in his own words the work he performed at this time under Lindemann. He is referring to the work in the field of spectroscopy which he carried out in collaboration with H. Kühn, who came from Göttingen in the summer of 1934:

> Up to that time I had been examining the hyperfine structure of spectral lines in order to determine properties of the nucleus — the spin and the magnetic moment and also the isotope shift, from which can be discovered other properties of the nucleus. The experimental basis of this works depends on the separation of light into the rays of different wavelengths;

but the differences in the wavelengths are very small. A fundamental limitation in the smallness which could be measured was due to the Doppler effect. The light rays are emitted by atoms, moving rapidly in the gaseous state; the Doppler effect results in a change of wavelength, or frequency of the light emitted, similarly [sic] to the manner in which the note of the whistle of a train approaching becomes lower when the train passes by the hearer and recedes.

The change in wavelength due to the Doppler effect can be either to longer or shorter wavelengths since some of the atoms in the gas are approaching the observer, whilst others are receding; this results in the rays having their wavelengths spread over a band, and this spreading could be larger than the smaller hyperfine structure wavelength differences, and could thus prevent their being observed. Up to this moment the effect was minimised by making the temperature of the gas as low as possible, since the speed with which the atoms move is reduced at lower temperatures, and thus the spreading of wavelengths due to the Doppler effect is also reduced. But even with the most effective cooling, the spreading was too great and so large that in some instances hyperfine structure could not be observed, when on theoretical grounds it was expected.

I thought of a method of reducing the Doppler broadening to an amount at least ten times smaller than the lowest attainable by cooling; this was to make a beam of the atoms, in which they would all be moving in nearly the same direction, instead of in all different directions, as in a normal gas. This beam would then be observed from the side, so that all the atoms in it would be moving at right angles to the observer, and would thus have almost no component of velocity of approach or recession so that the Doppler effect would be greatly reduced — in practice to as little as one-fiftieth of that of a normal gas.

When Kühn came to Oxford, Lindemann decided that he should work in collaboration with Jackson, who welcomed association with an experienced physicist in a new and difficult project. Jackson had not met Kühn before he was brought to Oxford, but was familiar with his work, which was of the highest quality, and which had been performed in Franck's laboratory at Göttingen.

Jackson realized, as soon as Lindemann introduced them, that he had found the ideal collaborator, who agreed with enthusiasm to work with him on his new method of discovering hitherto unobservable hyperfine structures. They chose the atom potassium. It was an odd atomic number, and Jackson explained that both the isotopes have odd mass numbers, so that their nuclei should, on theoretical grounds, have magnetic moments which must give rise to hyperfine structures.

After a year's work their atomic beam was in operation, and they discovered the hyperfine structure, from which they could calculate the magnetic moment of the nucleus of the more plentiful isotope; it was five times smaller than the smallest nuclear magnetic moment measured up to that time. Consequently there was no possibility of observing the resultant hyperfine structure by any method other than their new atomic beam. It was thus established that this new method could be successfully operated, and virtually removed a previously fundamental limitation to the resolution of rays with a very small difference of wavelength.

Jackson and Kühn published the results of this research in 1934, and, from then until the outbreak of war, developed and improved the atomic-beam method of high-resolution spectroscopy. In the course of these researches an important advance was made in optical instruments to exploit to the full the possibilities of the atomic beam.

The only instrument with which the necessary high resolution can be obtained is the Fabry-Perot interferometer. With this instrument there is no limit to the smallness of difference of wavelength that can be resolved; but it has the serious disadvantage that if it is set to resolve very small differences in wavelengths, the range of wavelengths over which it can operate is also very small; it cannot therefore be used for observing a structure which has a large number of rays, some with very small wavelength differences, and others with larger ones, nor on the other hand a structure with a very large number of rays with very small differences in wavelength. The latter is just the type of structure produced when rays are emitted in a magnetic field. It is of the greatest interest for testing the newly discovered quantum mechanics, and also it gives the most reliable method of testing the nuclear spin. This limitation of the interferometer, therefore, had to be overcome; we were able to do this by using a suitable combination of the two interferometers, with a device for correctly phasing these, by adjustment of the pressure of the air surrounding them.

Those doubting Lindemann's achievements at Oxford should also consider his deep, if unorthodox, interest in nuclear physics. He wrote an important pioneer paper on the application of the Quantum Theory to nuclear structure as early as 1915. Although wrong in detail — for the neutron had not yet been discovered — it possessed two great merits. It was quantitative and recognized the importance of probability in nuclear physics. It had little influence on the contemporary development of the subject, being too far in advance of its experimental state. He also believed that artificial disintegration and the application of nuclear energy to useful purposes were not such remote possibilities as Rutherford supposed. He had carried out some initial experiments, which remained unpublished, on artificial transmutation by bombarding uranium with 100,000-volt electrons, and had believed that he had indications of a positive result, and had arranged for a young Oxford physical chemist to continue the experiments in the Clarendon. He was of course mistaken in the interpretation of his original experiments, but two or three students working on problems in nuclear physics remained in the laboratory as a result of this venture. He was thus less impressed by Rutherford's great achievement than the world at large, which knew nothing of Lindemann's early experiments in this field. When the neutron was discovered in 1932 he personally began to strengthen and develop this side of the Laboratory work. Almost without consulting the staff he ordered and obtained quick delivery of a 400 kv. high-voltage set with sealed-off valves. With this, sufficient experience was gained to design a high-voltage laboratory for incorporation in the new Clarendon in 1939. He took great interest in this and arranged for junior members to visit both Manchester and Eindhoven for consultations on detailed requirements. He also started with J. L. Tuck on the design of a betatron, while this instrument was but a pipe dream, causing D. W. Kerst, who ultimately succeeded where many others had failed, to remark: "Another unpublished investigation which would surely have succeeded were it not for the War in Europe was that of James L. Tuck at the Clarendon Laboratory, Oxford, who has designed his apparatus in collaboration with L. Szilard. . . . Of all the attempts to accelerate electrons before the initial success of the betatron, Tuck's scheme seems to have been the most promising and most complete in technical detail." [1]

Besides installing a high-voltage set, Lindemann's success in obtaining the loan of 1½ gm. of radium while the Cavendish had only ½ gm., showed how his social activities often contributed to strengthening the position of his laboratory. For many years he had been friendly with Jan Masaryk, the Czechoslovak Minister in London, and when he heard from him in the early thirties that in 1919 a large consignment of radium had been sent to London for safekeeping, he set to work and persuaded the Czechoslovak Government that it was better to lend it to the Clarendon than to pay for it to be stored in a

[1] *Nature*, 157, 94, 1946.

London bank. He carried out all the negotiations personally, arranged with Christ Church that the radium sources could be prepared in Christ Church Laboratory, and was present at the critical time when this precious but dangerous source was opened and dissolved ready for use.

Prof also persuaded Leo Szilard, a refugee who had collaborated with Einstein and worked with distinction in neutron physics, to join the small group already at work in the Clarendon. So it came about in the early years of the war that Lindemann was one of the few heads of departments with firsthand knowledge of neutron physics and fission. Although too old to have worked with neutrons himself, he had watched the new techniques grow up in his laboratory, and, by chance, was a personal friend of Hahn, who discovered fission in the Kaiser Wilhelm Institute in 1939. Indeed, when war broke out experiments on the number of neutrons emitted during fission were already under way in the Clarendon. This close acquaintance with the subject undoubtedly influenced him in his momentous advice to the Prime Minister that work on the subject should proceed in wartime.

Always bent on unification, he pressed strongly that the rare occurrence of nuclear physics and low-temperature techniques under the same roof should be exploited. He always supported experiments which used both techniques, and after twenty years of steady prodding had the reward of seeing nuclear aliment, which required the use of both techniques in highly advanced form, carried out in the Clarendon in 1951, the first undoubted "world première" which it had achieved.

This account of the work of Lindemann at the Clarendon in the interwar years should be a compelling answer to those who accused him of losing interest in science; those who made these accusations could have had little idea of the magnitude of the change which he had wrought in this derelict place. Nor did his habitual diffidence and modesty allow him to advertise his success, and he seldom referred to the Clarendon unless directly questioned.

These fruitful years were thus summarized by one of his research workers:

When the war started, the Prof had made a remarkable achievement; starting from literally nothing, he had made the Clarendon Laboratory one of the leading low temperature laboratories in the world, and also the leading laboratory for high resolution spectroscopy. It seems to me that, quite apart from the gain to physics in general and to Oxford prestige in physics which resulted from this achievement, this was of the greatest importance because it gave proof of the Prof's ability to organise and to direct research in addition to his ability as a physicist, which he had established before he came to Oxford; and the knowledge which all other physicists had of this ability, made them respect Churchill's selection of the Prof as his scientific adviser. It was of immense value to us physicists to know that we had, via the Prof, virtually direct access to the Prime Minister. We knew that the Prof would not only understand our ideas, but would also present them clearly and without distortion to the ultimate authority.[1]

It had been no easy task to persuade Oxford of the importance of physics, or indeed of science in general, and by 1939 there were only some six fellowships in physics in the whole University. It was for this reason that he fought so hard to raise the status of scientists, and it was his great achievement that at last he awakened the University to the importance of the subject, and that the new Clarendon Laboratory was built, and opened in 1939, and new fellowships created. It was the best of its kind in Britain, and its staff, kept almost intact during the war, enabled it to start research again immediately afterward, with all the apparatus and technique

[1] Professor Derek Jackson, F.R.S., to author.

acquired in the meantime. This object, of raising the derelict Clarendon to the level of the Cavendish, had constantly been before him, and although his method of attaining it had not been the traditional one of precept and the conduct of research, the credit was his alone.

If there are still those who remain skeptical about Lindemann's achievement, this opinion of a former President of the Royal Society, Sir Cyril Hinshelwood, surely places the matter beyond doubt:

> Before he came to Oxford Lindemann's most important contribution had on the whole been theoretical rather than experimental. He had one of the most brilliant analytical minds I have ever known, and he continued throughout his life here to take deep interest in the fundamentals of science. His views on all matters of theory were always worth hearing. He was always interested in the work of others, and although his criticism at times tended to be destructive, he was always fertile in suggestions about interpretations which at their best could be intensely illuminating.
>
> He had been a brilliant young man moving in the most distinguished European scientific circles, and he came, still young, into a University where science was on the whole looked down upon by the dominant schools. He found himself playing two very important and stimulating roles. On the one hand he became something of an oracle in scientific circles, and, on the other hand, he began the rehabilitation of science among those people who were forced to respect the brilliance of his mind and to recognise in this rather glamorous continental figure someone very different from the image they liked to make of the man of science. Add to this Lindemann's charm and *mondain* predeliction, and it is not hard to see him devoting a great deal of his energy to the playing of a kind of Socratic role.
>
> As far as physics (and chemistry) went this was by no means a dereliction because his analysis often was of the greatest

help to other people, and I would say that he had made a great and real contribution to the modern rise of scientific studies in Oxford. He continued to think deeply about the major problems of his subject. He did not solve them: they have not been solved yet. And we must bear in mind that Cherwell was a man who would have scorned to publish anything in the nature of a "pot boiler," even to use that word in its least pejorative sense. He stimulated many things for which he never claimed credit. (I think experts would confirm, for example, that the well known "Saha equation" is virtually contained complete in an early paper of Lindemann.)

He published a book on the quantum theory in 1932.[1] It was brilliant but was on the whole judged not to have come off, perhaps because he attempted what was then impossible. Some people have said that he preferred social success to science. I think they are wrong. He preferred it to anything but the finest vintage of science, and because it was not given to him to solve the deepest problems he was not much interested in lesser things.

Perhaps to all this one must add a certain element of indolence: though I am sure it would be wrong to place major stress on this. I think that the feeling that only the best was good enough for him inhibited quite a lot.

But he was, as I have said, greatly interested in what other people were doing. Some found him sarcastic and destructive: others responded to his charm and brilliance and were helped by him. (I belonged to the latter class though I confess to having been very angry with him on occasion.)

As time went on and he had received people like Simon into the laboratory, and his government connections could be used to initiate work in the Clarendon, he exerted himself in a way which may justly be said to have laid the foundations for the laboratory's present eminence.

To return to the theme of personal research. Most professors have too much to do to undertake large amounts of work with

---

[1] See also Appendix II.

their own hands. They work with and through research students. Why did Lindemann not produce more effect in this semi-vicarious way? He was primarily interested in fundamental theories; much less in the small change of the laboratories. He was analytical rather than a discoverer. I cannot imagine him saying "let's do so and so and see what happens." He would propose tests of theories, and I am afraid the plain truth is that what he proposed was often too difficult for the ordinary research student to carry through successfully. If things were proving impossible, Lindemann was not the man to see what could be salvaged from the wreckage, and turned to account in some other way — often a useful thing to do. And so instead of being the officer among his troops as it were, he tended more to be the stimulating Socrates of larger circles. This passed into the later phase when as patron and organiser of the great expansion he rendered "elder statesman" service of inestimable value.[1]

[1] Sir Cyril Hinshelwood to author.

5

The Interwar Years II:
The Oxford Scene

WHILE THE Clarendon Laboratory gathered strength under his hands, Lindemann had begun his close association with the great families of England, the leading politicians and industrialists. His serene progress in this direction was a source of irritation and jealousy to the enemies he had already made by his alien derivation and by a caustic wit which he made little effort to control.

He had that peculiar disability often found in vituperative men of failing to realize the effect his sarcasms produced on others, and, although aware that he had enemies, he had no conception of their numbers or their malice. Like La Rochefoucauld, he enjoyed plucking out the tail feathers of man's self-esteem, and he did so, secure and happy in the circle of those who dearly loved him, who recognized the constancy of his friendship and the almost canine loyalties which lay beneath an exterior which intimidated many, and repelled some. His humor, within its limits, was brilliant and his conversation engrossing, well informed and full of sardonic reflections. One of his close colleagues well described the impression which his private talk produced on the listeners:

His special form of humour, however, arose out of the way in which he saw things; through his vision the sundry stupidities of mankind became droll, ridiculous, laughable. It was part of his idea of the way in which life should be conducted that in conversation there should be a constant by-play with fun and jokes. Indeed his attitude was a sort of challenge to oneself. If one had a ponderous point to make to him one thought it a good plan to dress it up in an amusing guise. Thus everything was kept gay and light. He was appreciative of jokes; he sometimes gave a little chirrup, sometimes a loud guffaw, followed perhaps by a "No; not really?" [1]

Harrod adds that his laughter was monosyllabic and that it was impossible to imagine him even as a schoolboy having a fit of giggles; but here he was mistaken, for Lindemann as a boy was subject to long, devastating attacks of giggles which he was unable to suppress.

The voice was soft and often inaudible, and his jokes were usually followed by a little high confirmatory grunt. When he was angry or stung by some contradiction, the voice assumed an ugly rasping note, jarring to the ear. He was a dialectician and arguer of a high order, his memory as formidable as his power of sudden calculation, and his logic inexorable. It was unfortunate that his golden words were so often lent to the support of untenable propositions, but, right or wrong, his opponent's ground was bitten away piece by piece by the remorseless encroachment of his arguments. He would not shrink from using an argument which he knew to be wrong if by so doing he could tie up one of his professional opponents.

It often appeared to his friends that there was a naïveté in him which produced an almost protective reaction, but such intimate glimpses were naturally concealed from his enemies, who encountered only the offensive side of his character. Nor can it be denied that his behavior went far to account for their hostility. Always apt to resent criticism, he was prone to regard views opposite to his own as a personal insult. Immersed in his own dedicated task of raising Oxford science from the

[1] Sir Roy Harrod, *The Prof*, pages 84–85. (Throughout, page references are to British editions of works cited.)

ignominious position into which it had fallen, he showed a contempt for classical studies which offended humanists.

These, he thought, long accustomed to intellectual predominance at Oxford with their School of Literae Humaniores, regarded the scientific research worker patronizingly as some superior form of garage mechanic, and he was led to attacks on classical education which went far beyond his true opinion. Fervently believing that the future of the world would be determined by science, he regarded it as his solemn duty to see justice done to it.

He relieved his feelings strongly in his intimate circle when he thought others had behaved foolishly or ill toward him.

" 'I should like to castrate him,' I remember him snarling out about one of them, adding in a discouraged tone, 'not that it would make any difference.' "[1]

He was inclined to be dogmatic when talking of the classics, poetry, pictures or other subjects of which he had little understanding, and he was too prone 'to rub the gold dust from the butterfly's wing.' To his enemies, therefore, whose numbers should not be exaggerated, he appeared an offensive man of alien extraction, professing an abstruse subject, and spending much of his time ingratiating himself with exalted people.

They drew attention to the fact that he apparently conducted little, if any, personal research, and from this inferred that he was no great shakes even at his own job. The ardor with which he fought for the cause of science appeared to them excessive, and his methods tortuous and ruthless.

Such was his early unpopularity in certain circles that he was at one time accused of embezzling the funds of the University Chest. This monstrous slur on Lindemann's immaculate honor led to the appointment of an impartial examiner, Professor H. H. Plaskett, who completely cleared Lindemann of the charge.

A long time elapsed before he gained general acceptance in

[1] Sir Roy Harrod, *The Prof*, page 39.

the Senior Common Room of Christ Church. In the early days he felt a sense of exclusion from the company — an uneasy suspicion that he was not one of the tribe. He assailed the philosophers with insensitive relish. A pamphlet by Reade of Keble was brutally demolished; against the logician, H. W. B. Joseph of New College, he was fierce and impressively destructive, and was sometimes a disturbing element amid the nuts and wine. At times he gave offense unintentionally under the impression that he was indulging in genial banter. Such an occasion arose when, probing among the Christ Church statutes, he claimed to have found a provision which enjoined celibacy on the Canons of the Chapter. When confronted with this, one of the Canons murmured something about "certain anomalies." "That is all very well," said Lindemann. "When you do it you call it an anomaly. When I do it you call it living in sin."

Most of his differences with his own colleagues — and they were never serious — can be traced to his determination to establish the cause of Oxford physics. We shall see him, in the last twelve years of his life when he had become a character, the most popular member of the Senior Common Room whose appearances were eagerly awaited and of whose welcome Harrod was to write:

> If we had some interesting guest dining, our eyes strayed over to the door at about 9.15 hoping that he would appear and add new life to our party. We were usually not disappointed. The door opened slowly, and his well-known figure appeared. He walked with measured tread, for he was already ailing. He took off that heavy greatcoat, and placed it methodically on the table and the bowler hat on top of it. Then he came forward to join us, ready and anxious to be interested in the affairs of whoever was there, attentive, quite unassuming, and full of jests and anecdotes appropriate to the person. Or if there was no one who especially wanted to talk to him, and a bridge

table was out, he liked to stand behind and watch the game. He knew all about it but only very rarely interjected a comment. Over and over again we tried to persuade him to play himself, but he declined to do so on the ground that, if he made a mistake, that would cause him to lie awake all night replaying the hand.[1]

He did not play bridge because he was a poor player, and it embarrassed him to play a game he did not understand in the company of those who did. It was another instance of that fear of being at a disadvantage, of making a fool of himself. It was impossible to imagine him joining in a game of charades, or acting.

His rooms were in the Meadow Buildings. Outside his windows the flat, tranquil Meadow stretched down to the river, where painted barges lined the bank, a green haven of peace in summer from the tumult of modern Oxford. They consisted of a sitting room, dining room, and bedroom, in which was a large collection of Dornford Yates and Wodehouse novels which he read to relax his mind, and a spare room. The Christ Church authorities, less inflexible than those at Wadham, put up little resistance to the installation of a bathroom and lavatory. He also had the use of another set of rooms on the opposite side of the landing.

Although he lived in great comfort, he was painfully unaware of the *douceur de vivre,* and his blindness to the aesthetic was at once apparent to the visitor entering these rooms. The sitting room was papered in white and contained two armchairs and a sofa in gray ribbed material. The walls were covered by aerial photographs of the Atlas Mountains which he had taken with his Leica. An upright piano stood against one wall, and a box of Fuller's chocolate creams upon a table. The piano was never played during term time, as with his usual thoughtfulness he did not wish to disturb

[1] Sir Roy Harrod, *The Prof,* page 37.

his neighbors, and later it was removed from the rooms. He found that playing it at night acted upon him almost like a drug, making him oblivious to the passage of time. The pendulum of a scientific clock oscillated maddeningly upon the mantelpiece.

Further shocks awaited one in the dining room, which had a small breakfast table in a bay overlooking the Meadow. Two embarrassing Victorian pictures hung upon the walls, one depicting kittens tumbling out of a basket, and the other a nymph and her dryad reclining in an orchard, both executed in garish color. These pictures became famous in Oxford circles, and were widely cited by the more spiteful dons as proof of Lindemann's hopeless philistinism in art, but there was also, in his obstinate clinging to the kittens and dryads, an element of family loyalty, as the pictures had been given to him by his mother when he moved into Christ Church.

He was also averse by nature to rearranging anything. The kittens were painted in Brussels by a celebrated Victorian cat painter called Madame Ronner. Some of his bolder friends begged him to remove the pictures as eyesores, their advice only making him more obstinate in retaining them. In the corner of the dining room stood a glass-fronted cabinet containing the many cups he had won at tennis in a disorderly heap, the silver long tarnished.

These rooms bring back to me delightful memories of lunches as an undergraduate with Lindemann before a game of tennis or squash. Relaxed and happy with those close to him, he was a charming companion. He never attempted to monopolize the talk, but listened courteously with unassumed interest to what one had to say. In spite of the difference in our ages and our relative positions, I felt perfectly at ease with him. He had a rare instinct for words and a genius for the succinct phrase, but his judgment of the character of men, as apart from their ability, was narrow and prejudiced.

Among scientists he was remarkable for the catholicity of his interests. When he discussed English history I was struck, as a student of that school, by his grasp of the subject. Of Napoleon he had almost a specialist's knowledge, and his general reading of history ranged far beyond the confines of the School of Modern History.

He derived an impish pleasure in Common Room from asking the historians questions about Genghis Khan and the Mongolian invasions, which he knew they could not answer. "They always say 'It's not my period,'" he complained. He spoke much of politics, in which he was fast becoming deeply interested, and he had arrived at settled and somber conclusions about foreign affairs, aided by his continental background, wide travel and linguistic power.

All these matters he would discuss at our lunch parties, and I was amazed at the knowledge he had accumulated of matters outside his own professional interests. His sparse diet did not make him a frugal host. You ate excellent food in his rooms, and he pressed the finest vintage port and cigars upon his guests. It was one of the most agreeable aspects of his character that he liked to see others happy and contented, although he pretended that the wine and cigars were intended to neutralize my youth in the squash court. We would walk to the courts across the Meadow as the winter evening fell, and take the ferry across the Cherwell. As we walked down the stone stairs outside his rooms for our first game he indicated a bolted door and remarked: "There's a bloody fellow called Katz who lives there, and he does too, blast him."

One played with him more out of affection than for pleasure. He had been taught the game by the amateur champion Victor Cazalet, who had grounded him thoroughly in the art of getting in the way, and his broad and unyielding back was a constant impediment to one's vision. He was inclined to be petulant if asked for a let.

Apart from his failure in interior decoration, Lindemann lived in great comfort. His personal needs were attended to by his servant Harvey and an assistant, and his cars were driven by a chauffeur.

Lindemann enjoyed sitting up late and would talk into the small hours of the morning, a habit that was to endear him to Winston Churchill. He would lie late the following day, rising at about eleven to carry out his inspection of the laboratory. "I think," said his brother Charles, "that F. A. was rather lazy, but he knew exactly what his students were doing. Every time I came to Oxford I would go round the labs with him on Sunday, and he'd tell me exactly what was going on in every research man's room."

His interest in cars had been first awakened at Darmstadt by the Grand Duke Ernst Ludwig, who had taken him and Charles for their first drive in an Opel. After this experience they urged their father to buy a car. He responded by buying a gigantic Daimler which he drove from London to Sidmouth and "nearly touched 40 miles an hour." F. A.'s first car, which he sometimes drove himself, was a 1919 Austin. He had at the time a dangerous weakness for speed and, after the Austin, bought a supercharged Mercedes, soon followed by a second, even faster. He had no instinct whatever for danger, and it was agony to sit beside him in one of those cars, its supercharger screaming like a projectile, madly driven by a chauffeur whom even he was forced to discharge for habitual drunkenness. Later he suffered a providential collapse of nerve, and his drivers were forbidden to exceed fifty miles an hour.

When forced to take the wheel himself, he did so reluctantly and was an execrable driver, at once timid and dangerous, and in a state of sustained tension which made him abusive to other motorists, shouting, "Keep your own side of the road!" and muttering angrily at some error of the vicar's wife at

Sidmouth. A Daimler and a secondhand Rolls Royce with a bed in the back followed the Mercedes, and a Packard the Rolls Royce.

His two main anchorages at Oxford were the Clarendon Laboratory and the Senior Common Room, but it was soon apparent that he had no intention of being yet another scientist dedicated to work at the bench and oblivious to the world outside. Devoted to foreign travel, he would set out on leisurely voyages of exploration in Rolls Royce or Mercedes, often accompanied by his friend and protégé Bolton King. He traveled in patrician comfort, his progress resembling that of some English milord in the eighteenth century. He complained in Common Room that there was no second class on the Golden Arrow. An astonished chorus of voices protested:

"Oh, but Prof, you surely never travel second class?"

"No, but I mean that one has to have one's servant with one."[1]

His relations with Bolton King, whom he had made the first Duke of Westminster Research Student in 1924, were intimate. The younger man felt not only admiration for Lindemann, but also an intense personal affection, clear proof of the fascination Lindemann exerted on those who had joined their fortunes with his. "I really *loved* the Prof," he told me. "Between 1922 and 1940 he was the biggest factor in my life." Lindemann stood godfather to Bolton King's child, as he had to Tizard's son.

He loathed the English winter, which chilled and depressed him, and he would stand by a streaming window, muttering: "Isn't it absolutely foul?" Thus his journeys often took him in search of the sun, and his energies revived in the sunsplashed piazzas of Italian towns, or in the tumult of the Ramblas in Barcelona with its shoeblacks and flower stalls, an explosion of color. He was more interested in historical than

[1] Sir Roy Harrod, *The Prof*, page 90.

in artistic sight-seeing, only entering a picture gallery when there was nothing else to do that appealed to him more, such as crossing a river that had played a critical part in some by-gone campaign, or visiting a famous battlefield.

Bolton King did not resent the fact that he was used by Lindemann in the role of someone intelligent who was there to listen. He found himself becoming a foil in Lindemann's arguments about air defense, which was always, on these leisurely wanderings, in the background of his mind, somber and disturbing, intruding itself between them and the beautiful places they visited.

It came as a surprise to Bolton King that in his company Lindemann in no way resented opposition. He was obstinate, but it was possible to convince him, although it was not in his nature to admit that he had been made to change his mind by argument.

Bolton King retains glowing memories of those journeys, unclouded by a single dispute — to Savoy, and at Easter to the Riviera, which Lindemann loved, with its terra-cotta-colored houses aching in the heat, its aromatic smells, its bougainvillaea and mimosa, to Rome and Naples, and to Barcelona and Morocco through the Atlas. .

They passed Lindemann's fiftieth birthday at a mean hotel in Midelt in default of a better, and he came downstairs at the incredible hour of 6 A.M., wrinkling his fastidious nose at the odors of a French provincial *estaminet*, at the upturned tables, at the rolls and crusts of bread, the debris of the night before.

They drove out in the fresh morning through the mountains to the valley of the river Ziz, past the town of Ksar es Souk, reminding them of some biblical city, into the ravine full of palm trees, and in the shade ate omelette and French bread and cold asparagus with a tingling sauce — the happiest birthday, Bolton King thought, that his friend ever had. Together they went, again via the Riviera, to Venice, which Lindemann loved more than any other Italian city, more even than Rome, Florence and Padua.

I was his companion on a motor tour of the valley of the Loire where he showed considerable knowledge of the history of Chenonceau, Amboise and Blois, and pointed out the reaches of the river where the infamous Carrier had instructed "a reliable boatman" to carry out the Noyades. He took brilliant photographs with his Leica and cinecamera. In those interwar years we made a notable journey to Russia together on the yacht of the late Lord Camrose, a journey which tested to the full Lindemann's moral and physical courage. He was a miserable sailor and the shallow Baltic was in churlish mood. Gale followed gale, and he kept his cabin in the extremity of grief, but no one heard him utter a word of complaint.

At the Park of Rest and Culture in Moscow, where the younger members of the party jumped with trepidation from the parachute tower, he ascended it in his uniform of bowler hat, Melton overcoat and umbrella, and was bitterly disappointed when the Russians refused to allow him to jump on account of his weight. Suspicions of his sinister hosts increased when he tried in vain to see the Russian physicist, Professor Peter Kapitza, lately returned from Cambridge.

His host on this trip to the Baltic, Lord Camrose, proprietor of the *Daily Telegraph*, was one of Lindemann's most valued friends, and it was in his house that he spent some of his happiest hours. He was impressed by his host's journalistic genius and wonderful financial ability, but even more by the steadfast integrity of his character. He thought how remarkable it was that a man could reach such a position in the cutthroat world of journalism without a blemish on his name and with such an admirable reputation, and he took particular delight in his company, frequently asking his advice and seeking his judgment, which he greatly respected, on world affairs. Lindemann often used the correspondence column of the *Daily Telegraph* when he had some particular thunderbolt to launch, and appreciated the hospitality of its pages, which were always open to him.

The word "snob" was often on his enemies' lips, odious as the cry of "cheat" in a card room. On this theme they improvised spiteful jokes with a malice that matched his own. In one of the Oxford elections, contested with a venom that only the dreaming spires can engender, they passed round the riddle: "Why is Professor Lindemann like a Channel steamer?" expecting the answer: "Because he runs from peer to peer." The charge deserves consideration, for it cannot be denied that Lindemann enjoyed the company of the great. When considering his progress from one stately home to another, it is necessary to observe both his relations with other classes in the community and the attitude toward him of the various aristocrats who became his friends.

Lindemann had not the slightest rapport with either the lower or the middle classes. In the opinion of Lady Townsend, the able wife of the Professor of the Electrical Laboratory, twice Mayor of Oxford, and one of the women he most admired, he had no comprehension of the way of life or manner of behavior of the vast majority of the population of the British Isles. He was as remote from the proletariat as an aristocrat of the French *ancien régime,* and he knew little more of the retired clergyman type, with whom she had so often to deal, or of the professional classes who were working and issuing publications at the same time as himself. There was thus a great hiatus in his comprehension of the English people which was partly due to his foreign background, and which, coupled with his natural diffidence and hatred of raw emotions, would have made him an uneasy member of the House of Commons. It meant that long contact with a person was necessary before appreciation came and made possible that constant and fiercely concealed altruism to all who worked with him and under him.

Why then was he so happy in the society of the aristocracy and the leading men in politics and industry? Why was his success with them so lasting and complete? Partly, no doubt, because in his male descent he came from a country in which birth and quarterings were held in such fussy and exaggerated regard, and had an inherited reverence for historic names, but there is some force also in this explanation of his success:

> I have the idea that what he sought more than anything else was an assuagement of his own interior malaise, of which he showed so many symptoms. There, in high society, if anywhere in the world, one finds consideration; all runs smoothly, and nothing can go amiss. These people have been bred through many generations to make those they favour comfortable and happy and, yes, above all, at ease. It is to be remembered that the suspicion and hostility to which the Prof became progressively more the victim right up to the outbreak of the Second World War, originated among the professional classes, the scientists, the dons, the civil servants. But these other more aristocratic people had no such suspicions and were not interested in the matters that gave rise to them. They accepted the Prof simply for what he seemed to be and liked him for it.[1]

They found much to like in him, for it was not by his own pushfulness that he became a cherished guest at almost every great house in England. Nor was it because he professed a difficult subject which none of them, except perhaps Balfour, appreciated. When he entered these houses he left science and all her rancors behind him. The battle and the whiff of cordite were forgotten, and in these graceful surroundings the many charms of his character could unfold themselves without restraint.

[1] Sir Roy Harrod, *The Prof*, page 92.

His hosts were not slow to perceive what an excellent guest he was. With his Rolls Royce, chauffeur and valet, he lived in a manner they understood, which came as a surprise as they did not expect a scientist to be an *homme du monde*. They found his manners perfect, his presence sympathetic and his conversation stimulating. It was a relief to them that he knew many of their friends, so that there was no embarrassing need to grope for topics of conversation from which he was not excluded. They discovered with surprise that he was an exceptional tennis player, in a different class from most of the young men in the house party. He loved feminine society and was adept at talking to women, for whom he reserved a fund of up-to-date, somewhat malicious gossip, punctuated by giggles. The men were also impressed over the port which he did not drink, by his views on politics. He appeared usually to be fresh from contact with some Cabinet minister whose opinions on the vital questions of the day he relayed to his friends, and they recognized the authority with which he made their flesh creep as he spoke of our terrible vulnerability to attack from the air, and the supine indifference he had found to it in the Government.

Thus in time these distinguished hosts and hostesses who invited him to their homes, at first perhaps out of curiosity, became devoted to this strange, gifted man. They were touched also by his love of children and young people, one of his strongest impulses, for the mere fact of youth was for him delightful. It would have been out of the question for him to become *persona grata* in so many great English houses if his motives had been only snobbery and social climbing.

In June 1921 he was invited by the Duke of Westminster to Eaton Hall, and the satisfaction he found in this visit is apparent in his rather effusive letter of thanks to the Duchess about that memorable occasion, and the evening when he first met Winston Churchill:

Aug. 19, 1921

MY DEAR DUCHESS,

I really do not know how to thank you for the most enjoyable week I spent at Eaton; it will always remain one of the most delightful memories of my life. If it were permissible to express my gratitude in a mathematical symbol, I should not be at a loss. As it is not usual to do so however and as I am far too little of a poet to express my feelings in words, I will confine myself to thanking you and the Duke once again for having allowed me to spend a perfect week end every moment of which was full of pleasure and interest. . . . I must thank you also for the delightful evening I spent with you yesterday. Quite apart from the interest of meeting such a man as Winston Churchill, the evening will be memorable to me for having allowed me an opportunity of seeing you and the Duke again.

He wrote to his father of this exciting encounter, which was to have such a momentous influence on his life, in a letter which casually indicates the new trend of his friendships in the great world, and offers undeniable proof of his addiction to famous names.

Aug. 19, 1921

I am very glad we can come to Sidholme after all as I refused an invitation to the Marquess of Headfort and another of the Duke of Westminster to Scotland to meet Winston Churchill on the strength of our plans. The Duke was very keen on my meeting Churchill and arranged a special meeting in Town last night for the purpose. It was interesting but Churchill was rather "distrait."

Blenheim Palace, conveniently near Oxford, soon made him welcome, and there he encountered a duke whose knowledge of the byways of history was as extensive as his own, and who still held sway like a Renaissance prince. He found much in his visits there with which to regale his father, and it is diverting to note his acid comments on some of the eminent people he met there and to wonder what would have been the reaction of H. G. Wells:

> The Blenheim dinner and dance was most amusing. They had got H. G. Wells of all people, and the Duchess made him dance, a most comic business. He is very second rate as regards brains and was told off well by Fitzwilliam who is not considered clever at all. The Spanish Ambassador was there and numerous weird people like Jimmy Rothschild.

He had already met Lord Birkenhead, for whose brain he had formed an admiration equal to that he felt for Winston Churchill. They first met in the early summer of 1919, when Lindemann was taken to Charlton to play tennis by J. C. Masterman, then a Christ Church don and a famous athlete, and E. F. Herring, an Oxford Lawn Tennis Blue and former Captain of the Oxford side. They became close friends, and he made many visits to Birkenhead's house at Charlton before and after his host's death. He made his first impact on this house by his excellence at tennis in a place where the game was held in high esteem, and on courts where some of the greatest players in the world — Brugnon, Austin, Norman Brooks, Señorita Alvarez and Mrs. Lambert Chambers, among many others — had appeared.

Birkenhead knew nothing of science, but was soon, like Churchill, captivated by Lindemann's brain and afterward conquered by his charm. He became a familiar figure in the house, and his friendship with Birkenhead so matured that he became a companion on his foreign holidays, easygoing and witty, but always with a faint aura of mystery about him, and the pleasure with which he was welcomed by us makes it easy to understand the favor with which he was regarded by others.

It was at Charlton that the nickname "the Prof," by which he came to be known almost universally, was bestowed upon him by Birkenhead's eldest daughter, Eleanor. The name suggested an intimacy, which pleased him; perhaps it somehow denoted friendship and acceptance to his uncertain mind, and provided a welcome alternative to the abhorred "Peach." So wide was its acceptance that it will be convenient to use it in future references to Lindemann.

As with Birkenhead, so with Winston Churchill; Prof's relations grew closer and more intimate, Churchill indeed sometimes bending his powerful and restless brain to a consideration of the Prof's own subject:

4 April 1926

I was so much interested in your book that I have consumed a morning which ought to have been devoted to the Budget in dictating this note while the impression was still fresh in my mind. I would be so much obliged to you if you would correct it for me, and I shall then have a true general view in my mind.

There are a great many points which I want to ask you about, and I look forward very much to our next meeting. I will only mention one now. Have the relations between music and mathematics been examined in the same way as those between mathematics and physics? Is there any sort of correspondence? If so, there will be a correspondence between music and physics other than mere sound waves. Might there not be a notation which would cover not merely sound waves but harmonies and discords, rhythms and cadences; and might not this notation be found in the absolute?

With all good wishes

WINSTON S. CHURCHILL

It was no doubt this growing friendship with Churchill which prompted the latter to take him on to the *British Gazette* during the General Strike in 1926. Churchill was delighted with the opportunity of editing a newspaper, and ordered his

Private Secretary, Oliver Locker Lampson, to collect as many students from the universities as he could find for the purpose of training them in the operation of the printing presses. One of these, Mr. E. L. Delmar-Morgan, remembered that:

> I was one of the students, and upon arriving in cars at the premises of the Islington Daily Gazette in Gough Square we were met by Lindemann and a couple of the non-striking operators. We soon had the outfit running. One of the two instructors composed the few paragraphs given on the photostat and towards midnight Winston turned up . . . with the typescript for the Sunday Gazette. Lindemann was enjoying himself immensely and was, of course, *ipso facto,* our chief. He stayed with us at Gough Square until the last copies of the Gazette had left the building just as dawn was breaking.[1]

It is perhaps significant that Prof in 1926 already felt himself sufficiently advanced politically to offer Churchill a draft letter to be sent to the Prime Minister on May 11, 1926 at the end of the General Strike:

> DEAR P.M.,
> The point to which I wish to draw your mind is that there must be a clear interval between the calling off of the General Strike and the resumption of the coal negotiations. The first tonight—the second tomorrow. But nothing simultaneous and concurrent. That will I am sure be fatal.
> No question of subsidy even for a fortnight can be mixed with the withdrawal of the General Strike. Tonight surrender. Tomorrow magnanimity. On the interval between these two depends the whole result of this deep national conflict.[2]

Prof's life was saddened by the death of his mother in 1927. Their later relations had not been harmonious, but he must

---

[1] E. L. Delmar-Morgan to author.
[2] Cherwell archives.

have agreed with Mrs. Winston Churchill when she wrote in condolence: "The loss of one's mother is a sad milestone in one's life. After that one is nobody's child and it is a lonely feeling."

After his mother's death he drew even closer to his father, writing him long and regular letters, and visiting many houses in the attempt to find somewhere agreeable for him to live. His scientific work was honored when in October 1927 he was proposed for a nomination to the Council of the Royal Society. Throughout these years his friendship with Churchill runs like a steady thread. After a visit to Oxford, Churchill wrote warmly to Prof:

> I did enjoy our Sunday with you. It *was* nice. Let me know when you will come at Christmas time. Yours ever W.

He often stayed at No. 11 Downing Street on visits to London when Churchill was Chancellor of the Exchequer, and when the latter needed advice about the new water garden he was to build at Chartwell it was to Prof that he turned, expressing the hope that the problem was not beyond Oxford mathematics:

> Chartwell Manor,
> Westerham, Kent.
> 31st May 1928.
>
> MY DEAR PROF,
> I am so grateful to you for the wonderful calculations you have made. There is no doubt about the 10 ft. command. As I am using new pipes I expect all will be well. I hope the water will be flowing into the upper lake by the end of the week.

One of the greatest of his friendships was that with Maurice the Duc de Broglie, and his family. It was an intimacy which lasted till his death, and was one of the main reasons for his frequent visits to France. The Duc de Broglie, who had been co-secretary with Lindemann at the Solvay Conference in 1911, was a brilliant physicist, a member of the Académie des Sciences de l'Institut de France. Prof was made a Corresponding Member of the Académie des Sciences, and the Duc's brother, Prince Louis de Broglie, a Nobel prize winner, was one of the signatories of the notification. Prof enjoyed his regular visits to Broglie, Eure, where the whole family foregathered in the summer, and his friendship with this gifted and delightful family was an important factor in his life. Intensely patriotic himself, he admired their fierce devotion to France in the black years of the Occupation.

He continued his visits to the great houses, sometimes breaking new ground, with the Duchess of Portland at Welbeck Abbey and the Londonderrys at Mount Stewart. He was invited by Mrs. Churchill to go to Biarritz in 1929 in a letter full of affection, suggesting the growing intimacy between them, and the grandeur of the holiday:

> Therefore after the 6th come on the wings of the wind (or less poetically and more practically on the wheels of your Mercedes) as quick as you can to Biarritz. Bendor[1] has not told us when he intends putting in at Bayonne on his yacht on his way to Portugal. I believe this week he is entertaining the Prince of Wales at Mimizan. Oh Prof — this is a lovely place, a Henri IV chateau surrounded by a moat. You can feed the swans out of your windows. The Eure winds its way through lovely meadows close to the house . . . Au revoir dear Prof. What fun it will be to see you.

By this time the Prof's veneration for Churchill was such that he willingly gave his services on many occasions as "devil" in the preparation of his friend's articles.

"I am extremely pleased," wrote Churchill, "with the notes on Moses which will be a great help to me in writing the ar-

[1] The Duke of Westminster.

ticle. Pray let me know how much I owe you in money;[1] for the rest my debt is incommensurable."

"I am very glad," answered Prof, "that you were satisfied with our theological efforts."

Churchill was fertile in suggesting possible subjects:

> *Women and the future.* To what heights will the ascendancy of women go? Will there be a woman Prime Minister? Women and finance. A world controlled by women? *If they had lived long ago.* Take a number of the world's most prominent men and imagine their careers in past eras. Henry Ford in Cromwellian days, maybe yourself in Caesar's time. Mussolini with Henry VIII, Ramsay MacDonald in the French Revolution, Bernard Shaw with the ancient Greeks, and so on.

In January 1929 Prof went to India as a member of a committee set up by the Government of India to inquire into the activities of the Forest Research Institute Dehra Dun. It seems probable that he was invited to serve on this committee on the advice of Birkenhead, who had been Secretary of State for India until October 1928. This visit enlarged his knowledge of India and brought him into contact with the Viceroy and the Governor of Bombay.

All this activity was interrupted by a telegram on August 23, 1931, from his brother Charles: "Father very ill. Come at once." When A. F. Lindemann died, Prof was deeply stricken. In his grief he wrote to me that "at moments such as this success loses its savour, failure its sting." The death of those dear to him struck him with a terrible impact. With his mother he had, at the end, bitterly quarreled, but with his father his relations had been perfect, unclouded by a single serious difference. He found recovery difficult; too many memories of the past, so ripe in shared achievement, came back to him, and he remained for a time dull and apathetic, deriving from the

---

[1] The money was given to the young man who prepared the notes.

knowledge of his father's pride in him only a bleak consolation.

Of all the letters of sympathy he received he was most moved by that of Lady Desborough, that brilliant woman who had suffered so much personal sorrow in her life, and in whose garden at Taplow, descending through green paths to a lovely reach of the river, he had so often wandered:

> Taplow Court,
> Taplow, Bucks.
>
> *Sept. 1, 1931*
>
> My dear friend — I cannot tell you how grieved we both are to know of the great sorrow that has befallen you — or how deeply we think of you. I know something of what the bond was — its strength and affection — and I do mind knowing what you will be suffering. But what healing there must be in the thought of all you were to him — of his pride in you — and that you had spent all these last weeks in caring for his health and well-being. All that cannot make up for the terrible missing and sense of loss — but it will help in time to heal the pain. Dear Prof, do not think of answering — this is only a syllable of a most true and sad sympathy
>
> From your most affectionate friend
>
> ETHEL DESBOROUGH

In 1932 Prof was disturbed to hear the news that Winston Churchill had been run down by a taxi in New York. By some Churchillian miracle he had escaped with a severe bruising. No contemporary could then have measured what his death would have meant to the world, but there was a chorus of thanksgiving for his escape in which Prof joined in his own peculiar way:

> CHURCHILL, WALDORF ASTORIA, NEW YORK.
> Just received wire delighted good news stop Collision equivalent falling thirty feet on to pavement equal six thousand foot

pounds energy equivalent stopping ten pound brick dropped six hundred feet or two charges buck shot point blank range stop Shock presumably proportional rate energy transferred stop Rate inversely proportional thickness cushion surrounding skeleton and give of frame stop If assume average one inch your body transferred during impact at rate eight thousand horsepower stop Congratulations on preparing suitable cushion and skill in taking bump Greetings to all LINDEMANN HOTEL CONTINENTAL NICE.

His admirably lucid and trenchant pen was always at hand ready to defend his friends, particularly those who were no longer able to answer for themselves. Birkenhead's famous speech containing the words "The world has still its glittering prizes to offer to those who have stout hearts and sharp swords" had been a desperate and forlorn attempt to stir his countrymen from apathy and pacifism in the face of international danger. Cogent in its warnings, it had already been grotesquely misunderstood and assaulted, particularly in clerical quarters.

On February 16, 1933, Prof wrote to the editor of an Oxford magazine deploring an anonymous article in the latest issue, misrepresenting once again his dead friend's Rectorial Address to Glasgow University. His letter is at once a good example of his power on paper, and a just expression of contempt for a writer who skulked behind anonymity when traducing a dead man who could no longer answer:

Christ Church,
Oxford.

16 February 1933.

SIR,

In an article on the Union Society and War in your issue of the 16th February the following sentence appears: "Lord

Birkenhead urged the students of Glasgow to adopt the philosophy of battle for its own sake and for its glittering prizes."

I regret that you should have permitted this slander to be resuscitated. It is clear to anybody who takes the trouble to read the late Lord Birkenhead's Rectorial Address, that he inculcated precisely the opposite thesis. Yet the writer of the article brands the late High Steward of the University as "bloodthirsty" because he recommends that whilst abstaining from provocation we should maintain in our hands adequate means for our protection lest we become the glittering prize of those who have stout hearts and sharp swords.

It is scarcely necessary to express my opinion of the character of a writer who, relying upon his anonymity and the fact that no action can lie for libelling a dead man, is content to besmirch the memory of a political opponent whom he would not have ventured to insult to his face.

Although it is tedious to blow on dead embers, a few of the major controversies in which Prof was involved during the interwar period must be related. The first concerned the election for the Chancellorship of Oxford University in 1925, of a successor to Curzon who had recently died. There was a considerable Conservative majority among the voting M.A.'s, but no obvious Conservative statesman worthy of this greatest of all academic honors.

The eyes of the dons, therefore, turned in the direction of the Liberals, and fell upon Lord Oxford and Asquith and Sir Edward Grey. Between the claims of these two men there could be no possible doubt. Asquith's wonderful academic record and great public career, joined to his intense love of Oxford, and Chairmanship of the Royal Commission on Oxford and Cambridge, would seem to have made his claims impregnable. This, however, was Oxford, and there were those, including the Warden of All Souls, Dr. Pember, who seemed to regard Asquith's great gifts as a positive impediment and preferred to play safe with Grey.

In this he was accompanied by the Liberal elder statesmen of the University. Harrod, who was closely involved in this affair, wrote:

> The Prof bade me come round to his rooms one evening in a state of some excitement. F. E. Smith was very keen that Asquith should be Chancellor. Despite their political differences F.E. had a great regard for Asquith; furthermore his high sense of the dignity of learning made him wish that the man who was, in his own person, a truer embodiment of learning and culture, should be titular head of his beloved Oxford.

The Prof then explained to Harrod the nature of the intrigue on which Harrod was to embark. F. E. Smith having obtained the consent of prominent Conservatives, including Salisbury, to support Asquith, it was clearly necessary that well-known Liberals should also favor Asquith. On this point there was doubt, and the object of the intrigue as proposed by the Prof was to treat the nomination of Asquith as an accomplished fact, using as an argument the support already obtained from the Conservatives. Harrod, a Liberal himself, had been cast in the role of seducer, and his task was to gather as much Liberal support as he could on this basis of a *fait accompli.*

H. A. L. Fisher, the Warden of New College, was with them, a two-edged weapon as his recent spell of Cabinet office had given him an altogether exalted opinion of his own powers, and he was given to pontifical speeches often containing the phrase "When I was in the Cabinet," which caused much coughing and shuffling of feet. Professor Gilbert Murray was regarded by the plotters as the key point in this strange charade, but he was drawn to Grey by his association with the founding of the League of Nations, to which Murray so idealistically and hopefully adhered.

He refused to support Asquith unless Clark, the Corpus Professor of Latin, also agreed to do so. The breathless Harrod hurried to Clark and gained his consent; he made flying visits to The Wharf to see Asquith, and to Charlton to see Birkenhead who was pulling the strings in the background. As so often happens in these strange Oxford intrigues, all their efforts were vain. Asquith was too much for the diehard Conservative backwoodsmen, among whom Grundy, a Fellow of Corpus Christi, industriously burrowed, and a few weeks later Lord Cave was nominated. He was to die a few years afterward and to leave the Chancellorship to Grey on an uncontested nomination.

It is strange that so great an Oxonian as Asquith should have been defeated by one so obviously inferior, a man whose love of Oxford was less than his own. Such appointments at Oxford are, however, not always decided on merit, and mistrust or jealousy of a distinguished man has often paved the way to the triumph of mediocrity. In this tangle of intrigue it is interesting to note the reasons given for Asquith's failure:

1. He had not taken his M.A. degree and was only plain B.A.

2. His choice of the title of Oxford had given offense.

3. His Chairmanship of the Royal Commission on Oxford and Cambridge weighed against him.

4. His handling of the Welsh Church had been resented.

These ridiculous pretexts were more than enough to offset his academic record, his love of Oxford and his international fame.

The next major issue in which the Prof was involved took place in 1929–30 and concerned the Radcliffe Observatory. The Observatory had, by arrangement with the Radcliffe Infirmary, acquired an allocation of £100,000, a gift which was made possible by the generosity of Lord Nuffield to the

Infirmary. This sum was sufficient for the construction of a great modern telescope, but the question arose as to where this new telescope should be situated. It was pointed out that the value of the gift would be largely neutralized by the Oxford climate with its clouds and mists, and that a more desirable home for it was South Africa. Prof was, from the outset, strongly opposed to this suggestion.

It was natural that one who so fiercely embraced the cause of Oxford science should contemplate the loss of this instrument with consternation. It was pointed out to him that John Radcliffe had left this bequest for the advancement of astronomy, but Prof argued that Radcliffe's other benefactions, the Radcliffe Camera and the Radcliffe Infirmary, indicated that his real object had been to assist Oxford, that he had not been thinking of the general advancement of astronomy, but of astronomy at Oxford in particular.

His difficulty in putting this case forward lay in the fact that the Observatory was managed by the Radcliffe Trustees and was independent of the University, which had no authority over it. He was driven to the argument that Oxford had for centuries acted as custodian for any high studies, such as astronomy, that were carried out in Oxford City, and that if the Radcliffe Trustees were flouting their benefactor's wishes by transporting the telescope far from Oxford, the University was entitled to prevent such action.

His views on the question were set out in a letter on December 8, 1930, to Mr. Newman, the Treasury Solicitor:

> We are convinced that a great deal of exceedingly useful work can be done if we have an adequate observatory in Oxford. According to the meteorological charts the climate here is scarcely inferior to any in the British Isles, certainly better than the climate of Greenwich or Edinburgh, and no worse than that of Cambridge. It cannot be denied that the Cambridge astronomical school has been highly successful.

Edinburgh has just installed a new 3½ foot mirror-telescope. If astronomy is worth supporting in Scotland surely it should not be dropped in Oxford. . . . It is important in this connection to remember that the great advances in astronomy have usually come from observatories working in conjunction with Universities whose sites were not selected primarily on account of climate. The discovery of new principles and the application of new methods can only proceed if mathematicians and physicists work hand in hand with astronomical observers. . . . Mere observation is very different from the sort of inspired investigation which leads to new discoveries.

Another most important point to the future of astronomy is whether young men are attracted to the subject. Unless they are enabled to obtain a first hand knowledge of astronomical work and methods which is only possible in an observatory, it is difficult to persuade undergraduates to take any interest in astronomy. It is just as important for the sake of astronomy to train students and ensure a good supply of young astronomers as it is to take a few more photographs of star clusters in the Southern Hemisphere.

On the South African observatory he wrote:

Of the second question as to the possibility of the University working in conjunction with an observatory in South Africa. Obviously the students could not be trained in South Africa as the large number of courses in ancillary subjects such as mathematics and physics could not be transferred there. The only advantage they might gain would be if they were invited to work at such an observatory as post-graduates. Very few students can afford to stay up for post-graduate courses, even if offered a free passage to South Africa; if they should be able to afford such a prolongation of their study, it would be far better to send students to Mount Wilson or one of the large American observatories. . . . the scale of these observatories is of quite a different order to anything contemplated in South Africa.[1]

[1] Cherwell archives.

Prof proceeded to fight this issue strongly and gained valuable support from the incoming Professor of Astronomy, H. H. Plaskett, to whom he wrote, saying that their own University Observatory was poorly equipped and that they had just launched a scheme to turn it into a first-class astrophysical station, and that the scheme of the Radcliffe Trustees to alienate the Radcliffe Observatory would stultify this intention.

Plaskett suggested ways in which the University case could be strengthened before it came to the courts for decision. He warned the Prof that the case of the Radcliffe Trustees from a purely astronomical point of view was absolutely foolproof, and that any astronomer, with the single exception of himself, would back the Radcliffe scheme against that of the University.

He believed that it would be wise to make each observatory (University and Radcliffe) independent in internal administration and scientific direction; the two observatories and the meteorological sections would form a loosely knit Institute of Cosmical Physics under Prof's or Milne's direction. He urged that whether or not the University was given the Radcliffe money to found such an institute, they should proceed with the plans for such an observatory, and he begged the Prof to approach the University for the necessary £5000 plus the annual sum of £500. The Professor of the University Observatory, E. A. Milne, was in broad agreement with their views.

The Prof must have felt a glow of triumph when he induced the great Einstein to testify emphatically upon the University side:

I have examined the affidavits of Professors Lindemann, Milne and Plaskett and am in complete agreement with the arguments and views expressed therein.

1. A university can only make sure of obtaining a really valuable scientific recruitment in an experimental subject if observational equipment adequate to the needs of time is avail-

able. Failing this the men who are to be trained will either study other subjects or go to other universities. Furthermore, teachers in these subjects would not have the possibility of remaining in constant contact with experiment. The University would therefore indubitably suffer serious damage.

2. It is true that a certain part of the observational material which is of importance for astronomy, can only be obtained in atmospheric conditions which are but seldom found in Europe. Observatories in regions with a favourable climate are therefore certainly necessary. There are already various such observatories in South Africa. The erection of another observatory there . . . that did not far outstrip existing observatories in equipment and resources, would in no way compensate astronomy for the disadvantage produced by damaging teaching and research at the University of Oxford.

3. For the investigation of many important problems, the collaboration of the researchers with others in an active scientific centre is more important than better observational circumstances obtained at the price of such co-operation. Decay of mental activity of workers in isolated research institutes is a phenomenon that has frequently been observed. . . .[1]

All this activity did not save the Radcliffe Observatory, although the University case was strong enough for the Prof and others to resort to litigation. The University lost its action, and the telescope was built near Pretoria. The Prof was an angry spectator in court, and he returned to Oxford saying that the University case had been mishandled, that their counsel, Sir Wilfred Greene, did not even appear, being engaged on some other case, and that it was yet another example of the contempt in which science was held in Oxford.

It could not possibly be said that the University had any actual legal right, although they had a strong moral claim, for it is clear to anyone who studied Dr. Radcliffe's life in connection with his will that he intended the use of the residue

[1] Cherwell archives.

to be in, and for, Oxford. His sole personal bequest outside Oxford was a fixed annual sum to St. Bartholomew's Hospital in London, of which he had been a governor.

There would appear to be a certain pettiness in the next dispute, which concerned the Prof's precedence at dinner at Christ Church and which went to the length of the parties taking counsel's opinion.

We have seen the reasons why Prof, although a member of the Wadham Governing Body and a Fellow of the College, was also a Student of Christ Church with his rooms there, but without a seat on the Governing Body. The question at issue was whether, owing to his unusual position, he enjoyed precedence from the time of his appointment as Student of Christ Church, or whether he ranked below the Students who were also members of the Governing Body.

At the time of the dispute Prof and one other Student only were not members of the Governing Body. He felt that although the question of his precedence was of no immediate consequence, it would be humiliating for him in thirty years' time as one of the senior members of the Common Room, perhaps bringing a distinguished guest to dinner, if some young man recently appointed took precedence over him and occupied the Chair in Common Room. He also looked forward to a long residence in Christ Church, having been appointed before the enactment of a retiring age, and it was clear to him that he would often in the future find himself in this unbecoming position.

Both parties in this storm in a teacup generated more heat than they could contain, and the College decided to take counsel's opinion as to the true nature of the Prof's position. Mr. Gavin Simonds, K.C., held that the Prof ranked below members of the Governing Body. Prof turned in disgust to Sir John Simon, who gave an exactly opposite opinion which, coming from such an authority, carried great weight. An argument followed among the learned men as tense as though they were debating some fatal issue in foreign affairs, some counseling firmness on the grounds that Prof would never dare risk the mockery of his exalted friends by litigation as to his seat at the Common Room table, others urging generosity. In the end the College wisely decided to yield, and it would have been more prudent if they had done so at once.

Another sharp disagreement in 1930–31 with the Governing Body, over the position in the College of the Duke of Westminster Research Student should not be allowed to convey too sinister an impression of the relations of Prof with his Christ Church colleagues, nor of serious disharmony in the Senior Common Room.

In 1924 the Duke of Westminster, a personal friend of the Prof, made a benefaction under covenant, as a result of Prof's persuasion, to support a research fellowship. A great deal of sapping and mining had been necessary to make sure of the gift. It was part of the agreement with the Duke that the studentship should carry with it full privileges. It was not known whether the Statutory Commission, which had not yet published its findings, would confirm the rule that all Fellows of Colleges must be members of their Governing Bodies.

The Christ Church authorities were not prepared to admit the new Student to their Governing Body. The first holder of the title was the Prof's friend and protégé, Mr. Bolton King. When the time came for him to be succeeded, the term of the original grant had not expired, and it was accepted that the new Student would be appointed under the terms of the original agreement. This arrangement was negatived by the fact that when the new statutes came into operation they laid down that all Fellows of Colleges must be members of their Governing Bodies. To the Christ Church dons who did not want the Research Student on the Governing Body, the difficulty was a real one, far more than a contest between bigotry and the light.

They felt that in the case of a man who was primarily a research worker and did practically no teaching, and only held his post for five years, it would be making unnecessarily hard demands on him if, by being placed on the Governing Body, he was burdened with the innumerable details of the administrative work of the College. He was there to research and should be allowed to do so. A less convincing argument was that the Governing Body was already overcrowded, for the addition of one extra member could have made little difference.

Their case is also supported by the fact that this question is still a bone of contention today, and after the war two Colleges altered their statutes in order to exclude research students from their Governing Bodies.

The Prof made it plain that he rejected their arguments, and stood square behind the new statutes. Once again he was fighting for the cause of science against what he regarded as obscurantism. He pointed out that the new statutes affected all Colleges alike, and applied equally to professorial fellowships, research fellowships or any other. He claimed that this change in the statutes had the intention of furthering the interests of scientific research by giving scientists proper representation on College Governing Bodies, and that there was no legal method by which Christ Church could avoid appointing this Student to their own.

The Prof's opponents argued that the new Student should not be regarded as an ordinary Student, but as a "Duke of Westminster" Student, who was somehow excluded from the normal privileges conferred by statute. This contention was rejected by Prof, who answered that the Duke would never have made the benefit on such humiliating terms, but his opponents were probably on stronger ground in maintaining that the case was different in that Prof exercised the equivalent of a veto. But it was his determination to see that science was not downtrodden or lightly regarded that animated him, as always, in this matter. His own exclusion from the Christ Church Governing Body had convinced him that it was only fellowships with the full privileges of that membership that counted at Oxford in terms of prestige and executive power.

If scientists, the men who would dominate the future, were to be properly recognized in Oxford, they must enjoy a position in their Colleges equal to that of the representatives of other faculties. It was this fervent belief that made him inflexible in his demand that the new Student must be a member of the Governing Body. He explained his position to a member of the opposition whom he liked, Mr. Barrington Ward, in a letter which clearly shows his dissatisfaction with the committee which his main opponents formed to prepare the case for the Governing Body, and his general exasperation with their behavior:

DEAR B.W.,

I gather from Harrod that you have complained that I exhibited a knowledge of the details of the meeting of a committee of which I believe you are a member. I think there must be some misapprehension about this, for the best of all reasons, namely, because I am not acquainted with the proceedings of your committee.

Of the recommendation submitted to the Governing Body, I have been informed. Since I am a party to the contract I have the right to know what is proposed and what is being done in this particular matter. In my view, it would have been proper for me to have been apprised officially of the position. I am sure you would not advocate concealment.

Perhaps I might take this opportunity to raise a somewhat wider issue; I do this the more willingly because I have always believed you to be more free from academic preoccupations than others and more ready to take a commonsense view. I refer to the secrecy with which some members of the Governing Body endeavour to surround its proceedings. To my mind this is undesirable, not to say unwise. The Oxford Colleges administer large endowments left for charitable purposes. It is a remarkable and fortunate fact that so much power has been entrusted to bodies recruiting themselves by co-option and relieved of Government interference, save during the periodic overhauls of the various Royal Commissions.

Nobody can be more anxious than myself to maintain the College system with all that this implies. One of its implications is, however, that the charity should be administered in conformity with the intentions of the benefactors . . . that the Colleges should be entitled to present affected parties with a "fait accompli" arrived at in secret conclave is an untenable position.

As you have no doubt observed some of your colleagues on the Governing Body seem concerned to envelop its proceedings with an air of mystery as unnecessary as it is futile. I am sufficiently charitable in general to concede this meagre prop to their self-importance. When however matters closely affecting questions that I have at heart arise, I must claim the right to express my opinion. You have elected to exclude me from the Governing Body. Of this I make no complaint. I do maintain, however, that it leaves me in a position of complete freedom to take all steps which may occur to me to impede and if possible to prevent the passage of measures which I consider not only deleterious to the prestige of the College but detrimental to the interests of the University as a whole. Of that power I intend to avail myself. I cannot believe that you of all people will blame me for so doing.[1]

In the end, at a Governing Body meeting Dean White arrived at a decision on the Prof's side. Enough were with him and the way of the Westminster Student was cleared to the Governing Body.

In spite of an apparent atmosphere of discord, life in the Senior Common Room proceeded along normal and harmonious

[1] Cherwell archives.

lines. The Prof was not unpopular there once the ice had been broken. Rather was the feeling that it was agreeable to have such a distinguished man who had been proposed by Bishop Strong, and he was regarded as a considerable asset. He was always the center of controversy, but this he enjoyed. He was not even unpopular after the squabble over the Westminster Research Student. No one resented the fact that he produced legal opinions because the case, after all, hinged on legal points. Naturally each side took legal advice, but no serious ill-feeling was engendered. The mistake he made over such matters was that he thought that they were highly important and reflected on his dignity, and that they could be resolved by strong administrative decisions. Perhaps this attitude was due to his foreign origin and rigid sense of hierarchy, causing him to make a hard and fast case about such issues instead of settling them quietly.

In the case of the Westminster Student he believed that there was a principle involved. The principle was the honor and dignity of science. He thought that since he was not a member of the Governing Body himself, it was essential for his Student to be in order that science should be recognized on a proper equality with other studies. He relieved his irritation on this occasion by remarking of one of his Christ Church opponents that "he is one of those people who are always doing one down from the highest possible motives."

The Prof's next encounter was to come in his spirited participation in the General Election of October 1935, and the Oxford by-election of February 1937. His interest in politics and economics had been steadily growing. All the great houses in which he spent so much time were political houses, and he had long heard the affairs of the day discussed and argued by the most prominent actors in them.

He had particular reasons for wishing to enter the House of

Commons: his knowledge of aeronautical defense, his experience of Europe, and the fact that he was a scientist. He was appalled by the apathy with which the Government toyed with the question of England's defense against air attack, and he was already somberly convinced of the approaching agony. It also seemed to him deplorable that there should be no single Member of Parliament who had made science his profession, and who could ask the necessary technical questions without being fobbed off as a layman could be by evasive replies from the Defence Ministries.

He had no wish to enter Parliament for any other reason, or to make politics his career. He had discussed the question of standing with his two greatest friends, Birkenhead and Churchill. While Birkenhead was alive he had done his best to dissuade him from the intention. Perhaps he realized that Prof was ill-suited by temperament to the rough and tumble of the Commons; but a stronger reason for his advice was that, unlike Churchill, he had been bred in Oxford life, had married the daughter of a great Latin scholar, and was deeply conscious of the glory and dignity of Oxford. He felt it far more seemly for his friend to stay on the exalted plane of his Oxford Chair, rather than become immersed in the intrigues of party politics as a backbencher. But Birkenhead had died in 1930, and Churchill, who desired Prof to buckle on his harness and plunge into battle with the rest of them, had become his guiding star.

Once again, in 1935, the old machinery of intrigue and lobbying was wheeled out. Again the outsider was baffled by the complexity of Oxford politics. At that moment she was represented by two Burgesses, Sir Charles Oman and Lord Hugh Cecil, both Conservatives. Conservative affairs were controlled by the Oxford University Conservative Committee, generally known as the Caucus, whose main function was to secure suitable candidates for the offices of Chancellor, High

Steward and Burgesses of the University. Prof disapproved of the Caucus, and poured ridicule upon it at every opportunity as being unrepresentative of University opinion. It was composed of Oxford members, a selection of dons, and external members who were Oxford graduates and mainly Conservative members of the Houses of Parliament. In 1934 Prof himself was a member of the Caucus.

There had been formed in the early thirties the Oxford University Conservative Association composed of undergraduates, to which a senior branch of graduates was added in 1936. From this organization, of which he was a Vice-President, and from Mr. Ian Harvey, its first President, the Prof received strong support in 1935 and 1937. Indeed, he was the chief architect behind the scenes in organizing the Association, which went from strength to strength and was formally recognized by Conservative Central Office. It was through this Association, as much as through his graduate friends in the Houses of Parliament, that the Prof conducted his battle against the Caucus.

After the old Caucus had precipitated the election of Lord Irwin[1] as Chancellor of Oxford University in 1933, its character was reconstituted, largely owing to the Prof's activities. It was decided to appoint a representative Committee of Oxford Conservatives to maintain Conservative principles in the University constituency, and that it should consist of two branches, the Oxford branch consisting of Oxford residents, and the London branch consisting of Conservatives on the Oxford Parliamentary Register not resident in Oxford.

This Committee was to summon once a year a general meeting of Resident Conservative members of Convocation for the appointment of the Oxford members to hold office in the ensuing year. It was decided that there should be one Committee consisting of forty members, including two women,

[1] Later Lord Halifax.

and that any Resident Conservative member of Convocation should be eligible to serve on it. The Committee was to call a general meeting of Conservatives at Oxford to choose a candidate for Burgess when a vacancy occurred. Prof arranged for Bolton King to be appointed secretary, but later he was forced to resign as the price of his support of Prof.

All this spadework which was intended to clear the way for Prof's triumph went for nothing. In March 1935 it was decided that his nomination as candidate in place of Sir Charles Oman should be supported by the Oxford University Conservative Association. The Caucus was incensed by this irregular proceeding, and on June 3rd came the great day when a meeting of Oxford graduates was called at Livingstone Hall, Westminster, to select a candidate. It was a bitter blow for both Prof and his energetic lieutenant, Bolton King, when, despite their efforts, the reformed Committee chose C. R. M. Cruttwell, the Principal of Hertford College, as official Conservative candidate. He was, in fact, the choice that might have been expected from the Caucus, a distinguished historian with an acid wit, but with no experience in public affairs and no gift for oratory. Prof was deeply humiliated.

It was at this moment of despair in his campaign that A. P. Herbert arrived with a hilarious splash, and offered himself as an Independent candidate for the Burgessship. A Socialist candidate, J. L. Stocks, lurked without hope in the background. Herbert disdained the normal procedure of issuing a short election address signed not by the candidate but by eminent sympathizers, and for statutory supporters relied mainly on assistant masters from the Dragon School.

Again flouting tradition, he wrote his own election address, prominent in which was the statement: "I know nothing about agriculture." The originality and panache of this unusual candidate struck the voters like a breath of fresh air, and he was returned as the second Burgess with Lord Hugh Cecil, while

Cruttwell forfeited his deposit. This last happy event did much to raise Prof's drooping spirits, remembering that his defeat had been contrived by the Caucus and the resident element in Oxford, which was only 700 out of 22,000 voters, hardly more than 3½ per cent of the electorate.

Harrod recalls that on the announcement of the result "I ran as fast as I ever have done in my life . . . I got through to the Prof and announced briefly, 'Cruttwell has forfeited his deposit.' The Prof was not addicted to manifestations of joy and enthusiasm or to throwing his hat in the air. I have never heard from the Prof such a whoop of triumph, such genuine joy in his voice as it came to me over the telephone. It was pleasing to be bearer of the news that would salve his wound after the deep humiliation of the Committee's choice."

A further source of satisfaction was that it was generally agreed that the majority of his supporters had voted for Herbert and not Cruttwell. The sentiments of Prof's friends were well expressed in a characteristic letter from Brendan Bracken:

MY DEAR PROF,

Many thanks for your charming telegram. I was delighted beyond belief that the Oxford Caucus got such a knock, but I wish you had been the Independent candidate.

The truth is that the recent happenings at Oxford have made many people believe that University representation is a deplorable anachronism.

Just consider the arguments addressed to The Times by Caucus leaders and minions. One oleaginous undergraduate, anxious perhaps to flatter the President of his College, had the impudence to write a letter attacking Herbert and praising Cruttwell. And a whole stream of sedentary troglodytes were foolish enough to suggest that a party label is the principal requirement of a University member.

But you have had your revenge. Herbert owes a great many votes to your efforts. And now I trust you will get ready to fight a by-election. I doubt if Linky Cecil [1] is going to remain for the whole of this Parliament.

It had been known that a vacancy would occur in the University representation in view of Lord Hugh Cecil's impending resignation on being appointed Provost of Eton. Prof decided to stand as a supporter of the National Government, and on July 11, 1936, issued a notice to the electors, on the same day addressing a curt letter of resignation from the Caucus to its secretary, W. O. Hart:

DEAR HART,
   As you know, I have not attended meetings of the Oxford Conservative Committee for over a year now. I gather from the fact that I recently received a circular that I am still considered a mere member. As I hear that all work in Oxford has been dropped (indeed at one time it was designated as eyewash) and as it seems that only nine people turned up at the general meeting of whom six were members of the Committee, I can scarcely recognise this body as representative of the electorate. . . . For this and other reasons, I wish formally to resign from the body. [2]

Whatever else might have been said about his candidature, it could not be denied that he got his blow in first. He got it in before the Member, whose place he wished to take, had formally resigned, and before the reconstituted Caucus had any opportunity of considering the matter. He was taking no chances with them.

As at the 1935 General Election, he gave his reasons for putting himself forward as his knowledge and experience of aeronautical matters, and his extreme uneasiness at the state of our aerial defenses. His action in doing so without prior con-

[1] Lord Hugh Cecil.
[2] Cherwell archives.

sultation with the Caucus further outraged those on that body who were hostile. These he ignored, preferring to pin his faith on powerful friends in both Houses of Parliament, some of whom were external members of the Caucus. Bolton King acted as his agent.

Meanwhile Winston Churchill helped in the drafting of a letter which was sent out to Members of Parliament, Lords and Commons, not all Oxford men, in support of Prof. When their names had been obtained, the letter was duplicated, published in the press and sent out to a further and much longer list of people, all Members of Parliament, for signature.

As Churchill said: "We ought to get pretty near a hundred acceptances, which after all is talking." In August 1936, during Prof's absence in Russia, Bolton King kept him posted with the progress of the campaign. The register had been revised and a new card index made in duplicate; volunteers had been organized to address envelopes.

It had now become evident that Sir Arthur Salter would command considerable support, should he allow his name to go forward for selection. Churchill and Prof were not deterred by the news. They realized that Salter was well left of center in politics and that it would be easy to work up a campaign against him as the advocate of a popular front. Churchill wrote:

> I should think your chances were greatly improved by Salter coming out as "Popular Front" candidate, as he should be called, supported by Cruttwell and Co., by Gilbert Murray and G. D. H. Cole. This should really give you the Conservative official support.

Salter came from a famous boat-building family, and A. P. Herbert was to say later that Oxford University was represented by a boat-builder and a buffoon. An able but somewhat negative man, he was a less glamorous figure than Prof, pale, squat, courteous with black clothes, wing collar and dark surprised brows.

When Prof returned from Russia his main anxiety was the possibility of an official Conservative candidate standing, and, by splitting the vote, letting Salter in, and he began to pull strings in high quarters to prevent this happening. He appealed in vain; his friend Lord Wolmer felt that he could not write to Central Office, as the Prof had broken the rules by coming out on his own, and Lord Wolmer had put himself out of court by supporting him; and a letter from Duff Cooper met with a cold reception from the Chairman of the Party, Sir Douglas Hacking. The ever-resourceful Bracken cheered Prof by writing:

Sept. 23rd.

I've just been reading in the Political Quarterly (July–Sept) an article by the All Soul's Socialist Rowse, advocating disestablishment of the Church of England. Sir Arthur Salter's name graces the first page of the P. Quarterly as a member of the Editorial Board. The numerous parsons who are Oxford electors ought to know about this.

The closing stages of the election were notable for the almost eighteenth-century animosity with which it was fought, and in the words of one newspaper: "In a thousand country rectories parsons are filling in ballot forms; at Oxford dons are scurrying, scheming, writing little notes in spidery scholarly hands, cutting each other, arguing over their port. In this election there are no public meetings, no hustings. There has been plenty of intrigue. There is, in the good old tradition, a refreshing amount of ill-will. There has been no nonsense about 'avoiding personalities.' "

In view of Socialist intrigues to get the Caucus to put up

an independent official candidate against him, which would split the vote, Prof tried to muster all his effectives when the Caucus arranged a meeting on Saturday afternoon, October 24th, in Oxford to choose a candidate. The Oxford University Conservative Association were allowed to send two representatives, Lord Birkenhead and Mr. Michael Berry.

The Prof's supporters urged the Committee not to do anything which would split the Conservative vote and so let in an opposition candidate. The Committee decided by fifteen votes to ten not to support the Prof, and by fourteen votes to eleven that a selection committee should be appointed to see if some other candidate could be found sufficiently eminent to win the seat. The danger of splitting the vote was brushed aside. Thus were his hopes dashed, but not submerged, as this was not the final meeting.

Prof's worst fears were realized when the Caucus put up Sir Farquar Buzzard as official Conservative candidate, well aware that by doing so they would split the vote, and let in a man who was more Socialist than Conservative and who was likely to vote against the Government as often as for it. The Caucus was not disturbed even by this probability, provided they could humble the detested Lindemann. Sir Farquar was an elderly Royal Physician and Regius Professor of Medicine, specializing in mental diseases. The undergraduates, who had no vote, were solidly behind Prof, and their summing-up of the three candidates was: "If you want to be cured of shell-shock, vote for Buzzard; if you want to avoid shell-shock, vote for Lindemann; if you've *got* shell-shock, vote for Salter."

On October 30th, Winston Churchill went to Oxford to speak in the Oxford Union Hall on behalf of his friend. It was a bold and unorthodox step as he was out of favor with the Conservative Party at the time, a prescient figure in the wilderness, and was addressing an audience predominantly undergraduate, and therefore without a vote. It was also against recognized practice to hold political meetings on behalf of candidates at University elections. He was further handicapped by not being an Oxford man. To a packed audience in the Union Hall, where many stood, he described the Prof as "possessing one of the most attractive and fascinating minds with which I have ever been brought in contact."

Of Salter he said with impish malice: "Sir Arthur Salter is a most engaging gentleman and a great authority on economic subjects. But like all of us he makes his mistakes from time to time. There was an instance when he eulogised highly the late Mr. Ivar Krueger as one of the financial guides of the world, who had blazed the trail along which men should follow. While the book was still in print Mr. Krueger found it necessary to commit suicide because of his gigantic frauds. This was one instance when Sir Arthur's judgment did not actually hit the bulls-eye, or even the circle." He added that Sir Arthur was supported by Mr. Cruttwell, "an historian who ought really to write a book on the Decline and Fall of the Conservative Caucus."[1]

The final meeting of the Caucus Selection Committee was held at 6 P.M. at Caxton Hall on Wednesday, December 9th. Even at this late hour Prof believed that victory could be snatched by a narrow margin if all his supporters attended. The issue was between him and Sir Farquar Buzzard. His optimism was yet another example of his pathetic divorcement from reality. He both despised and underrated the opposition, and was completely unaware of the extent of their hatred and determination. Bracken's "sedentary troglodytes" had achieved a masterpiece of organization and whipping in, and Prof's supporters were hopelessly outnumbered from the start.

The meeting was a fiasco, for which Prof considered Mr. Leo Amery partly responsible, as he had given no warning of his intention not, as expected, to open the proceedings. Amery's

[1] *Oxford Mail,* October 31, 1936.

own explanation of the disaster was that the meeting was packed by Buzzard's supporters by at least three to one. If the question was put to the vote, Buzzard must win, so, after consulting Lennox-Boyd, he decided that the best course would be for one of the younger members to rise and express his views as to the unwisdom of putting forward another Conservative candidate, and that Amery should speak at the end.

By some incredible blunder, after Buzzard's proposer and seconder had finished, none of Prof's supporters sprang up in protest. There was a pause before the Chairman put the matter to the vote, and to the stupefaction of Prof's friends it was all over. It was indeed an occasion which illustrated the tactical value of brevity in public speaking. The Prof's supporters had been outmaneuvered, and were unprepared for the warning which had obviously been given to those of Buzzard to be ready for a snap division.

Many of the Prof's supporters had been drawn from London Oxonians, who were unable to leave their offices so early, and after the meeting was over a stream of intending voters was still arriving in taxis and on foot. The voting was 129 to 45.

Amery lamely explained the defeat in a letter of December 10th, and attempted to persuade Prof to withdraw his candidature:

> I consulted with Lennox-Boyd and decided that in the circumstances the only thing to do would be to express our views as to the unwisdom of putting forward another Conservative Candidate without pushing the matter to a vote. Further, expecting a discussion and wishing to intervene most usefully towards the end of it I asked him to get up early or get Emmett or one of the younger members to do so. When the Proposer and Seconder had finished there was a moment's pause and while I was looking round to see which of the young men would get up, the Chairman promptly put matters to the

vote. . . . In view of the strength of the support Buzzard has got you ought to consider carefully whether you should go on yourself.[1]

Stung and humiliated as he was, the Prof probably never seriously considered withdrawing his candidature, because he vainly hoped that the mere fact of his standing might stir up the Air Ministry. The weeks before the poll he spent in organizing letters to the press instead of campaigning in Oxford. The result was:

Sir Arthur Salter (Ind.)	7580
Sir E. Farquar Buzzard (Con.)	3917
Professor F. A. Lindemann (Ind. Con.)	3608

As predicted, the vote was split and the "Popular Front" candidate admitted. It was a result which reflected great discredit on the Caucus, and it was largely inspired by personal dislike. The Prof's familiarity with the great, particularly Churchill, and his use of their help were bitterly resented. The fact that he did not understand and had few social relations with the ordinary Oxford professional classes alienated hundreds of the voters he most needed. He was not one to take tea in North Oxford.

His tactlessness further inflamed the hatred, and the exuberant support of the unenfranchised undergraduates did him little good with the dons, who regarded him as a prophet of war rather than its opponent. One of them, Sir John Masterman, afterward Provost of Worcester College, had the honesty to admit to the author many years later that he did not then realize the importance of exterior dangers and the vital necessity of putting the defenses in order.

The Prof had from the beginning at Oxford taken a great interest in technological education. He had also incurred

[1] Cherwell archives.

some unpopularity by criticizing the predominance of the classics in both schools and universities, the lack of scientific learning in the schools, and the uneven balance between the number of scholarships for classics and science. Many years were to pass before the iron grasp of the classics was even slightly relaxed, and in this matter the Prof may be regarded as a pioneer. He expressed his resentment of the attitude of the humanists to science in a satirical letter to the press in 1938:

Sir,

Much has been written about the reason "science" is feared and distrusted by the man in the street, if indeed it is. But the reason why the intelligentsia in our colleges dislike it is abundantly clear. It is the fault of the scientists. They are getting above themselves. Formerly a scientist, if tolerated in college at all, was a scrubby little man who knew his place. In Common Room he was expected to remain modestly in the background and to confine his interventions to an occasional respectful honking noise designed to convey appreciation and wonder when his refined colleagues showed by their polite merriment that a more than choice classical morceau had been recounted.

How different it is today. The scurvy knave jostles his way to the knight's table; the varlet disputes with the tonsured scholar; the sans-culottes declaim in the salons.

The modern scientist seems unable to realise how much more important it is to know about Greek participles than about the origin of the species, how immeasurably superior is a man who comprehends the niceties of the connections between the gods of Olympus to the mere empyricist who studies the gross interactions between the chemical elements. The young scientist thinks that such common snippets of information entitle him to an equal rank with the cultured scholar, to take part in the conversation, to have opinions on education, or even, about college elections. In the University he has the effrontery to ask for thousands of pounds for apparatus when he knows, or should know, how difficult it has been to scrape together a million to enable scholars to read in comfort in the New Bodleian. And your correspondents enquire why intellectuals dislike "science"!

Sir, it behoves everyone in a position to exercise any influence on the budding scientist to impress upon the malleable youthful mind that a mere knowledge of natural processes can never set off a false quantity.

Seven years before he had written in more serious vein to the *Times* about a letter from the Headmaster of Charterhouse. In his contribution he makes his own position on the question of technological education abundantly clear:

We deplore as deeply as he does, the tendency to undue premature specialisation often inflicted upon boys by the nature and character of scholarship examinations. Indeed some of us would go even further if perhaps in a direction scarcely emphasised in his letter. We feel that it is not only science scholarships which may produce individuals of narrow and illiterate outlook; we think that a far greater evil is the distorted and one-sided education often imposed on boys who specialise in other directions.

While none of us deny the immense importance of familiarity for a young man with the order of battle at Leuktra or the character of Claudius, we cannot but feel that it is at least equally desirable for him to have some elementary knowledge of the reasons and causes of that vast complex of phenomena which makes up his daily life. Some slight study of meteorology might lend zest and variety to his standard topic of conversation with strangers. Some rudimentary knowledge of physiology, while costly to the quack, might prove invaluable to health. Even a remote acquaintance with the principles of physics and chemistry enable a man to look upon a crystal or a flame with very different eyes to those of the pure humanist.

To anyone with a scientific education the ignorance of this aspect of nature displayed by men who claim to be possessed of knowledge and culture is almost appalling. Smith minor, painfully piecing together a translation from Cornelius Nepos, has delved far deeper into the recesses of classical learning than most of his masters have penetrated into the mysteries of science. How many headmasters, apart from the professional scientists, could discuss the most simple scientific question without perpetrating howlers which would result in most in-humane punishment if committed by a pupil in a humane subject. . . .

That Dr. Fletcher can refer to the "excessive demand for advanced knowledge upon candidates for (science) scholar-ships" is symptomatic of this condition. Really the standard of these examinations is deplorably low. It is connected with the vicious circle which maintains that the cleverest boys must have the best teaching in classics because there are more scholarships in these branches of knowledge, and which is completed by the argument that the universities must give most scholarships in classics because the cleverest and best taught boys affect these subjects. Unfortunately too, the best scientists are not often attracted to teaching, nor are the prizes offered in the scholastic profession comparable with those available in industry or the Civil Service. Whatever the cause, the facts are beyond dispute. While "science is claiming year by year a larger share in the control of our thoughts and our life," the average man has scarcely mastered the A.B.C. of the subject.

None of us would deny the need for a well-balanced edu-cation including the foundations of all branches of knowledge. Few would decry the charm and ease of manner associated with those older forms of learning, which, whatever else may be said against them, have never been accused of fostering in their proponents an inferiority complex. But anyone who has devoted his life to a study of nature, will not be inclined to perpetuate a system which is tending to produce in such overwhelming numbers a race of charming, well-mannered, scientific anal-phebets.

Prof had been solaced by the visits to Oxford of his old friend Einstein in 1931, 1932 and 1933. Although he had never had cause to revise his opinion of Einstein's childlike naïveté in the practical affairs of the world, he was stimulated by his genius and soothed by the calmness of his disposition.

Einstein was given rooms in Christ Church and dined at high table. His relaxation was playing the violin and he possessed a fine Stradivarius. After profound mathematical thought he would turn for comfort and peace to his violin, and those crossing the Quad could hear the plaintive music floating through the windows of his room. "In our Governing Body I sat next to him," said Harrod. "We had a green baize tablecloth; under cover of this he held a wad of paper on his knee, and I observed that all through our meetings his pencil was in incessant progress, covering sheet after sheet of equations."[1]

The young Christ Church dons pressed Einstein for his opinion of Prof as a physicist, and there is a story that he is said to have answered that he was essentially an amateur who had teeming ideas which he did not bother to work out himself, but that his knowledge of physics was thorough. He could at once assess the significance of any new discovery in the sense of its significance for physics as a whole, which very few people could do.[2] Mr. Collie of the Clarendon Laboratory is, however, in a position to provide firsthand evidence of Einstein's opinion of Lindemann as a scientist. When tackled by R. H. Dundas at high table at Christ Church as to how good a scientist Lindemann was, Einstein replied that he had always regarded him as the last of the great Florentines, a man who embraced all science as his province, a great man in the Renaissance tradition.[3] After the 1931 visit, when Einstein had charmed

[1] Sir Roy Harrod, *The Prof*, page 47.
[2] *Ibid.*, page 48. This report of Einstein's opinion of Lindemann is third-hand and should be accepted with reserve, although Sir Cyril Hinshelwood considers it to be accurate.
[3] C. H. Collie to author.

all by his modesty and kindness, he was made a Research Student of Christ Church, and fulfilled his engagements in Oxford in 1932 and 1933.

By the summer of 1933 Hitler's anti-Semitic outrages were affecting even one so eminent as Albert Einstein. After disgraceful behavior by the Prussian Academy, he wrote to his friend:

> Le Coq-sur-mer,
> b. Ostende,
> Villa Savoyarde.
> 1st May 1933.

DEAR LINDEMANN,

I am sitting here in my very pleasant exile with Professor Mayer. I shall be in Glasgow on the 20th June. Could I this year come to Oxford in June? Do you think that in June Christ Church could find a small room for me? It need not be so grand as in the two previous years.

You have probably heard of my little duel with the Prussian Academy. I shall never see the land of my birth again. I have worked out with Professor Mayer a couple of wonderful new results of a mathematical-physical kind.

Meanwhile my warm wishes.

> Yours sincerely,
> A. EINSTEIN

Einstein and the Prof were agreed that Hitler was bent on war, and Einstein wrote on May 7, 1933:

> I think that the Nazis have got the whip hand in Berlin. I am reliably informed that they are collecting war material and in particular aeroplanes in a great hurry. If they are given another year or two the world will have another fine experience at the hands of the Germans.

And in January 1935 he wrote from Princeton, where he was able to work in complete peace of mind:

> The German situation interests me particularly on account of the danger which it represents to the rest of the world. It seems to me that people are gradually recognising the full import of this danger. Two years ago it could so easily have been stopped, but at that time nobody wanted to hear about it.[1]

When Einstein died in 1954 the Prof was affected by a grief and melancholy which was probably far greater than he expected to feel at the passing of this gigantic figure, and in an obituary article in the *Daily Telegraph* he wrote:

> I first met Albert Einstein at the Solvay Conference on Quanta in 1911. Though he had already published so many masterpieces, none had then been actually put to the test and his theories were looked on rather as tours de force than as definitive additions to knowledge. But his pre-eminence among the twelve greatest theoretical physicists of the day was clear to any unprejudiced observer. I well remember my colleague as secretary, M. de Broglie, saying that of all those present Einstein and Poincaré were in a class by themselves.
>
> He was a young man, singularly simple, friendly and unpretentious. He was invariably ready to discuss physical questions with a young student, as I then was. And this never changed though the adulation showered on him might well have turned any man's head. During the months he spent in Christ Church he was loved not only for his friendly disposition and keen sense of humour but for his readiness to help and advise all those who approached him. . . .
>
> Like many scientists Einstein was politically rather naive. He hated violence and war and could not understand why his own natural sweet reasonableness was not universal. Absolutely

[1] Cherwell archives.

truthful himself, he tended to be credulous in political questions and was easily and often imposed on by unscrupulous individuals and groups. Indeed, his innate kindness of heart and loyalty to his race were often exploited especially in his later years when his signature to documents, no matter on what topic, was held to give it special importance.

As a theoretical physicist Einstein stands alone in this century and perhaps in any century. His brilliant originality, his fecund adventurous imagination, his uncompromising logic, and his clear exposition have probably never been equalled. As a man his simplicity and kindness, his unpretentious interest in others and his sense of humour charmed all who knew him. A very great man has vanished.

When the nerve-racking years 1938 and 1939 had passed, and the Second World War which he had long predicted had come at last, the Prof's character had become more clearly defined. There was an evident dichotomy in his nature, but his main principles in life were simple and hard as a pikestaff — absolute loyalty and love for his friends, and sustained rancor toward his enemies. The mind had an almost Prussian habit of discipline, and it was also a German failing he never overcame that he was usually incapable of understanding or even considering the opposite point of view.

It would be difficult to pretend that he was not aware of his own intellectual eminence, but on the few occasions when he spoke of science to his friends he gave an impression of modesty and even of diffidence. Some deep psychological condition in his character which it would be fruitless to probe made him abnormally inward and caused him a positive horror of blowing his own trumpet, and it was this which made dramatic accounts of the spiral spin so odious to him.

This aspect of the Prof was apparent to his more perceptive friends. It caused Lady Egerton, who was one of the few who could use with impunity the detested name "Peach," recall: "I went with Ehrenfest and Lindemann to see the Sidney Webbs.

That evening Ehrenfest gave a lecture which was difficult. Lindemann said: 'I understood it all, and found it most interesting.' I asked him why he did not do research himself. He replied: 'I can understand and criticize anything, but I have not got the creative power to do it myself.' From which I realised that he was fundamentally very humble."[1]

Allied to self-depreciation was the shyness and terror of flamboyance which went to ridiculous lengths in his conservatism in matters of dress. We have seen him climbing into primitive aircraft in heavy velvet-collared Melton overcoat and bowler hat, and observed his rejection of wrist watches as effeminate adornments. It would have been impossible to imagine him in a pair of bathing trunks, although he found great delight in bathing, in which he indulged clad in an ample Victorian costume. Something in the holiday atmosphere of Madeira must have given his spirits a little lift of freedom, for he sometimes added to this dress a Panama hat much crushed by folding, with a black band around it.

We have seen that the Prof made many enemies at Oxford outside Christ Church, and he was dimly aware of this fact, but it is fanciful in the extreme to infer, as Harrod does, that he was on this account afflicted by a persecution mania, and clung to his bowler hat as a helmet against aggressors. Verbal assertiveness is common in Oxford, but physical aggression by one don on another is happily rare. Although he knew that he had stirred bitter enmities, he had not the faintest conception of why he had done so, and it was the same fatal absence of *gnothi seauton*, "know thyself," which led him to a grave underestimate of the implacable forces ranged against him at the by-election. Apart from this natural incapacity for self-analysis, he was further hampered by being cut off from the great mass of human beings and having no bond of sympathy with people who were not brought into personal relationship with him.

[1] Lady Egerton to author.

He led a sheltered, and even pampered, life, with every accessory to comfort. He met only those whom he chose and in whose company he felt himself appreciated. In his rooms at Christ Church, his home, he was free to devote his brilliant mind to all the stimulating ideas that entered it. He felt no desire or obligation for social inquiry into how others lived. In spite of this insulation from the majority of the people, he was by nature kindly and compassionate, and he was alive with impulses of warm affection and generosity which, as we shall see, he concealed as jealously as his own nickname.

With his birth and upbringing it was inevitable that he would become a strong, and indeed a reactionary, Conservative. Sir Maurice Bowra had observed with distaste the harshness he advocated to undergraduates guilty of moral lapses. The risqué stories with which he sometimes embarrassed his friends were a mere reflex action void of meaning and bearing no relation to the narrowness of his view upon questions of sexual delinquency.

Lady Townsend discovered that his views on penal conditions were medieval. He sincerely believed that prisons should be made as gruesome as possible, and he was in favor of setting back the clock by intensifying hanging and the use of the cat-o'-nine-tails. Being compassionate himself, he was shocked by brutality in others, and regarded with contempt those more preoccupied with the criminal than with the victim, or, in a wider sense, with the black rather than with the white. Harrod thus summarizes the Prof's character:

> He was a person in whom the emotions normal to mankind seemed to be raised to a higher intensity. Devoted in friendship, fierce in enmity, revengeful in thought, sensitive, angry, scornful, courageous, resolute, obstinate, abounding in humour. . . . In himself he was every inch human, palpitating with life.[1]

[1] Sir Roy Harrod, *The Prof*, page 274.

There is nothing in these words which is false, but it is an intellectual estimate which leaves much to be said before the full complex of this man's character can be grasped. There is another side to it, a far better one, obscured by shyness and inhibition, and it can be seen in vivid detail through the eyes of his servant, James Harvey, who began as his valet and ended as his invaluable general secretary and devoted friend. After the death of his master he wrote:

> Almost without exception tribute has been paid to his great intellectual powers and both moral and physical courage. It is the other side of his character which I feel has been so ungenerously assessed. As it was my privilege to serve under him for over thirty years, the last twenty as personal private secretary accompanying him everywhere in peace and war, I consider I can speak with greater accuracy than has so far been achieved.
>
> When I see such adjectives used as "austere," "cynical" and "intolerant" to describe the warm and generous nature my late chief possessed, I cannot help trying to correct the cold picture which so many who did not know him have painted.
>
> I have taken dictation from him in the small hours of the morning when he was endeavouring, invariably successfully, to extricate somebody, in whatever station of life, who had foolishly got into difficulties; not just giving financial aid, as he often did, but sacrificing his rest, however busy he happened to be.
>
> He would fight as fiercely and unremittingly for anybody who had had a raw deal, as he would, and did, on any major issue. I have known him to be late for dinner in order to free a bird which had become trapped on the college staircase.
>
> His heart was as great as his mind. The world is a much poorer place for his passing — only people like myself, whose appreciations are rarely made public, will know how much poorer.[1]

[1] The *Daily Telegraph*, July 9, 1957.

It is probable that Prof disclosed to Harvey more of his true character than to any other man alive. He had him taught shorthand and typing, and encouraged him to study foreign languages. As the years passed an easy intimacy grew between them; and in the evening Prof would ask Harvey what he had done during the day. They had long conversations, and Prof confided to him that he was always afraid that Harvey would be the first to die. A highly intelligent man, Harvey had great natural accomplishments. He had played football for Oxford City, and was an amateur boxer of note. He cooked the Prof's demanding meals, drove a car, painted pictures, played the piano, and skillfully developed the Prof's photographs, besides being a master of shorthand and typing.

He soon discovered that at bottom his chief was extremely tenderhearted. He observed that Prof could not bear discharging servants and only did so with real pain, and after repeated warnings. It was Harvey also who typed out the letters and who realized the full extent of Prof's sympathy with those in trouble. He knew that no one whom a mischance or folly had placed in danger would appeal to him in vain. He remembers endless secret benefactions, all jealously screened against the world.

In the course of their many conversations, Prof gave Harvey much good advice. He fell into the habit of telling him stories, and his dressing in the morning was always accompanied by long discussions on the topics of the day. He would invite Harvey in to watch certain programs on the television, and give him showings of lantern slides. Harvey noticed his refinement in personal matters, and how, when showing slides, he would go behind a curtain to mop his brow.

When Prof returned from the Common Room, at the beginning of their association, and found Harvey typing back a sermon he had taken down in shorthand that morning, the pantry was enlarged and filled with the necessary office equipment. "It was the beginning," said Harvey, "of the happiest years of my life during which I received so much kindness, help and guidance."

He found the Prof pernickety about details. He would become indignant at a badly packed Port Salut cheese or a defective fountain pen, sending them back angrily to the shops.

> If the Professor ever lost his equanimity it was usually as a result of small matters. A loose button on his clothes; paper knife not to hand; a piece of thick toast, and collars which did not quite meet above his tie caused him to get cross. My error in sending the Professor on a 120 miles journey to attend a grand party on the wrong date; losing the Oxford by-election, or any major setback, made no visible impression on him. . . . In my early years with him I made the mistake of trying to whitewash myself, but I soon discovered that it was much better to be honest. He would always let one off lightly if he knew you were genuinely sorry.

The Prof from the beginning of his time at Oxford had a strong affinity with the undergraduates. He had, as we have seen, a singular feeling for youth, and was far more successful in his dealings with them than he was with their seniors. His many undergraduate friends were first attracted by his reputation, then conquered by his friendliness. They were filled with respect for his legendary reputation as an aeronaut, and intrigued by his caustic humor.

His patience, which was often surprising, led him to tolerate noisy parties on his staircase, and he was never known to report the young men to the Censor or the Dean. If the tumult became insupportable he would send Harvey with a message asking them to be a little quieter.

He was extremely fond of animals, keeping always in his room a gray Cairn terrier bitch, Dinah, given to him by Lord Birkenhead. It was also part of Harvey's duties to see that a small tin of scraps was kept in the passage so that he could feed the squirrels and birds. After his dog's death he acquired a black kitten, well named the Tasmanian Devil, which Harvey kept in his office.

> He would ring for it when he felt so disposed. Regularly every night after the Professor had prepared for bed, he would ring for the cat. The Tasmanian Devil became used to this routine, and directly I opened the door it would tear along the passage and into the bedroom, and straight under the armchair. After a few seconds it would dart out at the Professor and then the fun would start. Usually after about twenty minutes the Professor would ring for help, and I had to suffer the indignity of crawling about the floor trying to catch it. The Professor enjoyed every minute of it.[1]

The Prof was constantly exercised about the well-being of this indispensable servant, who soon became part of his life. In a rash moment he gave him a motorcycle, constantly warning him of the dangers of the road and drawing his attention to the motorcycle accidents. When this anxiety became too great, he gave Harvey his second car, the 16 H.P. Austin, and forbade him to use the motorcycle again.

It is difficult to overestimate his unaffected love of young people. A tender unguarded smile often illuminated his face when observing them, and in their company he became simple and natural. He took an unfeigned interest in their games and work, and after watching the schoolboy sons of his friends playing tennis, he would walk onto the court and explain to them what tactics they should have used to win.

He never parted from any of them without pressing a note into their hands with a secretive gesture. When he encountered a young man or girl who seemed to possess promise of a high order, he felt the delight an astronomer must feel when the long-sought planet swims at last within the field of his tele-

---

[1] James Harvey to author.

scope. He would arrange demonstrations in the Clarendon for the amusement of his young friends, when incredible freaks of nature were exhibited in dramatic form, and set them scientific puzzles.

His affection for the young was amply returned. His godson, Richard Henry Tizard, would ask his mother: "When is the nice man coming again?" Madame de Pange's son, a Westminster schoolboy, whom Prof invited to Oxford, wrote home: "I have spent a lovely week end at Oxford. On Saturday evening I dined in Christ Church Hall at the High Table with all the dons which was considered to be a very great honour. . . . Mr. Lindemann was very kind to me, showed me the different colleges, his big new laboratory etc. In the afternoon we had a long motor drive and dropped in to tea at some friends of his. I went back in the evening greatly pleased, with a big box of chocolates."[1]

It was generally accepted in Oxford that Prof was an atheist, and Sir Maurice Bowra had found repugnant what he considered a freethinker's lip-service to the Church of England for political reasons. It was not a subject on which it was easy to draw him out. Direct questions were parried with an evasive reply accompanied by a nervous giggle. It is true that he regarded the Church of England as a bastion of Conservatism, but he reserved his full admiration for the Roman Catholic Church.

The organization of that Church made a strong appeal to his instinct for discipline and obedience, and its control over its members seemed to him desirable and right. He approved of this control, and thought it admirable that Roman Catholics should be made to go to church, and be prevented from divorce on frivolous pretexts. He also felt great admiration for the dialectical skill of the Jesuits, and the ecclesiastical friend in Oxford he most liked and admired was Father Martin D'Arcy, S.J. The two men appeared to have a

[1] Sir Roy Harrod, *The Prof*, page 96.

mutual respect for the potency of each other's weapons, and in the Oxford debates in which they took part they were always to be found on the same side, an intimidating combination.

In spite of his frequent sneers at the higher clergy, Prof approached the question of the existence of God with a strange humility and no trace of scientific dogmatism. Father D'Arcy did not believe that he was an atheist and wrote to the author:

> There is a side to the Prof which you may not have known. It is shown in an incident shortly after I returned to Oxford in 1927. I promised a paper to the Essay Society at Christ Church, and forgot all about it. A few days before it was due Wystan Auden and some others called to remind me. Wystan told me to my dismay that they had billed me to talk on "Freedom and Authority in Religion." I said it was controversial; I could not do it, so then they said laughingly — "You must because we have invited Canon Rawlinson, Jacob and Professor Lindemann who is a strong atheist and the rudest man in Oxford. He will keep you in order." It was an amusing and satisfying evening for me because to my surprise the Prof sided with me throughout and mocked at those who attacked me. I said: "I was told you would be so opposed to my point of view; I want to thank you." He answered: "Father, your position is impregnable, granted the major premise of the existence of God. And what are we poor scientists to know about that?"
>
> I was so touched by this that I formed a firm friendship with him on the spot, and we became very dear friends. He used to delight to drop in on evenings into our Senior Common Room at Campion Hall; many members of the Hall had a great affection for him.[1]

It is improbable that anyone except Winston Churchill could have persuaded the Prof to set down his views on the

[1] Father Martin D'Arcy, S.J., to author.

relationship between modern science and religion. This he did in October 1936 in a paper unique among his documents:

The modern scientist does not claim that he knows all about the external universe. He only tries to make a mental picture, map or model to represent those aspects of it with which he is concerned. There can therefore be no conflict between his view and that of other people who may be concerned with totally different facets of experience.

The purely artificial conflict between Science and Religion which embittered relations in the nineteenth century arose from the fact that the scientist believed,

(1) that his map really was the reality

(2) that it worked on absolutely predetermined mechanistic lines, i.e. that it was like a clock which had been wound up where each motion was governed and that the whole future had to be run along certain lines determined by the Laws of Nature.

Modern science has shown quite definitely that most, if not all, of these laws of nature are statistical; that like the predictions of a life insurance company they can tell you with great accuracy what will happen to the average of an immense number of particles, but that they are just as incapable of predicting what will happen to an individual particle as a life insurance company is of predicting when any individual will die. In other words, science can never predict what will happen to any individual particle. If there is no interference, of course, individual uncertainties will average out and he can tell with fair accuracy what will be the result when he is dealing with billions and trillions of particles. But, of course, if there is any principle which interferes systematically within the domain of uncertainty, the scientist's predictions will fail. In the physical sciences we select phenomena in which, so far as we know, interference does not occur, and the Laws of Nature suffer no exception. *I personally am inclined to believe that there is some active principle which interferes with the crude play of chance which we have in biological phenomena when we are dealing with what we call "Life."* [1]

These considerations, of course, resolve any possible conflict between science and religion; indeed anyone who maintains that such a conflict is necessary stamps himself as an out-of-date Victorian.

Thus the Prof's character was a complicated one, windswept by many passing gusts. If we may attempt brevity in a matter so entangled, we may take refuge in the compact summary of Sir Robert Watson-Watt, pioneer of radar: "He was a mysterious complex of personal simplicities."

[1] Author's italics.

6

Air Defense

ONE CONSTANT APPREHENSION clouded Lindemann's mind during his years at Oxford between the wars. Long before most people he had foreseen the coming war and the destruction of our cities by bombing. It was this fear alone which caused him to stand for Parliament, as it was his belief that the presence of a scientist in the House of Commons was essential in order to prevent questions on air defense being fobbed off by answers so wrapped up as to be incomprehensible to a layman.

He had sensed the approach of the First World War, and he was now equally certain of the arrival of the Second. He made a vain attempt in September 1933 through Lord Lloyd to see Hitler, and through Signor Grandi to see Mussolini, saying that he had always been a friend of Italy, and felt sure that much could be done to improve relations between the two countries.

In November 1937 his uneasiness is evident in a letter he wrote to Patrick Donner, the Member for Basingstoke, about a recent speech:

> I need scarcely say that I approve of its general lines. It is extraordinary that there is anyone who can disagree in principle. The trouble is to know what to do. The situation seems to grow daily worse and we are now beginning to appreciate the full seriousness of "the years which the locust hath eaten."

Owing to our *penchant* for teaching other countries a lesson without considering whether we can enforce our view should they fail to come to heel, we have alienated practically every Great Power in turn. Now we can only rely upon assistance from those threatened equally with ourselves.

No doubt the Lord President — if he is allowed to see Mr. Hitler — will come back assuring us that he is a man transparently honest and sincere. Röhm thought the same before 30th June 1934, but this did not save him, nor do I see any reason to suppose it will save us.

At the height of the Czechoslovak crisis, Prof and Winston Churchill had an interview with Konrad Henlein, leader of the Sudeten Germans, at which Prof acted as interpreter. Henlein proved to be a subtle and able subject for interrogation, and they got little from him. So skillfully did he play his part that he even succeeded in leaving on them an impression of honesty and a desire for compromise. "I hope you are not going to turn out to be another Seyss-Inquart,"[1] said Prof. "Good God, no," said Henlein heartily.

We had quite an interesting talk with Henlein and I hope that some reasonable compromise may be reached. That these questions should be of such enormous importance is only part of the result of the disgraceful state of weakness, which our Government . . . has allowed to develop in our defences in the last few years. Defences, of course, like other physical quantities are relative, and in my view, if we were not going to stop Germany re-arming, we ought to have started doing so ourselves long ago. When we add to this the vacillating foreign policy which has allowed Italy to get strong, and at the same time forced her into Germany's arms, it is not surprising that we are now in such a dangerous situation. Our main hope is that the other side is also having difficulties of which we know nothing.[2]

[1] The Austrian puppet leader, executed at Nuremburg.
[2] Professor Lindemann to Dr. Noetzlein. Cherwell archives.

The Munich Agreement further increased his gloom and contempt for the Government, and his constant dread of air attack on England. On October 14, 1938, he wrote to Lord Tweedsmuir, the Governor-General of Canada:

> I must confess I am very anxious about the Munich Settlement, especially after the Saarbrücken speech. But still we can only hope that Hitler for once meant what he said and that he will be content to let us enjoy our Empire whilst he establishes himself in South-Eastern Europe. If only we had developed the defence against aircraft, for which I have pleaded for so many years, our position might be very different.

It was inevitable that, holding these views, Prof should have regarded a proper air defense as the most vital of all current needs, placing it above research into cancer or tuberculosis. In his days at Farnborough he had been close to the various sections of the Air Ministry, and his association with its Aeronautical Research Committee had begun soon after the war. He served on the Meteorology Sub-committee from 1921 to 1924, and in 1925 became Chairman of the Kite Balloon Sub-committee, a project dear to his heart, and in 1926 was invited to become a member of the Main Committee of Aeronautical Research, on which he served for two terms of office, from 1926 to 1929 and from 1929 to 1932.

In 1927 Sir Maurice Hankey, then Secretary to both the Cabinet and the Committee of Imperial Defence, wrote to Prof asking for his views on air defense. By then he was also a member of the Anti-Aircraft Sub-committee of the Committee of Imperial Defence. On the death of its Chairman, Lord Haldane, this committee was dissolved, and he replied to Hankey's letter informing him of this fact, in terms which express the position he adopted from the beginning and from which he never wavered:

Though the results attained by this particular Sub-committee may not have been as gratifying as could be wished, I am convinced that there is not only room but a very decided need for some such Sub-committee provided a suitable Chairman and personnel can be found. As I have often told you, it seems to me that general scientific information and advice are essential for any proper consideration of defence problems, and a Sub-committee to suggest and discuss new problems and methods would seem to me an important adjunct of the C.I.D.[1]

On August 8, 1934, the Prof wrote in the *Times* a strong appeal for work to be undertaken on new modes of defense against invading aircraft, and in September he and Winston Churchill descended on Baldwin during his annual holiday at Aix. Several circumstances must have conspired to make this visit unwelcome in the extreme. Baldwin regarded this holiday as a sacrosanct period in which no newspapers were allowed, and which was devoted to literature, reverie and general recuperation. No interruption would have been welcome to him, least of all one demanding attention to the odious subjects of foreign affairs and military preparation. Churchill and the Prof shattered the Prime Minister's repose by urging upon him new methods of defense, such as the construction of small aerial mines.

As a result of this initiative the Committee of Imperial Defence invited Prof to lay his proposals before Sir Robert Brooke-Popham's committee, which was then considering the defense of London against enemy air attack. This invitation did not appeal to him. He had, he said, no specific proposals to put before a committee whose attitude, he believed, was that "the bomber would always get through" and that counter-bombing was the only effective reply. He demanded nothing less than a revolution in the official attitude toward air defense. He argued that no weapon had yet been invented

[1] The Committee of Imperial Defence.

to which an antidote had not ultimately been found. He held
that the whole question should be referred to a body without
preconceived notions, and it was essential to proceed from the
assumption that such a defense could be found if sufficient time
and money were devoted to the search.

> What I have in mind is a committee under the Chairmanship
> of a man of the type of the late Lord Justice Fletcher Molton
> or the present Lord Weir with two or three service representa-
> tives and two or three scientists whose definite instructions
> would be to find some method of defence against air bombing
> other than counter attack and reprisals.
>
> Some modus would have to be found to secure priority for
> researches initiated by the committee and some method of
> paying for them. With adequate support and the knowledge
> that the Government would not take no for an answer, I am
> confident that such a committee could hammer out a workable
> scheme within a very few years.[1]

Although Prof did, in the end, attend a meeting of Brooke-
Popham's committee, he was not reassured, and in the autumn
of 1934 began to urge Lord Londonderry, the Secretary of
State for Air and a personal friend, to appoint an outside committee of scientists to investigate the question of defense
against air attack. The response was disappointing, and a letter from Londonderry was so guarded in its terms as to suggest that it had been drafted by an Air Ministry official. Londonderry did, however, ask what was in Prof's mind, and
he was only too willing to divulge it:

> Mr. Baldwin some time ago made a speech which, it was
> generally understood, had the approval of the Air Ministry,

[1] Professor Lindemann to Mr. Baldwin, November 3, 1934. It was the
central point of his argument that the work should be delegated to a sub-
committee of the Committee of Imperial Defence, in order to give it the
authority to conduct experiments without interference.

in which he took the line that it was impossible ever to stop night bombers reaching their objectives and that the only hope of saving Europe from the welter of slaughter and suffering which the raids and counter-raids of hostile air squadrons would produce, was a general spread of the pacifist idea. I do not know upon what evidence this conclusion was founded; why for ten years the possibilities of the kite-balloon barrage were neglected, nor how much energy had been devoted to research into methods of this sort. Whatever the reason, I gather that until recently at any rate, it was definitely the opinion of the Air Ministry that no defence could ever be discovered.

This view appears to me profoundly improbable. An antidote has always been found hitherto for every offensive weapon and I see no reason to suppose that aircraft are the only exception, in fact, many general arguments would tend to prove the contrary. But once a Department has adopted such a defeatist line, it is clearly going to be very difficult to persuade those concerned to make very great efforts themselves to prove that they have been in error. For this reason and because some of the methods which ought to be considered would probably lie in intermediate regions between those covered by the various defence ministries, it seems unlikely that a purely Air Ministry Committee would attain the desired end.

My suggestion would therefore be that a small committee consisting, say, of three scientists and three service representatives should be set up under an independent Chairman (e.g. a man of the type of Lord Weir) to report directly to the Prime Minister. Its task should be to find a method of preventing bombers, and especially night bombers, reaching their objectives.* Some method would have to be found for ensuring priority for researches or investigations the Committee wished to have made by various Government Departments and some mechanism by which it would be possible for the Committee to supervise them and assure itself that they were being properly and seriously conducted. The cost in my view would

* I am not making a great point of day bombers as I take it the Air Force can deal with these.

not be excessive (not more than £100,000 a year at most and probably much less) and might if necessary be certified and brought in as a supplementary vote at the end of each year. In this way it seems to me one could get the necessary research initiated and carried through with the energy and vigour which the immense urgency of the problem requires.

As you will see, such a Committee would in no way be concerned with the organisation of air defence or be called upon to deal with the existing plans which the Air Ministry has worked out. Its instructions would be to discover or invent new methods. Defensive measures based upon such methods which might be devised and approved would be carried out by the appropriate ministry. There would be no need for the Air Ministry to inform the Committee of its present plans though I should hope it would work in close conjunction with it giving the Committee the benefit of its experience. After all there is no reason why there should be any more danger in confiding the principles of the existing methods to three carefully selected scientists (who could if necessary voluntarily put themselves under the Official Secrets Act for this purpose) than there has been in confiding in all the hundreds of air mechanics from whom they can scarcely be concealed.

I sincerely hope you will try to get some such Committee formed and given the necessary powers. It would, I am sure, meet with general approval in Parliament. It may be that the Air Ministry is right and that I am wrong and that there really is no defence. But even so, the Committee would serve a useful purpose. For it would prove to the people of England that every effort had been made to find one and that the issue had not been allowed to go by default.

Londonderry replied on December 20th, and the nature of his letter suggested to the Prof that he could not, without undue optimism, expect any support from this quarter. The Secretary of State informed him that he had for some time been contemplating setting up a departmental committee of the

Air Ministry under Henry Tizard to discover how far recent strategic research could assist in the problem of defense against air attack. It would be useful, he thought, if Prof would communicate with Tizard, and make suggestions for consideration by the committee.

Prof, instantly wary, recognized in this proposal the old departmental committee he so distrusted. He saw it as an ineffectual body, at the mercy of the Air Ministry officials, with no power to force through experiments, or to deal on equal terms with other departments concerned with preparations for war.

After consulting his friends Winston Churchill and Austen Chamberlain, he told Londonderry that, although he did not know the powers and composition of the committee, he could not believe that a departmental committee could fulfill the urgent purpose, and that he and his friends felt obliged to press for more vigorous action on the lines he had set forth.

He turned, therefore, to the new Prime Minister, Ramsay MacDonald. This charming but irresolute man for a brief moment raised the drooping spirits of Prof and his friends. He replied in an encouraging manner to a letter drafted by Prof, and signed by Churchill and Chamberlain, which had put forward the now familiar demands.

> 10 Downing Street,
> Whitehall.
> 10th January 1935.

Private.

MY DEAR AUSTEN,

I have seen your letter, also signed by Winston, and am glad to have your backing. All I can say at the moment is that I have had the matter in hand myself for a little time, as I know Lindemann very well. Just now I am so full of pressing matters, preparatory to the meeting of the House and the arrangement of its business, that it will be a day or two before I can return to it; but so far as I can see at the moment, it is a thing about which an enquiry should be made. I quite agree with you that it should not be a Departmental Committee, and have already made up my mind that it is something that the C.I.D. should take in hand.

I will write to you finally, however, as soon as I personally can, but am sending you this in the meantime to assure you that I have it under consideration.

Yours very sincerely,

J. RAMSAY MACDONALD

Having received, as he thought, the Prime Minister's support, the Prof began painting in the background to another man in a key position, Sir Maurice Hankey, and he ended his appeal by saying that if we could only get rid of the aerial menace, England would once again be an island, and the whole European situation would be transformed.

He was soon to learn the danger of reposing too much confidence in Ramsay MacDonald. After that misleading *démarche*, the "Boneless Wonder" began to assume a different shape, writing to Austen Chamberlain on January 15th to say that when he last wrote he had not been told that the committee under Tizard, of which Londonderry had informed the Prof, had already been set up, its composition being: Mr. Henry Tizard (Chairman), Professor A. V. Hill, Professor P. M. S. Blackett and Mr. H. E. Wimperis. The terms of reference were "To consider how far recent advances in technical knowledge can be used to strengthen the present methods of defence against hostile aircraft." Its official name was the Committee for the Scientific Survey of Air Defence, and the intention was to ask the Prof to give evidence.

This characteristic shift of allegiance on the part of the Prime Minister caused Chamberlain to write on the letter: "Most unsatisfactory. I have written at once to say that no

Departmental Committee will satisfy us." The Prof agreed that it was deplorable "the way Ramsay chops and changes," and that he understood that there would be no opposition to his ideas in the Cabinet, except possibly from the Air Ministry. "It does seem absurd," he said, "that they should claim a veto. The navy might as well object to the C.I.D. investigating coast defence."

Prof and his friends were now angry and dispirited at the course events had taken. He particularly felt the chill of despair at the years that had ebbed away barren of achievement, and he carried his proselytizing even into Mayfair drawing rooms, where after his lecture on the horrors to come dowagers were left in a state of nervous prostration. The little group had now abandoned MacDonald in disgust.

The Prof had now had time to consider the composition of the Tizard Committee, and he told Churchill that Tizard was, of course, a good man, but that the Committee was without power, and a mere waste of time. Would it be possible to get a committee appointed by Parliament? On February 13th he spoke again to Londonderry, who "at once raised the question and said he could not understand why we were not satisfied with his Committee, and that it seemed to him that an endeavour to bring in anyone from outside reflected upon the Air Ministry.

"I explained to him that in my view defence against air attack was not exclusively an Air Ministry question any more than Coast Defence was exclusively an Admiralty affair; that a great deal of work would have to be done by other departments, e.g. the War Office, and that an Air Ministry Committee would in these circumstances be singularly ill-adapted to ensure prompt and vigorous action.

"I further pointed out that it was essential to have work done on a large scale and not to be hampered by any departmental inertia and that this could only be assured if the committee were presided over by a man of Cabinet rank. I mentioned that if a committee were set up either by the House of Commons or with its specific approval, one could overcome all financial difficulties; for experiments demanded by the Committee and carried out by one of the Departments, could be charged at a figure agreed between the head of the Department and the Chairman of the Committee and put into the supplementary estimates of that Department; in these circumstances they would be certain of the approval of the House of Commons.

"Finally, in reply to his statement that he would be very much aggrieved if we found something his experts did not already know about, I pointed out that it was precisely the knowledge that this was so which would be bound to make them try and prove that our proposals would not work.

"In the end Londonderry said he quite saw our point and agreed with it and that he would write to the Prime Minister in this sense. Unless, on his return to the Air Ministry, he is over-persuaded by his officials, I have every hope he will do this, which should materially facilitate our task on Friday morning."

After all these uncertainties the Prof was encouraged again by reading in the newspapers that a proper C.I.D. Sub-committee was to be set up to deal with defense against aircraft, and in March he wrote to Sir Maurice Hankey saying how delighted he was by the report, and offering to forego his holiday if he could be of any use. He heard again on June 9th from his friend Chamberlain that MacDonald had veered again, that his reply to questions in the House had been satisfactory, and that at last they meant business on the question of the C.I.D. Committee, and that he would, therefore, urge Prof to join the Committee of which Tizard was Chairman — the Committee for the Scientific Survey of Air Defence.

He had already consulted Churchill, and agreed to join the

Tizard Committee, but he did so reluctantly and with little hope of making serious progress. To Chamberlain he wrote in June 1935:

> I am afraid that I am still not by any means satisfied with the Government's attitude. I can scarcely believe that the somewhat unimportant Tizard Committee can have the authority or power that is required, more especially if it is a question of getting work done by the War Office or some other Department. The Prime Minister, of course, at our meeting promised to replace the Committee by a more powerful C.I.D. Committee. Now they seem to want to whittle away the functions of the C.I.D. Committee and allow it merely to coordinate researches done by the various small departmental Committees. This seems to me a great pity, but I suppose that if they are determined not to attack the problem wholeheartedly nothing can force them to do so.

He was now a member of the Tizard Committee, and the stage was set for a merciless battle between the two men which was watched with astonishment by the scientific world. In the sessions of this Committee Prof fulfilled the functions of a Parliamentary opposition, subjecting the proposals of others to constant and searching criticism. It was a role for which his brain was eminently suited. Hostilities opened slowly on July 1, 1935, when Prof sent Tizard a long memorandum "on some of the questions anent air defence, which I have been advocating for the past year to a number of different people. The thing I am keenest on is to get ahead with the small aerial mines. I am sure with goodwill they could be made to work."

A further exchange of letters between them shows the Prof's growing irritation with what he regarded as the slowness of the Committee's proceedings:

> As I told you, I consider no time should be lost in starting work on small explosive mines whatever may be the ultimate

method of placing them in position. One should investigate how much explosive is required, what is the best arrangement for the metal casing, what is the best method of detonating, how they should be suspended and so on and so forth. These problems are independent of the question as to whether they can best be laid in one way or the other. As I told you, I think these sort of investigations ought to be started without delay and I hope work will not be postponed until the next meeting of the Committee, which I understand is to take place between the 15th and 20th of September.

Another point though of less urgency except from a personal point of view, is the question of infra-red detection and location. As I said, I am by no means satisfied that this should be dropped. The forms of location at present envisaged are obviously long-distance methods. The infra-red becomes more accurate the closer the aeroplane approaches and might prove invaluable if one wished to fire without using searchlights. At present things are much too uncertain to neglect a feasible method even if one thinks something better may exist.

As I mentioned before, I should like to know soon if investigations are to be dropped as the work on the subject now proceeding in my Laboratory should be discontinued before next term if it is of no importance.

He was not satisfied with Tizard's reply to this letter, and wrote:

I am sorry you think it necessary to postpone the work on the mines. There is so much to be done before a practical result can be obtained that I begrudge every week. As to the infra-red, I should have thought it would be mainly useful to the A.A. people. If they really think to do anything with their first burst before the aeroplane can take "avoiding action" it must surely be important to get the exact position without using searchlights.

R. V. Jones, whom we have met as a pupil of Prof's at Oxford, had been working on this subject at the Clarendon

Laboratory. At a meeting of the Tizard Committee in the autumn of 1935 it was agreed that he should be asked to undertake work on the Committee's behalf on an infrared method for detecting and locating aircraft, using electronic amplifiers instead of galvanometers.

On February 7, 1936, Prof wrote to Lord Swinton, who had succeeded Londonderry as Secretary of State for Air, giving his conclusions on the problems of air defense. In so far as his conclusions came within the reference of the Tizard Committee, he was pleased to find how nearly they agreed with him on the question of kite-balloons and antiaircraft artillery, but he was still impatient at the slow progress made on experiments:

1. There is no prospect of our being able, by existing means, to deal with night bombers if they come over individually instead of in large formations. We must therefore expect this form of attack.

The first sentence is quite certain on cloudy nights and practically certain on clear nights.

2. Anti-aircraft fire is not a practicable method for the defence of large general targets such as London. It may be of use in defending comparatively small specific targets which require accurate bomb sighting.

The first part of this statement is mathematically demonstrable. It is no more controvertible than a proposition in Euclid. The second part depends upon experiments; it expresses a hope rather than a realised ideal.

3. The only method which is definitely feasible at present to defend London against individual night bombers is the kite-balloon barrage.

The argument for this appears to be conclusive though it might be possible in the course of time to modify the German Air Fleet so as to enable it to fly slowly through the barrage.

Efforts will of course have to be made to raise the ceiling of the kite-balloons to the necessary height.

4. It should be possible to develop aerial mines which would supplement or, if the enemy machines are modified in the manner indicated above, perhaps ultimately replace the kite-balloon barrage.

This is perhaps a pious hope, but one which, given a free hand, I would lay considerable odds on fulfilling.

On February 27th he emphasized to Churchill the slowness of the Committee in forcing through experiments. In this letter he makes perfectly clear his belief in radar and his admiration for Watson-Watt, who was developing it:

The only part of the Committee's work which has so far been successful has been the development of methods of detection and location. The reason for this seems to me to be that it has been put in the hands of a man who suggested the method and believed in it and that he could and did push ahead with whatever experiments he thought necessary . . .[1]

I suggest however that the only way of making progress with the equally important development of aerial mines and the related question of shell bursts which remain effective for some reasonable period, is to put them in the hands of some enthusiastic believer who is not compelled to come back to the Committee every time he wants to make a fresh experiment, but is given authority and indeed instructions to think out and carry out experiments as fast as he possibly can. In view of the pressure on the Government Departments it may be desirable to consider whether the resources of private firms might not be made available for this purpose. But whatever the method, drive and energy must be instilled.

In a letter complaining of the failure of the Committee to tackle the questions of aerial mines, methods of increasing the

[1] Author's italics.

effective duration of shellbursts, kite-balloons and infrared detection, he again affirmed his belief in R.D.F.:

R.D.F. methods of Location

This is the only work which has made satisfactory (or indeed any) progress. It has been throughout in the hands of Mr. Watson-Watt, who suggested it, and believes in it and having had a more or less free hand, there is every indication that he will make it a complete success.[1]

It might be worth asking exactly what the Committee has done beyond giving its blessing to Mr. Watson-Watt. It has written reports and called for information, but it has not materially itself initiated or even seriously helped any new developments.

It is probably true to say that experimental work cannot be carried out by a Committee, since each experiment must be based upon the previous one and usually fifty or even a hundred experiments will be required before success is attained. If each new experiment must await a meeting of the Committee, progress can only take place at a snail's pace. The only method is to hand over research to people who are enthusiastic believers in the possibility of finding a solution and utilising the Committee, if at all, as an occasional advisory body to which those in charge can appeal if desired.

Meanwhile the atmosphere on the Tizard Committee had become dangerously charged with tension. Prof adopted a manner both superior and offensive which enraged his colleagues. Particularly exasperating to them was his habit of reporting every complaint about the Tizard Committee to Churchill, who could raise the matters on the superior Air Defence Research Sub-committee of the Committee of Imperial Defence, of which he and Tizard were both members.

By June 1936 the relations between Prof and Tizard

[1] Author's Italics.

F. A. Lindemann, Viscount Cherwell

Prof's mother (from a painting in possession of Mrs. Carson-Roberts)

Prof's father,
A. F. Lindemann

F. A. Lindemann (left)
with his brother Charles
at Sidholme

A painting of a stuffed jay
by F. A. Lindemann, while
at school in Darmstadt

Professor Nernst talking with his old
pupil Lord Cherwell, in later years

The Chudleigh Mess at Farnborough, 1918. Prof is top left

Sir Henry Tizard
(left)

Anglo-American shipboard conference, January 1952. Left to right, standing: Walter Gifford (U.S. Ambassador in London), General Omar Bradley, Sir Oliver Franks (British Ambassador in Washington), Lord Cherwell, Lord Ismay, Averill Harriman. Sitting: Sir Anthony Eden, Sir Winston Churchill, President Harry S. Truman, Dean Acheson (Secretary of State), John Snyder (Secretary of the Treasury), and Robert Lovett (Secretary of Defense).

The Prime Minister, Sir Anthony Eden, being shown a model of a heavy-water reactor by Sir John Cockcroft on his visit with Lord Cherwell to Harwell on September 27, 1955

Prof with his personal assistant Mr. E. J. S. Clarke holding a koala bear during their visit to Australia in October 1953

Prof with a young friend

had reached a point which prompted Tizard to send this letter:

161 St. James's Court,
S.W.1.

18.6.36.

DEAR LINDEMANN,

No doubt you already know that as a result of your personal criticism to Winston Churchill he made a written attack on the Research Committee without taking trouble to ascertain my views first. I was obliged to answer this categorically, whereupon he followed up in Committee with other wild criticisms presumably based on information from you. Needless to say I have no objection to your discussing with him the work of our Committee — on the contrary everyone concerned would welcome this if the object were to produce fresh ideas and constructive suggestions. But if the only result is to produce ill-founded criticisms then I am bound to say that however good your ultimate motives are, the only effect of your actions is to retard progress. I would really enjoy working with you if you were ready to work as a member of a team, but if you are playing another game I don't think it is possible for us to go on collaborating without continual friction. I have told Swinton this — so you ought to know.

I wish we could have settled such differences of opinion that exist in a friendly manner in our own Committee, but you have made things very difficult, if not impossible.

I am writing a general statement about the policy underlying the priority attached to different items of our work. I will let you have this next week. If agreed by members it will be circulated to the C.I.D. Committee.

Yours sincerely,
H. T. TIZARD

Prof, not a man given to turning the other cheek, discussed the letter with Churchill and replied:

23rd June 1936

DEAR TIZARD,

I thank you for your letter of the 18th June.

It is not worth while for me to attempt to discuss the relative wildness of the various statements which may or may not have been made in my absence at the meeting of the C.I.D. Committee, but I am sure that anything deriving from me was strictly accurate. If you would send me a copy of the statement of which you complain and of your "categorical" reply I would be glad to deal with the matter.

The point on which we seem to be in complete disagreement is the different urgency which we attach to our endeavours to find some method to deal with air attack. Your procedure would no doubt be excellent if we had 10 or 15 years time. I believe that the period available is to be measured in months.

Apart from Watson-Watt's work you will scarcely claim that any appreciable advance towards a solution of the problem has been made since the Committee has been in being. You appear to be perfectly satisfied with the rate of progress. I am not.

In view of the immense importance of the question and holding the views I do as to its urgency, you will not be surprised that I have used every means at my disposal to accelerate progress and that I am determined to continue so. I am very sorry if this offends you, but the matter is too vital to justify one in refraining from action in order to salve anybody's *amour propre*.

Yours sincerely,
F. A. LINDEMANN

Churchill, who had supported Prof throughout the hostilities, gave his own impression of the dispute to the Secretary of State for Air, Swinton:

22nd June 1936

Confidential

I am sorry you do not feel able to allow an impartial examination to be made of the points in dispute. I certainly did

not agree to the procedure which you say was "decided" at
the end of our meeting. In fact I well remember saying that I
was not at all satisfied. I will however await Tizard's promised
report. His first step has been to write a very offensive letter to
Lindemann which I should have thought would make, and was
perhaps intended to make, their future relations impossible.

What surprises and grieves me is your attitude and that you
should be apparently contented with the way the work is going.
We are at present entirely defenceless from the ground (except
for a few vulnerable points where batteries are massed) against
any attack from the air: and it must be at least more than a
year before anything practical can be done. During the ten
months I have sat upon the Committee I have been shocked at
the slowness with which every investigation proceeds. I well
know that this branch is a very small part of your labours. All
the more therefore I should have thought you would welcome
the assistance of others in trying to get things done.

The differences upon the Scientific Committee are not as you
suggest of a technical or abstruse character. They are differences about the method and procedure to be used in testing
certain ideas, which if found sound would open a new domain
to anti-aircraft artillery, as well as helping in other ways known
to you. The experiments are neither large nor expensive, but
they must be numerous, and can only advance by repeated trial
and error.

Last August we decided to try to find out what happened
when an aeroplane was brought in contact with a thin wire at
the end of which was an explosive charge, and how big that
explosive charge should be. If this enquiry had been entrusted
to a private firm, it could have been completed in two or three
months at the outside at a cost I should suppose of less than
£1,000. Instead of this we have the long series of delays set
forth by Lindemann in the paper which you have circulated at
my desire. Apart from knowing that a very modest explosive
charge will suffice to do serious damage, we have not made any
progress. I certainly thought that an idea like this if adopted
provisionally would be tested day in, day out, until it would

either be proved sound or futile. But if these small experiments are to be agreed to one by one, and then fitted in with the mass of important experimental work being discharged at Shoeburyness and elsewhere, with reports in each case back to the Committee which meets about once a month, and with no one person given the means to pursue the quest, then it is certain that nothing will result before the period of maximum danger has come.

It is always difficult to have a public controversy about unmentionable topics. I am however quite sure that if instead of serving on your Committee Lindemann and I had pressed our points by all the various methods and channels open to us, these ideas would have had better treatment than they have received.

I have dwelt upon this particular set of experiments because I have followed them more closely. But I fear that a similar slowness and intermittence characterises other lines of research in this field.

I hope you will weigh what I write without resentment or prejudice.

The Tizard-Prof conflict which divided the scientific world was lent an added piquancy by their former close friendship. This had by now fallen completely apart. Prof at this time referred to Tizard as "that intriguer." The pleasant memories of the past, the risks shared in common in the air, and the fact that he was godfather to Tizard's son counted for nothing. Tizard was now an enemy and therefore an object of that long-sustained rancor. Prof was regarded in the Committee as Churchill's mouthpiece, and his habit of getting his complaints about what he considered to be their lethargy ventilated by Churchill in the superior Committee caused strong resentment. As he was inept at subterfuge or compromise, he frequently became offensive on the Committee, where he gave his sarcasm and waspish tongue full play, and his fatal insensitiveness to atmosphere or the feelings of others occluded him from any real knowledge of what they thought of him.

Tizard in particular was enraged by the attack made on his Committee in June by Churchill, at the instigation of Prof, in the A.D.R. Committee on which both Churchill and Tizard sat. He was so stung by Churchill's criticism that, as he confessed to the author: "From that moment the Prof and I became mortal enemies; when he was on the Committee he was incapable of admitting that he was wrong. Things got so bad that Churchill got up on the main Committee and attacked me. I defended myself in no mean manner. Had Mr. Churchill been a gentleman, he would have come to me first."[1]

He added that in his opinion Churchill was prone to swallow whole anything that Prof told him about air defense, and that there was much opposition in the scientific world to his views. Tizard had for four years been Chairman of the Aeronautical Research Committee. Its members included many who had known the Prof at Farnborough, but, according to Tizard, there was a loud cry of protest at the mere possibility of his re-election.

On the Tizard Committee the Prof's objections were less to the work it attempted than to what he thought its aimless tempo and supine attitude to the delay of invention trials. It was behaving, he thought, as though it had fifteen years to produce an antidote, and proceeding on a peacetime basis on work that was in fact an immediate matter of life and death.

There was another aspect of this deplorable feud which had nothing to do with clashes over infrared or aerial mines, and was, in fact, a naked struggle for power between the two men. They were once bosom friends. Both had studied under Nernst, and they had a high opinion of each other's abilities, Tizard saying that Prof was the cleverest man he had ever known, "as clever as Rutherford."[2] Both had been test pilots, and in the election to the Oxford professorship Tizard

[1] Sir Henry Tizard to author.
[2] Sir Henry Tizard to author.

had pulled every string, as only he knew how to do, to secure the Chair for his friend.

Both men were intensely ambitious to dictate the scientific policy of the country, and, in their grapple for power, there was room only for one at the summit. It was as though two men desired to ascend to the top of a house by separate staircases. Tizard had taken the staircase which he climbed under the aegis of Rutherford, and the Prof ascended the other staircase under that of leading statesmen — Birkenhead, and afterward Winston Churchill. Each man desired to lead, and to lay down the experiments which were to be made. It was undoubtedly, as Prof said, a serious error on the part of Londonderry that he did not appoint as chairman of that unquiet Committee a man of Cabinet status, versed in affairs and more detached from the scientific world. Under such a chairman, perhaps a man like Sir John Anderson, these troubles might never have occurred.

This struggle for power was ultimately won by Prof when Churchill first appointed him his scientific adviser, and afterward took him into his administration. Tizard's hopes of high scientific employment were dashed at that hour, but he was later to entertain hopes of high office from the Labour Party which were realized when in 1946 Attlee appointed him Chairman of the Defence Research Policy Committee and the Advisory Council on Scientific Policy.

Intrigue and jealousy were at that moment not uncommon among scientists. The old patronizing attitude toward them, which Prof so resented at Oxford, was also evident in London. One senior civil servant had minuted: "It is contrary to good administration that scientists should sit in conference with senior officers." Wilmot, the Minister of Supply in the Socialist Government, was to reflect with ineffable condescension: "What I like about scientists is that they are a team, so that one need not know their names"; and Walter Elliot had observed that "Scientific men should be on tap but not on top." The scientists who were already in the departments resented the intrusion of other scientists, and there was continual jealousy among them of other men's work. This jealousy of scientists of one another's achievements took many forms, but none more disgraceful than the treatment of Watson-Watt. He was harried during his development of radar by others who had not troubled to pursue the research on it beyond first principles, and who were jealous of the fact that Watson-Watt had developed this war-winning device. None of those who were jealous of him was big enough to admit his greatness. Professor Hill was right to say that no one appreciated him as much as Watson-Watt himself. They did not appreciate him at all, and expected him to remain almost anonymous. Some even tried to prevent him being elected to The Royal Society, but were happily thwarted, and he would probably not have been knighted had Prof not appealed personally to the Prime Minister.

It is not difficult to see what happened to the Committee on Prof's arrival. The pleasant old club was suddenly ruined, as any other club might be, by an offensive outsider who, they thought, ought never to have been elected, and who was insolent enough to criticize the rules. The other scientists on the Committee were friends and had social contacts with each other. With Prof they had none. He lived in a different social sphere, and, apart from scientific arguments, had no communion with them at all.

Sitting on this Committee then were these men who had come to detest the Prof. In addition to his arrogant behavior and sarcastic tongue, he was the type of scientist who had separated himself from the herd. He had no social relations with them except at meetings, but slipped into his Rolls Royce with relief, and glided away from discord to more harmonious company.

Sir Henry Tizard, former Secretary of the D.S.I.R., was a notable figure in British science, and made great contributions toward winning the war, although many leading scientists[1] are of the opinion that he had a far less acute brain than Prof. It is probable that the two men had begun to fall out before their association on the Committee for the Scientific Survey of Air Defence, and Prof was believed to have referred to Tizard as "that insufferable little man" before the air defense trouble began. Professor R. V. Jones considered:

> The first signs of differences between the two men appeared some years after Tizard had left his Fellowship at Oriel in 1920 to become Secretary to the D.S.I.R. From his uncompleted autobiography it is clear that there was difficulty about Committees. At Tizard's instigation Lindemann was appointed a member of the Council of the D.S.I.R. in 1926, but his critical attitude made him unpopular with the other members. The Aeronautical Research Committee refused to have him as a member in spite, it seems, of Tizard's support. Lindemann probably knew that Tizard had proposed him and blamed the rebuff on Tizard's unsuccessful advocacy. Certainly from about this time Lindemann showed signs of impatience with Tizard, although Tizard still regarded Lindemann as a friend.[2]

Tizard's greatest contribution was perhaps not scientific, but lay in his consummate skill in making the service chiefs conscious of the importance of science, while Prof was indispensable not only for the guidance that he gave to Churchill, but as a most penetrating scientific critic. Unfortunately he made no effort to conceal his contempt for people whom he regarded as his intellectual inferiors, and this was his outstanding folly.

Air Marshal Sir George Mills made it clear to R. V. Jones

[1] E.g., Professor R. V. Jones and Sir Thomas Merton.
[2] Professor R. V. Jones: *The Times*, April 6, 1961.

that Tizard's keenness and his capacity for asking provocative questions was one of the main factors in getting the Royal Air Force disposed toward the use of radar.

> It is quite true [said Jones] that the original proposal for radar was made before the Tizard Committee actually held its first meeting, and Watson-Watt must be given great credit for the way it developed. An almost equally important matter, however, from the point of view of our salvation in 1940 was not only that we had radar, but that our Air Force knew how to use it. This may seem an obvious point, but it might not necessarily have happened that way at all. The Biggin Hill interception trials of 1937 were undertaken largely, I believe, as a result of Tizard's saying (at a time when radar was by no means an operational device) "Let us assume that we have a radar system, and that it is capable of providing this particular kind of information. Now let us see whether the Air Force can make use of it, and let us develop interception techniques based on its use." Sir George Mills gave me a firsthand account of the effect that these trials had, with the result that in 1939 we were ready not only with a chain of radar stations, but with a cadre of Air Force officers trained in its use, and alive to the possibility of further developments. . . .
> . . . Thus we had a fighter defence matched to the use of radar in 1940, whereas the Germans only realized the mistake in their philosophy in about 1942. The fact that we have the right philosophy, when we might easily have made the same errors as the Germans did, was probably almost as vital to us as the invention of radar itself. Someone on our side must have the credit for this, and certainly the apex of the pyramid of operational liaison between scientists and serving officers was Tizard. I should certainly be inclined to give it to him.[1]

It is a further indication of Tizard's influence with the Air Force that he persuaded them to take a scientist, R. V. Jones,

[1] Professor R. V. Jones to author.

into Air Intelligence, and that he afterward became Chief of Scientific Air Intelligence. While Tizard's judgment was not always sound, it is unquestionable that he played one of the most important parts in the prewar development of air defense. He was a brilliant and forceful man on committees, with a wonderful gift for getting scientists and serving officers to work together. His faults were that he was quick-tempered, liable to wander outside his own field, anxious to engross too much work himself, and to resent the submission of new ideas. He was without doubt a distinguished figure, but he was as wrong a Chairman of this Committee as Prof would have been himself.

The great abilities of both men and their old friendship make the pettiness with which they conducted their feud dispiriting to contemplate. Sir Frederick Brundrett, who spent some time with both of them said:

> My own conclusion was that, for two extremely intelligent grown-up people, their attitude towards each other was singularly childish. Cherwell always used to tell me, for instance, that Tizard was no scientist. I cannot help feeling that you have got to put your definition of a scientist very high if you are going to exclude Tizard from that category. Tizard, on the other hand, was never prepared to accept any opinion emanating from Cherwell as an honest one, and I frequently found it necessary to prevent the circulation of some particularly acid comments which were quite unjustified by the facts of the actual case under discussion.[1]

The charge that Prof did not believe in radar, and did his best to obstruct its progress until he realized its great potentialities, was made by Professor A. V. Hill, and was afterward unworthily revived by Sir Charles Snow in his Godkin Lectures at Harvard University in 1960. It is perhaps unnecessary to

---

[1] Sir Frederick Brundrett to author.

comment at length on the propriety of a British scientist washing such dirty linen in a foreign university. Sir Charles Snow's account of the dispute between the two men resembles a Victorian melodrama in which virtue in the form of Tizard is triumphant and the villain Lindemann hissed off the stage. In his assessment of Lindemann's character he was no doubt assisted by his imaginative powers as a writer of fiction, and his conclusions are so ignorant and misleading to anyone who knew the dead victim as to approach caricature.

As the insidious description proceeds, an unrecognizable figure emerges — an *éminence grise* of doubtful nationality, who neglected physics to go whoring after the false gods of rank and title, a sexless fanatic whose warped emotions found outlet in sadistic humor at the expense of others — in fact, a creature alien and repulsive. Sir Charles lingers over the personal habits of Lindemann, as though to discover something further detrimental to his character in the fact that he was a vegetarian and a teetotaler, and as though these private inclinations had some connection with his reputation as a scientist.

The cards are stacked against Lindemann in a manner so blatant as to become naïve in the effort to reduce him to a figure of trivial importance. The gift of sarcastic speech, which was common to both men, was found by Snow to be "misleading" in Tizard but "malevolent" and "sadistic" in the case of Lindemann. Both men were avid for power, but in the eyes of Snow that was fitting in the case of Tizard, but reprehensible in that of Lindemann. Snow sees Tizard as British to the core, and in contrast to this bluff, reassuring figure, Lindemann's foreign origin is stressed and the synthetic figure emerges — "Heavy, pallid, Central European." Snow tells us that Lindemann's was "the sort of character that makes a novelist's fingers itch," and it is clear that they have not itched in vain.

He has used the most questionable artifice to produce an

impression of Lindemann that is as odious as it is false. Lindemann's popularity in English society he attributes charitably to a combination of money and pushfulness, seemingly unaware of his charm as a companion. He does not hesitate to stoop to disparagement of Lindemann's powers as a scientist in comparison with those of Tizard: "The professional scientist did not take him seriously as a scientist, and dismissed him as a cranky society pet. Scientifically his name was worth little." It may be observed that in making this statement Snow is writing against some of the best scientific opinion of the day, and we shall find a truer estimate of Lindemann's achievement in the views of Sir Cyril Hinshelwood, late President of the Royal Society, or in those of Sir Thomas Merton and Professor R. V. Jones, both of whom expressed the opinion to the author that Lindemann's scientific powers were greatly superior to those of Tizard. No one reading Snow's lines would imagine that Lindemann's brain had excited the admiration of Einstein, nor that as a youth in his early twenties he had been co-author of scientific publications with the great Nernst, who regarded him as his most brilliant pupil, nor that his melting-point formula had been accepted by the famous Solvay Conference. Seldom can a writer more completely have given away his prejudices than Sir Charles Snow. He has violated the historian's first duty, objectivity, and his hostility toward Lindemann's person is only equaled by his misunderstanding of his character. This is no way to write history.

We have seen that one of the few really fruitful lines of research before the war had resulted in the chain of R.D.F. stations on the coasts of Britain, which had been established by Sir Robert Watson-Watt in time to play a vital part in the Battle of Britain. Far from decrying Watson-Watt's work on radar, as Snow suggested, Prof had regarded it with the greatest admiration, and had repeatedly pointed to Watson-Watt's development of radar as the one redeeming feature of prewar research.

One can turn to no better witness on this point than Watson-Watt himself, who held Prof in high esteem and was extremely generous in acknowledging the debt he owed to him: "Frederick A. Lindemann . . . was later to have a profound influence on the application of radar, as on all applications of science, to the winning of the Second World War."

He gave Prof credit also as early as the late twenties and early thirties for thinking of detecting aircraft by some method of measurement on reflected radio waves, but he had concluded that the packages reflected from anything so small as an aircraft would be too minute in energy content to supply the required information. "But he helped me greatly towards the fulfilment of my first proposals to use the cathode-ray tube in radio direction finding. Without his encouragement and help I might have had no 'C.R.D.F.,' and without C.R.D.F. there might have been no timely R.D.F."[1]

Watson-Watt's opinion is of particular value, as perfected radar was his unquestioned brain child, and as in the Tizard-Lindemann dispute his personal allegiance to either side was not involved:

I have, privately, asserted that I am one of the comparatively small number who had enjoyed the privilege of living in approximately equal amity with, and fidelity to, both the Prof and Tizard. I am deeply indebted to both . . .

The Prof's position on radar was, so far as I know, the following: —

(*a*) as he told me after radar was a "going concern," he had, before my memoranda were submitted, discussed with Bolton King the possibility of detecting aircraft by radio echo methods — presumably by the pulse method used by Breit and Tuve, in America, for ionospheric measurements in mid-1925. They had, however, concluded that the "engineering efficiency" of such a project was hopelessly minute, and did not carry the idea so far as a reasoned arithmetical examination.

[1] Sir Robert Watson-Watt, *Three Steps to Victory.*

In this pessimism they were in agreement with other highly competent physicists. Blumlein of EMI, who was killed in an experimental flight with H2S, and was himself a daring innovator, told me, after radar had been proved in practice but had not yet been disclosed to him, that aircraft detection by radio reflection was "looking for a mere speck in the sky," and hopeless as the familiar search for "a needle in a haystack." Professor Richard Whiddington, at Leeds (who had been at RAE at the time of Lindemann, Dobson and myself) told an insistent first year student — again long after radar was in use "in earnest" — that there was no hope of success for a workable proposal for the detection of aircraft at worthwhile ranges, by the use of radio echo techniques, put forward by the student.

Watson-Watt next referred to a memorandum he had written to Wimperis of the Tizard Committee and continued:

In July 1935 I reported following to 40 miles: in September 1935 I reported following to 56 miles, and pick-up at 37 miles. "The development of RDF had so greatly exceeded the expectations of the Air Defence Sub-committee of the Committee of Imperial Defence, which had assumed that a range of detection of 50 miles would not be achieved for some five years, that at their fifth meeting it was recommended with the Air Council's agreement that a chain of radio detection stations covering the approaches to the coast from the Tyne to Southampton should now be established" (Minutes of 16 September 1935).

In November 1935 an ambitious programme was proposed by the Air Staff for seven stations to be available for operations with the Service in August 1936, and for the first three stations to be in operation by June 1936.

.   .   .

It may well be that Prof had not had access to my Memorandum when he first heard of the project, in that case he would remember his discussion with Bolton King and wish to see the "numerical considerations."

As to Snow's charge that had Churchill become Secretary of State for Air, Lindemann would have stopped work on radar, Watson-Watt comments:

> Moreover, I hold to my view that the Lindemann letters to the "Times" and the Churchill visit to Baldwin at Aix-les-Bains, in the summer of 1934, may very well have compelled the appointment of the committees which took the wise but unheroic decisions to give Watson-Watt his head.
>
> "Had Churchill succeeded in becoming Air Minister at that time," I am modestly confident that I could have convinced him through the Prof, that my project was worth while, and that my slogan "Every week that passes is one per cent of the time we can count our own" would not have gone unheeded. I base this not merely on Scots stubbornness and pertinacity, but on the valuable support I had from these two after the "tea-milk-brandy" interview on mid-June 1936.[1]

Watson-Watt continued:

> I now add another pointer. On 2 February 1936 I addressed the Tizard C.S.S.A.D. on the desirability of the centimetric radar. In due time we discussed it further at the meeting of 25 February 1936, and I am sure that Prof was present and active, pressing for an early attack on this new line. So he was at this date enthusiastic for more radar.
>
> The Churchill, Lindemann, Watson-Watt meeting took place on 12 June 1936 and Prof was certainly pressing for a more "crash-like" effort then.
>
> In sum, then, I would say (*a*) that I could at all times talk more easily and comfortably with Prof than with the somewhat staccato Tizard, but that I was at no time conscious of any reserve in zeal for radar on the part of either; (*b*) that nothing could have been more in tune with the Churchill-

---

[1] Sir Robert Watson-Watt to author. The interview referred to was arranged by Lindemann in order to bring Watson-Watt, the pioneer of radar, and Winston Churchill together. Three different beverages were consumed during the meeting.

Prof campaign of 1934–35 for science in air defence than was radar. I find it inconceivable that Prof did not welcome the whole programme as a thing in itself. At no time did I detect any other than anxiety for a bold and speedy programme. Prof had other projects which he pressed, but there was no suggestion, known to me, of any serious competition for manpower or money-power; (c) I declare with complete confidence that, in a project which met with initial scepticism in some military circles, and on which there was real sluggishness in departmental action, I detected no single sign of reluctance, resistance or scepticism from any scientifically qualified critic. I cannot conceive of any greater enouragement than I had from C.S.S.A.D. and from A.D.R. Subcommittee of the Committee of Imperial Defence, from every one of the members of these committees and from every Minister of the Crown whom I met in the research and development period.

To sum up: *Nowhere, in my memory, in my personal records, or in any official records in my possession do I find even the merest shadow of evidence that the Prof ever did anything whatever to obstruct the development of radar in accordance with my proposals. Indeed, from 1915 to the end of his life I had from him, without interruption warm friendship, valuable advice, encouragement, hospitality and inspiration.*[1] I would add that if I had at any time had to choose between Tizard and Prof as companions on a desert island (provided with eggs and olive oil whatever else was lacking) I would have plumped for the Prof![2]

Snow's accusation that Prof sometimes argued that radar should not be given absolute priority over other projects, if true, is explained in the following words of Watson-Watt, and endorsed by R. V. Jones in the remarks that follow them.

Nothing that I have written or thought on this matter excludes a potential overriding consideration about the tactics of

[1] Author's italics.
[2] Sir Robert Watson-Watt to author.

debate. The pre-existing Tizard-Lindemann hostility may well have caused Prof to say something which could be mis-estimated by those outside the small group of those directly concerned. As a mere tactical diversion, Prof may have made a flourishing feint against radar so that he might better the chances of those projects of his own which were being coldly received. Faced with a three to one opposition, he was entitled to freedom of manoeuvre.[1]

I remember [said Jones] discussing the various detection systems with him in 1935, and I am sure he appreciated the possibilities. He may have drawn attention from time to time to the weak points in radar, and in a Committee he may well have, as on another occasion, put himself into the position of advocatus diaboli, but he was much too good a physicist not to appreciate what radar might do. . . . He certainly saw what damage might be done to radar after I had pointed out to him that one could potentially swamp it by dropping spurious reflectors in the sky over the North Sea, and although this was certainly pointed out to Tizard and his colleagues at the Air Research Defence Committee, they made no attempts to make any trials of the idea, and it was left to Prof to initiate the trials in late 1940.[2]

It was true that Prof supported an investigation into the possibilities of infrared detection of aircraft, but his object in doing so was not to obstruct radar, but to have in reserve an alternative method should the enemy succeed in rendering radar useless. Although infrared detection did not mature in time to be used in the war, it has ultimately been justified by success. It was then, however, in comparison with radar, a weak method of detection, and the mere fact that Prof was aware, as early as 1935, that it was possible to receive back an echo from an aircraft would in itself have prevented him from disbelieving in radar.

[1] *Ibid.*
[2] Professor R. V. Jones to author.

Apart from this false accusation of the obstruction of radar, Prof was accused by his opponents on the Committee of wasting their time with wildcat schemes. The proposal which most incensed them was described by Professor A. V. Hill as "Lindemann's continual and violent advocacy of a fantastic scheme for dropping bombs hanging by wires, in the path of attacking aircraft . . . He became ruder, more objectionable and less co-operative on the Committee, until Blackett and I told Swinton we weren't going to stand it any more."[1] Hill claimed to have a list available in emergency of ten major scientific "crimes" committed by Lindemann, one of which was the rockets containing parachutes with mines, of which he remarked that they would take so long to get into position that the enemy would be far away before they could be effective. Another device, "equally futile," was incendiary "leaves" designed to set fire to enemy crops. Of course he made mistakes, but he also made a host of enemies who were on the lookout for them, and anxious to make as much of them as they could.

How unreal these proposals were is a matter of opinion, but if they were mistakes, then Prof enjoyed no monopoly in such matters. Was not Tizard also connected with a ridiculous idea to light up the whole of southern England, an idea approaching in optimism the proposal to construct an aircraft carrier made of ice? He refused to entertain a proposal of Sir Thomas Merton, afterward successful, for making fighter aircraft faster in short boosts of ten minutes by the use of nitrous oxide, because he was taken up with other things, until Cripps forced the scheme through, and when tip-and-run raids began it gave an extra forty-five miles an hour. He took no action about Window,[2] even when Churchill had raised it at an Air Defence Research meeting in 1937, after a conversation between Prof and R. V. Jones in which Jones had pointed out that radar it-

---

[1] Professor A. V. Hill to author.

[2] Code name for an anti-radar device consisting of metalized strips dropped from aircraft.

self was not invulnerable. The truth, of course, is that scientists, like lesser men, are not exempt from human fallibility.

Prof would probably have been a worse Chairman of the Committee than Tizard. Neither was temperamentally suited to the position. As a member, Prof was provocative, arrogant and destructive but the only other member of the Committee who could stand up to him intellectually was Blackett, whose ultra left-wing sympathies were not likely to endear him to Prof. Two men like Tizard and Lindemann, both with strong personalities and cutting tongues, both ambitious, and avid for power to dictate scientific policy, were bound to clash, and Prof's hopeless tactics left him isolated, and his three colleagues in a solid majority against him.

Our subject then was in a minority of one on the Committee. One of his opponents, Professor A. V. Hill, thus described the situation on the Tizard Committee in an elegant mythological poem,[1] written in 1936.

The following poem, in the style of the Earl of Derby's translation of the Iliad (1864), purports to represent the Minutes of a meeting of a Committee of the Air Ministry in 1936, together with a summons to the next one. These meetings were SECRET, *and even today, twenty-three years later, considerations of propriety, if not of security, require that pseudonyms should be used: this may explain how a Norse deity and a Geheimrat somehow got mixed up with a lot of Greek characters on a Trojan Committee.*

[1] Characters in the poem.

Sigma	the late Sir Henry Tizard.
Omega	the late H. E. Wimperis.
Theta	Professor P. M. S. Blackett.
von Alpha-plus	the late Lord Cherwell.
Phi	Professor A. V. Hill.
Odin	Sir Winston Churchill.
Lambda-Mu	Sir Harold Roxbee Cox.
Hermes	Air Chief Marshal Sir Philip Joubert.
Rho	A. P. Rowe.
Hopskipjump	the late Viscount Caldecote, formerly Sir Thomas Inskip.

Attending there on ancient Sigma sat
The Elders of the City: Omega
And Theta and von Alpha-plus and Phi.
All these were gathered at Adastral House,
By age exempt from war, but in discourse
Abundant as the cricket that on high
From topmost bough of forest tree sends forth
His music: so they sent their Minutes forth,
And all men wondered, even Odin wept
With tears of joy that Ilium was safe.

Von Alpha-plus arose and thus began,
"Oh ancient Sigma eminent in war
And in the council wise: thy present words
No Trojan can gainsay, and yet the end
Thou hast not reached, the object of debate.
This city cannot be immune from war
Until a hail of parachuting mines
Descend unceasing at its eastern gate.
So shall the long-haired Greeks remain at home
Nor lay their infernal eggs upon our streets."

Thus angrily, and round his body flung
His cloak, and on his head a billycock,
Then passing cocked a snook at Lambda-Mu,
Last called his shiny Rolls of eighty steeds
And soon without the tent of Odin stood.
Him, from his godlike sleep, he sought to rouse
Loud shouting: soon his voice his senses reached:
Forth in his slumber-suit bearlike he came
And spoke to deep designing Alpha-plus,
    "What cause so urgent leads you through the camp,
    In the dark night to wander thus alone?"

To whom von Alpha-plus of deep design replied,
"Oh, Odin, godlike son of destiny, awake:
For ancient Sigma's professorial crew,
With Hermes of the glancing wings and Rho

Who keeps the minutes but who wastes the hours,
Will not be happy till the long-haired Greeks
Upon this city lay their infernal eggs.
They have no mind to fill the sky with mines
Attached to parachutes: and precious days they waste
In vain experiment with R.D.F.
If, godlike son of destiny, we two
In place of Hopskipjump and Sigma were
The sky would rain with parachuting mines
Unceasing, and the land be safe." So spake
Von Alpha-plus of deep and bold design.
Him answering, Odin, son of destiny, replied,
"Many indeed, and fierce, the bombs I've dropped,
But never 2-oz mines attached by wires
To parachutes, by day and night alike,
In billions at our eastern gate. The like
Has never been before. We two will take
The tidings to the Minister of State.
    With Odin Lord Almighty of land and sky and sea
    And Alpha-plus to help him, how happy all will be!"

So ancient Sigma and his stag-eyed crew,
Theta with bright ideas, Phi with none,
Rho with the Minutes, weary Omega,
Sat long and silent in the deepening gloom,
While Lambda-Mu went out and hanged himself,
Snook-cocked by Alpha-plus of deep design.
At last with downcast visage Sigma spoke:
"The game is up. Without von Alpha-plus,
Of wily counsel and of deep design,
Who speaks with politicians and the Press,
And soon may be M.P. for Oxenbridge,
All hope is gone and many-murdering Death
Will hunt his victims in our streets." To which
Theta of bright ideas, Phi of none,
Rho of the Minutes, weary Omega,
Had nothing printable to add. But set

A day to meet Geheimrat Alpha-plus
And pray for mercy from his mighty friends,
From Odin, godlike son of destiny,
And from himself, the man of deep design.
Then ancient Sigma and his stag-eyed crew
Will make submission to von Alpha-plus,
(Except for Lambda-Mu who hanged himself).
Your presence is requested at 11:
The number of the room is 008.

In early July 1936 A. P. Rowe of the Air Ministry, "Rho of the Minutes," who acted as Secretary to the Tizard Committee, sent to Prof the Committee's draft second interim report. Prof disagreed with a great deal of it, being particularly incensed by the procedure adopted in issuing the report; he elaborated his grievances in a long and aggressive letter rejecting the report and enclosing his own substitute draft, adding sardonically: "The fact that you had three weeks to prepare the draft whilst I only had three hours, will, I trust, excuse any crudities of expression or omissions of substance." The intransigeant wording of this minority report did much to offset an admirable suggestion it contained — that Watson-Watt should be put in charge of communications as well as radar. It was one thing to have radar, but another to guide airplanes to the desired position by radio control, and to send messages to them. This recommendation was ultimately adopted. The last paragraph of Prof's minority report is relevant:

In order to improve efficiency in interception the Committee recommended in its last Report that Mr. Watson-Watt be put in charge of communications, etc., as well as detection and location experiments. It is regretted that this has not been done since interception depends not only on discovering where the enemy is, but also on the possibility of telling our defending aircraft in which direction to fly in order to find him. The problems are closely related and the Committee felt that they should be under one head. In its latest Report, however, the majority of the Committee thought it would not be wise to refer to the failure to carry out its recommendations. As the reasons which caused the Committee to make this recommendation still hold good, I think the failure to carry it out ought to be mentioned.

Prof had intended to toss this unbending document, repeating his arguments about aerial mines, into a Committee which was now simmering like a cauldron. The meetings had become a battlefield, and we are told by Professor Blackett, one of the original members:

On one occasion Lindemann became so ferocious with Tizard that the Secretaries had to be sent out of the Committee room so as to keep the squabble as private as possible.[1]

The time had come for the majority on the Committee to strike — the Bolsheviks to oust the Menshevik.

On September 3, 1936, the Secretary of State for Air wrote to Prof:

I have just received the resignations of three of the unofficial members of the Committee for the Scientific Survey of Air Defence. In these circumstances I have no option but to dissolve the Committee as at present constituted.

The resignation of his three colleagues was not prompted by Tizard, and it came as no surprise to Prof, who could only reply to Swinton that he realized his colleagues felt irritation because he had tried to accelerate the very slow progress which had been made in the investigations. He gave as examples two researches to be carried out concurrently at Farnborough and

[1] Professor P. M. S. Blackett, *Tizard and the Science of War.*

Shoeburyness: "Although it was agreed in November 1935 that this research should be undertaken, no experiments were put in hand at Farnborough until February 1936."

He had not long to wait for the chopper. On November 11th Swinton sent him a note at once friendly and dismissive:

2.11.36.
Air Ministry,
Kingsway W.C.2.

Personal

DEAR LINDEMANN,

I want to write personally to tell you that I have reconstituted a Committee of scientists under Tizard's chairmanship. I found that I could not secure the cooperation of the other members on the basis of the old membership; and my colleagues and I regarded the work of the Committee as much too valuable to be allowed to lapse.

It was I who originally asked you to join the Committee as then constituted; and I should have been very happy if the original Committee had felt able to continue to work together.

Yours sincerely,
SWINTON

The Committee was reconstituted with Tizard again as Chairman, but Prof was not invited to rejoin.

This was, for the moment, defeat. He had tried newspaper articles; he had tried influence; but he had been beaten by the machine. He experienced a fleeting moment of despair, and he complained bitterly about the inertia, or even hostility, of the departments. Questions in Parliament could be ridden off by answers in technical language in the absence of any scientist to challenge them. At this moment of low morale, he wrote miserably: "I suppose nothing will be done until the bombs begin to fall, and then it will be too late."

He put his remaining faith in the new Secretary of State for Air, Sir Kingsley Wood, hoping, without conviction, that he might regard the past record as one of the scandals which ought to be effaced, musing gloomily: "But once he gets into the saddle Tizard and Co. will nobble him."

After his humiliating dismissal he became a vagrant between the Admiralty, the Air Ministry and the Department of Scientific and Industrial Research — still pressing, often on heedless ears, researches into liquid hydrogen as fuel, the wire-carrying shell and the aerial mine parachute. He had by now clearly become anathema to the departments, and their replies to his barrage of letters were terse and almost exasperated.

It was, therefore, with surprise and pleasure that he received and gladly accepted an invitation from Kingsley Wood to serve on the committee of which Churchill and Tizard, Kingsley Wood, Inskip and Hore Belisha were also members. It was perhaps as well that the Prof had no inkling of the correspondence which passed on this subject between Sir Thomas Inskip, the Minister for the Coordination of Defence, and Sir Henry Tizard.

It must have been a severe shock to Tizard when Inskip wrote to him on November 15, 1938, that Churchill had approached Kingsley Wood with the suggestion that Lindemann should be appointed a member of the Air Defence Research Committee, adding that "Mr. Churchill has given Sir Kingsley Wood an assurance on behalf of Professor Lindemann of what I may call good behaviour."

After much tribulation Tizard had, he thought, dislodged for ever this vexatious old man of the sea. Vistas of calm and harmonious research at his own speed, and with men he liked, had appeared to lie open before him, and he now saw the dreary battle beginning again. He behaved, however, in an effort to resign, with dignity and restraint:

I must say that I feel in a personal difficulty about the suggestion. I fully realise that Mr. Winston Churchill's main object in anything he does is to strengthen the defences of the country, and therefore it seems wrong to oppose anything he suggests unless one has very strong reasons for doing so. But I also feel that the real reason behind Mr. Winston Churchill's suggestion is that he does not altogether trust the advice I give, and that he prefers Professor Lindemann's advice. I could quite easily foresee occasions when Professor Lindemann and I should not agree on the advice we gave you. We do not want that kind of disagreement on the Committee.

After further gentle pressure from Inskip, Tizard yielded, but not without making his own misgivings plain to the Minister. Among other things, he regarded the invitation to Prof as a slight upon the scientists who had worked upon this committee, and he was able to arrange that if Lindemann was invited to join the A.D.R. Committee, Professor Fowler should also be approached.

This was all he could do, and on November 24, 1938 he wrote to Inskip striking his flag:

I must say that you have put me in a difficult position about Lindemann. I think that the proposal to bring him on is wrong. It is very unlikely to lead to any good being done unless he has changed a good deal in the last year or so. Personally, as I foresee the difficulties, I would much rather go off the Air Research Defence Committee if he is coming on. But when you say that you would not have that for a moment, and that you would rather say "No" to Winston Churchill and put up with the consequences which you feel might be hampering to you, then of course you get me on a very weak point indeed, and I simply have to surrender.

An objective account of the Tizard-Lindemann breach must conclude that there were serious faults on both sides, and that the seeds of discord were inherent in a committee so constituted, and presided over by an interested party. The patriotism of both men was unquestioned, as was their ardent desire to find means of defense. Lindemann, with a clearer view of foreign affairs, was passionately convinced that it was a race against time. Tizard resented the tactless manner in which Prof presented his case, also regarding some of his proposals as ridiculous. Beyond this, it was a collision of two strong personalities whom ambition and sudden mutual dislike drove to unworthy behavior.

It was in accordance with Prof's character that of the two principals in the memorable battle he was far the more vindictive. His brother Charles made efforts to splice the severed bond, and even induced the two men to shake hands. It was an empty gesture on the part of Prof, whose heart was not touched, and who could never feel the same about his former friend, a gesture recalling the glacial handclasp between Giraud and de Gaulle. Tizard's temper was less lasting, and he asked R. V. Jones to persuade Prof to bury the hatchet at least for the duration of the war. It was an olive branch difficult to deliver to a man who hated emotional appeals, but Jones welcomed the opportunity. It was not accepted. "Now that I'm in a position of power," said Prof, "a lot of my old friends have come sniffing round." It is, however, agreeable to relate that this rancor did not abide, and that when Tizard retired as President of Magdalen College in 1949 Prof gave a dinner party in Christ Church for his old antagonist and friend.

7

The War

WHEN WAR CAME, it was soon obvious what part Prof was to play in it. He was called upon to follow his master. Churchill appointed him his personal adviser, thus inaugurating for him an extraordinary period of power without responsibility, power greater than that exercised by any scientist in history. It is to his lasting credit that on the whole he did not abuse this power, and it must be realized that it was to some extent restricted by the fact that from the start he had a considerable proportion of the scientific world against him. As the story of his public life unfolds we shall see how these small beginnings led to a peerage in 1941, membership of the Privy Council and a seat in the Cabinet as Paymaster General in 1942, and in the Shadow Cabinet when his Party was defeated in 1945. He was again to take office in 1951, to become a Companion of Honour in 1953, and to be created Viscount in 1956. He chose for his title the name of Cherwell, the lovely river that wanders through Oxford.

Churchill's first intention had been that Prof should advise him on scientific subjects, but in October 1939, when First Lord of the Admiralty, he asked him to form a statistical branch as well, and soon Harrod had collected from the universities a team of six young economists, for the leadership of which his eye had happily fallen upon G. D. A. MacDougall, now Investment Bursar of Nuffield College, Oxford.

The object of S-Branch, as it was first called, was to collect and co-ordinate Admiralty and other statistics for the First Lord, but when Churchill became Prime Minister in May 1940 its character was transformed into the Prime Minister's Statistical Section, and the scope of its work enormously increased. It remained in existence until the change of government in July 1945. When in December 1942 the Prof, by then Lord Cherwell, was appointed Paymaster General, the Section was sometimes known afterward as the Office of the Paymaster General.

The establishment of the Section was twenty, and at any given time would contain six economists, one scientific officer, one civil servant trained in economics to control the amateurs, half a dozen computers, two or three typists or clerks and a number of "chartists" employed in the early period when there was much drawing of charts and diagrams. In the words of its head, MacDougall:

> The staff had contacts with nearly every Ministry, most of all with the Service and Supply Departments, the Ministries of War and Transport, Fuel and Power, Food, Labour and Economic Warfare, the Treasury and the Board of Trade. They dealt with Departmental Officers at all levels, and Lord Cherwell had much conversation and correspondence with the various Ministers. Work was informal and intimate, and Lord Cherwell spent much of his time in discussion with his staff.

Although he was generally regarded as the Prime Minister's Scientific Adviser, the work during the war was directed at least as much to nonscientific questions — to economic problems and to other general matters on which a quantitative or analytical approach could make a fresh contribution. It was a contribution which could be made by a person trained in analytical disciplines and comprised the work of economists and statisticians as well as scientists. The economists in the

Section made the same kind of contribution through Prof as was made by the Economic Section of the Cabinet Office through the Lord President, Sir John Anderson, to the Cabinet and its committees. This analytical approach to problems of administration was something new in government, and it was of value over a range of problems which were a great deal wider than those normally covered by the term "economics."

The main method of communication with the Prime Minister, apart from the charts and plans which offered immediate clarification of confused issues, was through minutes from Prof which were supplemented by his close daily contact with Churchill. These minutes dealing with a remarkable miscellany of subjects followed one another in swift succession, totaling at the end of the period of six years about 2000, or roughly one minute a day.

The requirement insisted upon by the Prime Minister, who was bearing the burden of Atlas, was brevity. He was exercising control over every aspect of the war, engrossing, as some thought, far too much detail, and it was essential that Prof should not only be brief himself but should also inculcate habits of brevity into his staff. In this he was aided by a marvelous power of compression, which could present the inquiries of weeks in a minute of ten lines, and by a contempt for Civil Service jargon.

He regarded himself and his branch, thought one temporary member of it, as first and last servants of the Prime Minister, and his services to him were threefold: he presented quantitative problems to him in the way he could most easily grasp; he conducted original research into the quantitative aspects of the conduct of the war; he advised him on scientific matters.

Mr. Churchill's intellectual approach to the conduct of the war was essentially that of the military historian. As need

scarcely be said, he saw the importance of energy and belli-
cosity. Cherwell did not need to contribute to these. But
he knew too the supreme importance of the right assessment
of the opposing forces and the optimum deployment of the
Allies' limited strength: and he was not by training or taste
an arithmetically minded man. Cherwell's first job was to
present the quantities to the Prime Minister in a way he
could assimilate. He had to summarise the monstrous mass
of statistics thrown up by the administration so that the Prime
Minister could see what was happening and grasp the essence
of the big quantitative issues that arose for decision.

This meant charts and lots of them and an endless stream
of little minutes summarising and analysing and asking per-
tinent questions about Cabinet papers of all and every kind
. . . The charts used to be things of beauty and ingenuity
and they were just the kind of presentation the P.M. could
understand. In much the same way the Professor's briefs
reduced large tracts of official prose to manageable dimensions
and identified weak points in the argument for attack. He
had a positive genius for summarising and a splendidly
simple unadorned prose style. He could be guaranteed to
halve the length of any draft offered to him, ejecting super-
fluous words and finding two syllables to do the work of four
with obvious enjoyment. He used to receive a stream of fat
papers sent up from the P.M. tersely marked "Prof. 10 lines
please," and it was astonishing how often it could be done.[1]

It will at once become obvious in what an invidious position
the Prof was now placed. It was, in fact, so delicate that, had
he not behaved with unusual restraint, bloody mutiny might
have broken out in the departments. In spite of the immense
usefulness of its work, his Section had no definite status. He
was not a minister with a department behind him, yet he had
the task of requiring statistics from them, often with the object
of hostile scrutiny. Although never a member of the War Cabi-

[1] Note by D. M. B. Butt for Sir George Thomson.

net, he was in closer and more continuous contact with the Prime Minister than any other man.

This, in addition to the two men's old friendship and personal intimacy, gave him great power — the power he had so long wanted, the power to get things done. Nor was he always tactful in his encroachments on subjects which were not his business and which he did not understand, and throughout his life he had found difficulty in controlling his tongue when dealing with people he considered intellectually inferior.

The irregular advantage which the Prof's peculiar relationship with the Prime Minister afforded him and his tendency to interference emerge clearly in a letter to the author from Lord Chandos who, as Oliver Lyttelton, often found himself opposing Prof in economic squabbles during the war:

> First of all there is no doubt that Prof exercised a great deal of influence on Winston. This influence was natural and helpful on scientific matters, and he was able to give the Prime Minister in very simple language the essential points to enable him to follow the developments of radar and so forth. Unfortunately the Prof also fancied himself as an economist and I think (because I was opposed to most of his views) that in this field his intervention was unhappy and even mischievous.
>
> You know how unorthodox (to say the least of it) Winston was over matters of administration. A lot of Prof's unpopularity with the Departments was because he used to brief the Prime Minister on Cabinet papers, both when he was not a Cabinet Minister and when he was. The rest of us had to go through the usual procedure of having printed proposals as Cabinet papers to put before the Cabinet. These were examined and criticised where necessary, by other Ministers, backed up by their massive Departments. We never knew in advance what Prof's brief to the Prime Minister was, but he often read almost straight from it. Most of us knew when the initial at the bottom of the memorandum was "C."

You can see how embarrassing it was for Ministers to be knocked about on matters of fact, when they had not even seen the figures that were being used *against* them.[1]

In spite of this, Chandos at that time had the happiest personal relations with Prof, and musing over those days decided that "after Maynard Keynes I would be inclined to say that he was the cleverest man I have known in my life."[2] To Lord Beaverbrook, however, the memory of Prof was of an uneasy and far from popular figure without any settled office or portfolio, whose entry into other ministers' offices was seldom solicited and whose departure was invariably welcomed. His interference in the details of other peoples' business of which he had little knowledge irritated even one so fair and tolerant as Lord Ismay, who said that in the end the Prof was advising Churchill on every conceivable topic except the actual prosecution of the war. He thought that the Prof was sometimes extremely tiresome in pressing his views about strategy, thus proving once again that he was never deterred from pontificating about a subject because he did not understand it. To Ismay one of his most irritating habits was to send out strategic memoranda covering matters which had already been fully dealt with by Ismay, and thus making Churchill sometimes appear foolish in the eyes of the soldiers. Like others before him, he discovered that Prof had an obstinacy impossible to shake, that he always thought that he was in the right about everything, and was never prepared to yield or admit failure.

He detested bureaucrats and lost no opportunity of attacking them, his main objection to them being that by their system of work they made swift and efficient action in time of war impossible. His opinion of soldiers, contemptuously expressed to Ismay, was that they knew nothing about their job,

[1] Lord Chandos to author.
[2] *Ibid.*

and he was fond of referring to them as "brave animals," a jibe which did not endear him to the military.

His hatred of bureaucrats often led to admirable results, as in the case of M.D.1.[1] On this subject Ismay observed:

> General Jefferis was a free-lance in experiments of weapons of war, and both the War Office and the Ministry of Supply hated his guts. He operated under Prof's protection, and did a great deal of good work on experiments which were much more quickly undertaken than they would have been under bureaucrats. In this work Prof had the strong support of Winston, who had never forgotten the obstruction from official-dom of his attempts to introduce tanks in the First World War. All this suited the Prof very well. He detested bureaucrats, and, placed in this way, was able to score them off ad lib.[2]

The work attempted by the Section was immense in scope. An analysis of the minutes Prof presented to the Prime Minister shows that nearly one-third were addressed to the technical details of instruments of war, their development, production and use. On the nonscientific side of the Section's work, the range of subjects covered was staggering, so that it needed "the beautiful piece of mechanism," as Churchill called Prof's mind, to exercise even general supervision.

Of such minutes sent to the Prime Minister 30 per cent were concerned mainly with the armed forces, 20 per cent with shipping, 15 per cent with food, agriculture and raw materials, 10 per cent with postwar problems, and the remaining 25 per cent with miscellaneous topics over a wide field, from the building program to the shortage of matches, from economic warfare to the shortage of doctors, from the problems

---

[1] M.D.1. was an experimental research department under the Ministry of Supply. It was concerned with the invention of new offensive weapons, and its Director was Colonel Millis Jefferis, later Major General.

[2] Lord Ismay to author.

of Russia and the problems of India to export policy, rationing, inflation and austerity.

His views on austerity would have surprised those who regarded him as a bloodless ascetic. He was strongly opposed to any unnecessary privations for the civil population and became with Churchill the champion of a reasonable standard of living. In Harrod's words:

> . . . when it came down to brass tacks, I guess that he did more than any other person concerned with the planning of our war economy, except only for Churchill himself, to make the lot of the common man less dreary.[1]

In a minute, dated August 8, 1941, to the Prime Minister Prof wrote:

> I am glad that Lord Woolton agrees that beer in normal quantities should be made available . . . I personally consider the maintenance of normal amenities most important for the sake of morale. Believing as I do, that we shall beat the enemy not with large masses but with comparatively small numbers of men armed, equipped and trained to the highest degree (airmen, tank troops, navy) my inclination would be to leave labour required to provide reasonable amenities even at the expense of, say, the infantry. But I know that this view is not generally shared.[2]

In March 1942 the Lord President's Committee submitted a paper suggesting further stringent restrictions on home consumption. Prof was opposed to nearly all of them and made his views plain to the Prime Minister, who agreed with him. On March 5, 1942, the Prime Minister minuted Prof:

> I agree with the general outline of your minute. In particular I am opposed to the heavy taxation of entertainments.

[1] Sir Roy Harrod, *The Prof*, page 205.
[2] Cherwell archives.

It would be well worth while rationing bread in order to bring in the more nourishing Lend-Lease foods. It would be better to ration than to let stocks run down. Bread is scandalously wasted now and often fed to pigs and chickens. The great thing is to keep the price down so that the poorest can buy their full rations.

I deprecate the policy of "Misery first," which is too often inculcated by people who are glad to see war-weariness spread as a prelude to surrender.

The value of all the various self-strafing proposals should be estimated in tonnage of imports. If there is a heavy economy to be achieved on any article, let us effect it; but it would be unwise to embark on a lot of fussy restrictions in order to give, or try to give, satisfaction to the Fleet Street journalists who are exempted from Military Service, have no burden of responsibility to bear, and live in the restaurants of the Strand.

You should draft something for me couched in more decorous terms.[1]

Prof did so, but on May 7th he was again raising the subject, writing forcefully to the Prime Minister:

I suggest that the time has come for a general Directive from the War Cabinet on the subject of Austerity.

Obviously in wartime the civil population, and even the military, must be denied certain things they would like. But there is a limit beyond which direct gain to the war effort is outweighed by the deterioration of morale produced by the accumulation of minor distresses. We are told that the public is suffering from a sense of frustration because it does not see how it can help win the war and that depriving it of things it likes will cure this. I question this analysis.

As usual his arguments were couched in quantitative terms. He pointed out how cuts of any significance must fall on people living on incomes of less than £500 a year:

[1] Cherwell archives.

. . . All the cuts in the last few months, taken together, have not saved more than about 25 per cent of our imports or given us even 1 per cent of extra man-power. Is it for such small profits that we should expose the nation's will to win to the Death of a Thousand Cuts? . . .[1]

Since the Prime Minister insisted upon the quantitative aspect of problems, almost all Prof's submissions to him were based on figures. MacDougall said that "an argument to establish a prima facie case for action had at least to be illustrated by appropriate orders of magnitude . . . Before proposing to the Prime Minister that, say, the building programme should be curtailed, it would be necessary to show by some simple quantitative measures that further building on the current scale was relatively unnecessary and that the saving of imports and manpower to be achieved was large."

The Section was, therefore, far more than a purely statistical one, and every detail of its character was determined by the relationship between the two men, which was peculiar and subject to no normal practice. Its greatest danger was that of antagonizing departmental officers and their ministers. The danger was constantly in MacDougall's mind. He realized that these difficulties applied to most organizations without a departmental minister, and he knew "that except in cases of collusion between the Section and departmental officers, the latter may often be reluctant, and very naturally so, to divulge information that may be used to criticise their ministry." He concluded that the fundamental remedy for this trouble was for the Section to become sufficiently expert to gain the confidence of these officers, and this, in due course, it did. It was largely due to MacDougall's wonderful tact that such a position was reached.

MacDougall never forgot during his work with the Prof that the Section was intensely personal to the Prime Minister; that

[1] Cherwell archives.

it worked continuously for him; that it had some idea what was in his mind; that it knew the sort of thing he wanted to know and how he liked to have it presented; that its loyalty was to him and to no one else.

Prof could be obstinate, but his courage in standing by his own beliefs through thick and thin, facing hostile experts, alone, armored in his self-confidence, against a powerful opposition, was admirable. A good example of the kind of intervention he made is seen in the tigerish manner he fought for his own beliefs about the size of the German air force, a stand thus described by one of his colleagues:

> In the summer of 1940, when we were awaiting the German air attack, he expressed scepticism about the size of the German bomber force lined up against us. The official view gave the Germans a vast front line and a still vaster accumulation of bombers in reserve. The forecasts of the damage we were to sustain were hideous. Some instinct or fifth sense assured Cherwell that this was all wrong, and he hammered away at the Air Ministry and the Ministry of Economic Warfare about it for months, using good, bad and indifferent arguments and generating tremendous heat. But he finally won, and the conclusive engagement in the battle came when he confronted the Air Ministry with the inconsistency between the stock of aircraft and the scale of production over the past five years that the Germans were supposed to have had with the corresponding stock and production which we had.
>
> He ferreted out that our figures of current stock, past output and recorded wastage showed a "gap" of 5,000 aircraft. There were all sorts of wastage which we did not measure properly (e.g. aircraft sent for repair and never repaired), so that the wastage rates the Intelligence authorities were applying to Germany were far too low. Hence the German reserves were mythical, and even the size of their front line squadrons was not all it was said to be. It required intense self-confidence, great persistence (and eventually the services of a Judge) for an amateur to upset the experts on a subject of this kind:

but Cherwell had them all — and the conclusion was of high strategic importance.

The Prime Minister at the end called in a High Court Judge, Mr. Justice Singleton, to analyze the figures of the German air force and the differing estimates of Air Intelligence and the Ministry of Economic Warfare. Singleton's estimate of four to three to the Germans against the British was accepted as Churchill's working basis.

Prof's skepticism about the accuracy of our bombing also brought him into angry collision with high authority. He was an advocate of bombs with a high charge-weight ratio producing a great blast effect as opposed to the shards of steel which the Royal Air Force was using in the early days of the war. Always doubting the official claims to bombing accuracy, he went to look for himself at the flash photographs taken when the first of the new 4000-pound bombs were dropped to see what damage they had done, and bleakly contemplated pictures showing untouched stretches of open country.

He concluded at once that bombing must be seriously inaccurate, and he refused to be fobbed off by the stock explanation that, as the flash went off simultaneously with the bomb-burst and the aircraft was moving at speed, it was not likely that the photograph would show the site of the explosion. Prof insisted that the photographs, taken as a whole, were a significant indication of accuracy, and he asked the Prime Minister to arrange for a member of his staff to visit Bomber Command and make a full analysis of all the night photographs taken in recent months. It was an unpleasant necessity to be obliged to criticize brave men who were losing their lives, and it was only possible for one who, as everyone knew, had cheerfully imperiled his own in the air.

The unfortunate officer chosen to enter the lion's den thus suffered a distressing experience:

After a most uncomfortable week (morally speaking) his timid emissary returned with a somewhat shattering report which demonstrated fairly conclusively that in those early days our bombing was only a third or a quarter as accurate as anybody had realised. The conclusion was highly relevant to the question of research priorities, and led to a quick concentration of effort on navigational aids.

This discovery by Prof that, although Bomber Command thought that they had found the target, in fact two-thirds of the crews actually failed to strike within five miles of it, caused Churchill to send an instant and peremptory minute to the Chief of the Air Staff, Portal, demanding his proposals for action, and led to a series of devices for guiding bombers to their targets by radio aids, the first of which was Gee.[1] Another important invention, the proximity fuse, with which Prof was closely associated, was an aid to defense second only to radar in its war-winning potentialities.

Mr. Cobden Turner, a joint-inventor of the fuse, was grateful to the Prof for the encouragement given to him in its development:

> Thanks to the help which Lord Cherwell gave to us through Lord Beaverbrook, we were finally given a Blenheim Bomber and a Polish pilot, so that after that we were able to do our dropping tests, and finally the proximity fuse came into service. There is no doubt that it was thanks to Lord Cherwell that the slow progress which had hitherto hampered this invention was accelerated.[2]

The P.E. or proximity fuse was one of the most successful inventions of the war, but its perfection took a long time and progress was marked by many disappointments. The Prime Minister and others in high places, such as General Pile, chief

---

[1] The name given to a radio device by means of which bombers could fix their positions when operating over Germany.

[2] Mr. Cobden Turner to author.

of A.A. Command, at once realized the vital importance of the new weapon. By the time the P.E. fuse was ready in quantity the Battle of Britain was over, but it was soon to prove its exceptional quality:

> Attempts were made in 1941 to design a similar proximity fuse using a tiny radar set arranged to explode the warhead when the projectile passed near the aircraft. Successful experiments were made, but before this fuse was developed in England, the Americans, to whom we had imparted our knowledge, actually succeeded not only in perfecting the instrument but in reducing its size so much that the whole thing could be put into the head not merely of a rocket but of a shell. These so-called "Proximity Fuses," made in the United States, were used in great numbers in the last year of the war, and proved potent against the small unmanned aircraft (V.1) with which we were assailed in 1944, and also in the Pacific against Japanese aircraft.[1]

No one now is likely to question the late Chester Wilmot's words in *The Struggle for Europe*:

> The proximity fuse was so called because shells in which it was fitted would explode as soon as they came in close proximity to the ground or to objects in the air. This fuse, invented in Britain, and mass-produced in America, had played an important part in the defeat of the flying bomb, and was first used in ground operations during the Ardennes offensive. The invention of this fuse, the most important artillery invention of the war, is yet another example of the superiority of Allied over German science.[2]

The U.P., unrotated projectile, was developed by Dr. Crow[3] at the Projectile Development Establishment (P.D.E.) of which he was controller, at Fort Halstead with a firing

[1] Winston Churchill, *The Second World War*, Vol. 2, pages 350–351.
[2] Chester Wilmot, *The Struggle for Europe*, page 698.
[3] Now Sir Alwyn Crow.

range at Aberporth. In November 1939 the First Lord of the Admiralty asked Dr. Crow to produce urgently a means of laying an aerial minefield and to consider other methods of protecting ships against airplanes. A high-altitude barrage was developed — an aerial minefield up to 19,000 feet, the fast aerial mine up to 2000 feet, the P.E. fuse up to 18,000 feet, and the U.P. with aerodynamic (A.D.) fuse up to 20,000. All three services used the U.P. in various forms. The arrangements for Dr. Crow were somewhat similar to those under which Millis Jefferis worked. Both had access to the Prime Minister through Prof.

M.D.1., and its resourceful chief, Colonel Millis Jefferis, whose "guts were hated" by both the War Office and the Ministry of Supply, was a perfect example of Prof's ideal method of scientific research — leaving a man of inventive genius to pursue his own researches free from bureaucratic restriction and with ample material for conducting experiments. Watson-Watt's triumph with radar had convinced him of the desirability of one man working with carte blanche, and he gave Millis Jefferis a similar opportunity, which he took with both hands, ready to devote himself to any research which Prof thought worth pursuing. Jefferis was responsible through Prof to the Minister of Defence. In this way he had the special ear of the Prime Minister and his firm support for any invention and device which Prof considered worth backing. Had it not been for Prof, the life of his department would not have been worth a moment's purchase.

M.D.1. was originally a War Office branch known as M.I.R.(c) which was started in 1939 to develop devices for use in irregular warfare. Toward the end of 1940 it became unpopular because it was producing and issuing for service a number of weapons which had not been designed or manufactured by the orthodox branches. For this error it was transferred from the War Office to the Ministry of Supply and became M.D.1. under the direction of Colonel Jefferis. In 1940 workshops were requisitioned at 35 Portland Place, but after bomb damage in the autumn of that year other premises were found at Whitchurch near Aylesbury, where, in due course, fully equipped workshops, factory buildings and ranges were constructed, and Whitchurch became a completely self-contained experimental station and proving ground.

From this station at Whitchurch issued a steady stream of inventions of great effectiveness and originality, including mass-produced antitank weapons, such as the Blacker Bombard, PIAT, and the sticky bomb. The total number of developments at Whitchurch was sixty-five, and most of these were brought to a successful conclusion.

Of these developments and Prof's interest in them Sir Millis Jefferis informed the author: "He went down to Whitchurch regularly and was directly responsible. He was magnificent to work for, and there was never a cross word."[1] Millis Jefferis started the soft-nose shell, taken up after the war as an antitank weapon. He introduced the bombard, and the sticky bomb which was carried on a belt and blew holes in houses, to the sides of which it was attached. The bombard was a form of mortar accurate up to 100 yards, which filled in the gap in the desperate shortage of antitank weapons. He then turned to PIAT (projector infantry antitank), with a crew of two, one man to fire and the other to carry the weapon on the march. Jefferis was particularly proud of this weapon, although he admitted that he had stolen the idea for it — a hollow-charged shell fired off a spigot which had a nose fuse projecting four inches in front. The shell had to detonate before it struck the tank. When the nose struck and the shell detonated, a jet of steel poured out from the center and made a three-quarter-inch hole through the armor.

[1] Major General Sir Millis Jefferis, K.B.E., to author.

The Prof turned up for the trials of all these weapons at Shoeburyness. If you gave Prof the scientific basis of statistics, he gave the answer. He was not practical and I did the engineering work.[1]

Another weapon was the "Hedgehog," a multispigot mortar with twenty-four spigots on it actuated by a ripple-switch electrically fired. It was designed to be mounted on board ship for antisubmarine work in place of depth charges. Prof had to fight hard for this weapon against the Admiralty, who eventually made it into a successful antisubmarine weapon with at least thirty-two kills to its credit.

Through most of this period Prof was Paymaster General, and soon encountered trouble from Beaverbrook, who had recently taken over the Ministry of Supply and had, perhaps, been infected by their dislike of M.D.1. as an independent irregular body. Millis Jefferis described to the author how "Beaverbrook sent Lucas and Rootes down, both of whom reported adversely on the bombard. Prof, incensed by this intrusion, gave orders that a special demonstration should be mounted to vindicate the weapon. They turned out with steel plates, three guns and a tank, and never missed a target, the first shot extinguishing the lamps on Lucas's motor car. After this convincing demonstration Beaverbrook made a speech to say how wrong he had been." [2]

Extraordinary requests reached the department, which was prepared to take on anything. At one point the army asked for a "Beehive," with static demolition charges effective against reinforced concrete Japanese blockhouses. They wanted it to penetrate five feet of concrete, and requested a beehive in three pieces, which the sappers could assemble stealing up to the target at night. Jefferis responded with a beehive that would drill a hole through reinforced concrete

[1] Major General Sir Millis Jefferis, K.B.E., to author.
[2] *Idem.*

and steel, and the sappers were given the weapon and used it. Prof, as usual, arrived for the demonstration at the small experimental establishment, to which he had become strongly attached.

As the end of the war approached Prof and Jefferis were anxious that M.D.1. should be raised from a Grade B Directorate to Grade A, so that after the war it should not be co-ordinated or deprived of its individuality, "as," thought Prof, "is all too apt to happen to Grade B Directorates under the impact of impassioned rationalisation." Both men believed that M.D.1., so well proved in war, would have a useful function in peacetime in weapon development.

Although the Minister of Supply, Sir Andrew Duncan, apparently agreed to this course, M.D.1.'s status was not raised, but Jefferis was promoted to the rank of Major General. In November 1945 the organization was absorbed by the Armaments Design Department, and, with Prof still fiercely protesting, was closed down on January 31, 1947.

The great influence which Prof exercised in M.D.1. to short-circuit official delays also came into play when he found that the Germans were using aluminum powder to enhance the power of their aluminum nitrate explosives. Aluminum had been scarce in the early days of the war, and it had been decided to use all available aluminum powder for making depth charges, a custom which persisted even when aluminum had become more plentiful. It became essential to correct the ensuing discrepancy between the effectiveness of German and English explosives, and in Churchill's words:

17 Feb. 44.

At the end of September 1943, during discussions about the German long-range rocket, doubts were expressed about the efficiency of our high explosives as compared with those of the Germans. The Paymaster-General immediately dis-

cussed the matter with the Chief of the Air Staff, and the
latter proposed to the Chiefs of Staff Committee, who supported
his proposals strongly, that urgent action should be taken to
establish the true facts, and that if a substantial inferiority
was revealed the competent authorities should be called upon
to give an explanation and a proposed remedy.

2. At the suggestion of the Chiefs of Staff Committee the Paymaster-General undertook the inquiry suggested, and on October 6 submitted a report to the Chiefs of Staff Committee
which clearly established that our explosives were inferior
to the Germans' and that an improvement estimated by various
authorities as between 40 per cent and 100 per cent could be
made if aluminised explosives were used instead of the existing
types. Lord Cherwell recommended that the most urgent
possible preparations to change over should be made without
waiting for the result of further trials. With this recommendation the Chiefs of Staff Committee and I agreed, and immediate
action was taken to effect the change-over.

This was an example of the fact that he was usually at his
best in matters where he had no preconceived ideas. Where
he already had such ideas, or when he had passed a too hasty
judgment, he was incredibly obstinate in the face of new evidence which did not suit his case.

When he was demanding more aircraft for Bomber Command at the expense of Coastal Command he produced at a
top-level meeting some startling statistics regarding the number of depth charges used per U-boat attacked. On this occasion the furore was so great that he was forced to explain his
figures, when it transpired that he had used the number of
depth charges produced as a substitute for the numbers used.
This unhappy episode caused the Secretary of State for War,
P. J. Grigg,[1] to give orders that the War Office were not to sup-

---

[1] Rt. Hon. Sir James Grigg, K.C.B., K.C.S.I.

ply Prof with any information except through his private office.

Another device which would probably have languished in a pigeonhole had Prof not produced it and filled the Prime Minister with enthusiasm, was fog dispersal on landing grounds, known as FIDO. This dispersal was achieved by petrol burners on the runways and produced miraculous results. On September 28, 1941, he minuted the Prime Minister:

> It may well be that the expenditure involved is too great to justify the adoption of these methods in peacetime; but such arguments have no weight today. In view of the appalling losses we occasionally suffer from unexpected fogs . . . it seems urgent to take up this work again. . . . If we have even two or three aerodromes fitted to disperse fog in case of need, the cost would be recovered in a very short time.[1]

The Ministry of Petroleum were ordered to proceed, and FIDO, although expensive, was completely successful and saved many lives, besides allowing more bombing sorties, the captains of bombers being described as "wildly enthusiastic."

The "Wizard War" continuously waged by the scientists on both sides was vividly described by Sir Winston Churchill in *The Second World War*, and the part played by Prof in this secret battle admirably assessed:

> During the human struggle between the British and German Air Forces, between pilot and pilot, between A.A. batteries and aircraft, between ruthless bombing and the fortitude of the British people, another conflict was going on step by step, month by month. This was a secret war, whose battles were lost or won unknown to the public; and only with difficulty is it comprehended, even now, by those outside the small high scientific circles concerned. No such warfare had ever been waged by mortal men. The terms in which it could be recorded

[1] Cherwell archives.

or talked about were unintelligible to ordinary folk. Yet if we had not mastered its profound meaning and used its mysteries even while we saw them only in the glimpse, all the efforts, all the prowess of the fighting airmen, all the bravery and sacrifices of the British people, would have been in vain. Unless British science had proved superior to German, and unless its strange, sinister resources had been effectively brought to bear on the struggle for survival, we might well have been defeated, and, being defeated, destroyed.

A wit wrote ten years ago: "The leaders of thought have reached the horizon of human reason, but all the wires are down, and they can only communicate with us by unintelligible signals." Yet upon the discerning of these signals, and upon the taking of right and timely action on the impressions received, depended our national fate and much else. I knew nothing about science, but I knew something of scientists, and had had much practice as a Minister of handling things I did not understand. I had, at any rate, an acute military perception of what would help and what would hurt, of what would cure and what would kill. My four years' work upon the Air Defence Research Committee had made me familiar with the outlines of Radar problems. I therefore immersed myself as far as my faculties allowed in the Wizard War, and strove to make sure that all that counted came without obstruction or neglect to the threshold of action. There were no doubt greater scientists than Frederick Lindemann, though his credentials and genius command respect. But he had two qualifications of vital consequence to me. First, as these pages have shown, he was my trusted friend and confidant of twenty years. Together we had watched the advance and onset of world disaster. Together we had done our best to sound the alarm. And now we were in it, and I had the power to guide and arm our effort. How could I have the knowledge?

Here came the second of his qualities. Lindemann could decipher the signals from the experts on the far horizons and explain to me in lucid homely terms what the issues were. There are only twenty-four hours in the day, of which at least seven must be spent in sleep and three in eating and relaxation. Anyone in my position would have been ruined if he had attempted to dive into the depths which not even a lifetime of study could plumb. What I had to grasp were the practical results, and just as Lindemann gave his view for all it was worth in this field, so I made sure by turning on my power-relay that some at least of these terrible and incomprehensible truths emerged in executive decisions. . . .

However in June [1940] I received a painful shock. Professor Lindemann reported to me that he believed the Germans were preparing a device by means of which they would be able to bomb by day or night whatever the weather. It now appeared that the Germans had developed a radio beam which, like an invisible searchlight, would guide the bombers with considerable precision to their target. The beacon beckoned to the pilot, the beam pointed to the target. They might not hit a particular factory, but they could certainly hit a city or town. No longer then had we only to fear the moonlight night, in which our fighters could see at any rate as well as the enemy, but we must even expect the heaviest attacks to be delivered in cloud and fog.

Lindemann told me also that there was a way of bending the beam if we acted at once, but that I must see some of the scientists, particularly the Deputy Director of Intelligence Research at the Air Ministry, Dr. R. V. Jones, a former pupil of his at Oxford. Accordingly, with anxious mind, I convened on June 21 a special meeting in the Cabinet Room, at which about fifteen persons were present, including Sir Henry Tizard and various Air Force commanders. A few minutes late, a youngish man — who, as I afterwards learned, had thought his sudden summons to the Cabinet Room must be a practical joke — hurried in and took his seat at the bottom of the table. According to plan, I invited him to open the discussion.

For some months, he told us, hints had been coming from all sorts of sources on the Continent that the Germans had some novel mode of night-bombing on which they placed great hopes. In some way it seemed to be linked with the code-word Knickebein, which our Intelligence had several times mentioned without being able to explain. At first it had been thought that the enemy had got agents to plant beacons in our cities on which their bombers could home; but this idea had proved untenable. Some weeks before two or three curious squat towers had been photographed in odd positions near the hostile coast. They did not seem the right shape for any known form of radio or Radar. Nor were they in places which could be explained on any such hypothesis. Recently a German bomber had been shot down with apparatus which seemed more elaborate than was required for night-landing by the ordinary Lorenz beam, which appeared to be the only known use for which it might be intended. For this and various other reasons, which he wove together into a cumulative argument, it looked as if the Germans might be planning to navigate and bomb on some sort of system of beams. A few days before under cross-examination on these lines a German pilot had broken down and admitted that he had heard that something of the sort was in the wind. Such was the gist of Dr. Jones's tale.[1]

Clearly Churchill explained in language comprehensible to laymen how this secret struggle of the beam was conducted:

I will now explain in the kind of terms which I personally can understand how the German beam worked and how we twisted it. Like the searchlight beam, the radio beam cannot be made very sharp; it tends to spread; but if what is called the "split beam" method is used considerable accuracy can be obtained. Let us imagine two searchlight beams parallel to one another, both flickering in such a way that the left-hand beam comes on exactly when the right-hand beam goes out, and vice versa. If an attacking aircraft was exactly in the centre between the two beams, the pilot's course would be continuously illuminated, but if it got, say, a little bit to the

[1] Sir Winston Churchill, *The Second World War*, Vol. 2, pages 337–338.

right, nearer the centre of the right-hand beam, this would become the stronger and the pilot would observe the flickering light, which was no guide. By keeping in the position where he avoided the flickerings he would be flying exactly down the middle, where the light from both beams is equal. And this middle path would guide him to the target. Two split beams from two stations could be arranged to cross over any town in the Midlands or Southern England. The German airman had only to fly along one beam until he detected the second, and then drop his bombs. Q.E.D.!

This was the principle of the split beam and the celebrated "Knickebein" apparatus, upon which Goering founded his hopes, and the Luftwaffe were taught to believe that the bombing of English cities could be maintained in spite of cloud, fog, and darkness, and with all the immunity, alike from guns and intercepting fighters which these gave to the attacker. With their logical minds and deliberate large-scale planning, the German High Air Command staked their fortunes in this sphere on a device which, like the magnetic mine, they thought would do us in. Therefore, they did not trouble to train the ordinary bomber pilots, as ours had been trained, in the difficult art of navigation. A far simpler and surer method, lending itself to drill and large numbers, producing results wholesale by irresistible science, attracted alike their minds and their nature. The German pilots followed the beam as the German people followed the Fuehrer. They had nothing else to follow.

But, duly forewarned, and acting on the instant, the simple British had the answer. By erecting the proper stations in good time in our own country we could jam the beam. This would of course have been almost instantly realised by the enemy. There was another and superior alternative. We could put a repeating device in such a position that it strengthened the signal from one half of the split beam and not from the other. Thus the hostile pilot, trying to fly so that the signals from both halves of the split beam were equal, would be deflected from the true course. The cataract of bombs which would have shattered, or at least tormented, a city would fall fifteen or twenty miles away in an open field. Being master, and not having to argue too much, once I was convinced about the principles of this queer and deadly game I gave all the necessary orders that very day in June for the existence of the beam to be assumed, and for all countermeasures to receive absolute priority. The slightest reluctance or deviation in carrying out this policy was to be reported to me. With so much going on I did not trouble the Cabinet, or even the Chiefs of Staff. If I had encountered any serious obstruction I should of course have appealed and told a long story to these friendly tribunals. This however was not necessary, as in this limited and at that time almost occult circle obedience was forthcoming with alacrity, and on the fringes all obstructions could be swept away.

About August 23 the first new Knickebein stations, near Dieppe and Cherbourg, were trained on Birmingham, and a large-scale night offensive began. We had of course our "teething troubles" to get through; but within a few days the Knickebein beams were deflected or jammed, and for the next two months, the critical months of September and October, the German bombers wandered around England bombing by guesswork, or else being actually led astray.[1]

The Germans soon began taking measures against our successes. One of their formations, Kampf 100, by using a special beam of its own, the "X" apparatus, could still bomb accurately and they formed a pathfinding group from it which they used to raise the fires by incendiary bombs for the Luftwaffe, without Knickebein, to follow. By the end of 1940 "X" apparatus had been mastered. It was followed by "Y," which was in turn rendered useless, and the faith of the German air crews in this new invention was shattered as soon as it came into full operational use.

[1] Sir Winston Churchill, *The Second World War*, Vol. 2, pages 341–342.

When Prof first went to the Admiralty with Churchill, he had preserved intact his group of Oxford physicists as the Admiralty Radar Group. He believed that the vital need in radar was to develop a short-wave technique. In spite of strong opposition, he was convinced of the advantages of short wave (microwave radar), and of the possibility of it reaching such a state of development that it could be used operationally during the war.

The radar available at the beginning of the war, or within a year of the beginning, operated on relatively long wavelengths. The shortest was about 1½ meters; this was used in the Air Interception radar, fitted to night fighter aircraft to enable them to detect and approach the aircraft at night from a distance of two or three miles to the short range of a few hundred yards at which the target could see them.

Secondly, there was the A.S.V. (Air-to-Surface Vessel) radar fitted to the radar of Coastal Command, which enabled them to detect and approach surfaced submarines at night from ranges at which they would be invisible even in bright moonlight.

Thirdly, there was G.C.I. (Ground Controlled Interception) which was used mainly to enable the ground control to detect both the enemy bombers and our night fighter aircraft at ranges up to about sixty miles.

The longer range radar, which was used for the early detection of approaching formations of enemy aircraft, operated on a wavelength of about ten meters, and owing to this long wavelength it had been necessary for Watson-Watt to install it on carefully chosen sites on tall and consequently heavy towers. These were 350 feet high and formed conspicuous targets. The microwave radar which Prof advocated would operate first on a wavelength of about 10 centimeters and later on a shorter wavelength of 3 centimeters. On this question of short-wave technique Professor Jackson wrote:

To make oscillators which would radiate electromagnetic waves of microwave length required an entirely new electronic technique; on account of their own inherent capacitance, conventional valves, even when made very small, set the lower limit of wavelength attainable with tuned circuits powered by them, at about 50 cm. Microwaves could be produced only by newly discovered devices, the most successful of which was the klystron, at the time of the beginning of the war. But this was capable of producing only relatively low energy, adequate for operating a receiver, but much too low for operating a transmitter.

Before microwave radar could be produced it was therefore necessary to invent an entirely new high power oscillator to operate the transmitter, and to develop the klystron in a form in which it could be tuned satisfactorily, and with stability, and could be used in an aeroplane. This appeared to be a formidable task; and without the enthusiastic support of the Prof, it is doubtful whether the necessary scientific effort would have been provided. You might well ask why we considered it of this much importance to develop microwave radar, when the radar which we had operating at longer wavelengths was fairly satisfactory. The reasons for this were fortunately fully understood by the Prof, and he was consequently one of the most persistent advocates of its development.

The first application of microwave radar was for Air Interception, the radar carried in night fighter aircraft. Here it had two very important advantages over the longer wave radar. First, its range was greater and, moreover, was substantially independent of the height at which the fighter was flying; the range of the longer wave radar was always less since the reflections from the ground ("ground returns") were much stronger than the reflections from an aeroplane and consequently completely masked the latter, unless it were in the region free from ground returns, i.e. at a distance less than the height of the radar above the ground.

We were fortunate in the early days of night fighting in that the enemy bombers nearly always flew at 15,000 to 20,000 feet, so that our radar had a range of about 3 to 4 miles; but if the enemy had decided to fly at low altitudes, the range of our radar would have been so much reduced that it would have become almost useless.

The second, almost equally important, advantage was that it indicated directly and precisely the position of the target aircraft. A spot appeared on one cathode ray tube showing the exact distance and bearing of the target aircraft. With the longer wave radar we were only provided with rough indications of how much to the left or right, or how much above or below, the target aircraft was.

A fair comparison of the difference between microwave radar and longer wave radar is the difference between seeing and hearing; the microwave radar detected by means of a narrow beam and therefore its action could be compared with seeing, and the image it formed on the cathode ray tubes could be compared with the image on the retina of the eye; while the long wave radar had a very broad beam, and the echoes produced by the target aircraft could be compared with sound echoes, in which direction is determined only roughly by the different effect in the two ears.

A third advantage, which became of great importance in the later stages of the war in the air, was that it was much less easily jammed than long range radar. This, combined with its long range and accurate presentation, enabled the night fighters to operate without the aid of ground control. And this they did most effectively in the last two years of the night bombing campaign against Germany; they flew in company with the bombers and sought out German night fighters, and destroyed substantial numbers of them; they also used to patrol the German bomber stations looking for German bombers returning at night from England, with a view to attacking them. This operation was made much more successful, on account of the long range of the microwave radar, when the fighter was at a relatively low altitude.[1]

[1] Professor Derek Jackson, F.R.S., to author.

The second application of the microwave radar was its use against submarines. Here the short-wave radar used for this purpose was superior to the earlier radar as the microwave air interception was more effective than the earlier form. The range was far greater — about twenty miles compared with three or four miles with the old method — and the indication of direction was precise. In the opinion of Professor Jackson:

> Without the aid of microwave radar the effectiveness of aircraft of Coastal Command in destroying surfaced submarines would have been greatly reduced. I think it is no exaggeration to estimate that their killings would have been less than one-quarter what they were. Since, in the latter part of the war, more than half of the submarines destroyed were destroyed by Coastal Command, it is easy to estimate what we owe to Prof's unrelenting support for the development of microwave radar.

Another application of microwave radar was the navigational instrument known as H₂S, and its introduction into the aircraft of Bomber Command was largely due to the persistence of the Prof. This ingenious device produced an image of the ground underneath the bomber in which it was fitted, similar to a map showing towns and rivers; the towns appeared as bright spots in the image on a cathode-ray tube, while large rivers appeared as dark lines, the ordinary ground being fairly bright but less bright than the spots produced by towns. The presentation was in the form of a map fairly free from distortion; the range was about a hundred miles on the later sets using radar of 3 centimeters wavelength.

A great deal of the success of the air crews of the pathfinder squadrons was due to this device. The observer who operated H₂S and navigated the airplane was provided with a camera to photograph the cathode-ray tube, showing the presence of a target town as a bright spot near the center of the tube, and thus proving that he had successfully found his target. Professor R. V. Jones wrote on the advent of H₂S in 1943 and its impact on the U-boats: "U-boat sinkings by Coastal Command rose again to such an extent that the U-boat campaign had to be abandoned. Such was the single scientific invention which, in Hitler's words, defeated the U-boats."

Professor Jones, however, criticized Prof's proposals for the tactical handling of this weapon. It could have been used either for towns or U-boats, and he thought it should have been used against U-boats first and towns afterward. Prof had obstinately pressed for its immediate use against towns, and the Germans discovered the secret from the first shot-down aircraft. Jones, then head of Scientific Air Intelligence, had to try to persuade the Germans that this was not the same device as that used at sea, and that we were concentrating on infrared.[1]

Professor Jones took a serious view of Prof's pigheadedness on this occasion:

> The new airborne radar equipment, one of Lindemann's most cherished "gadgets," was used against German towns and its use against U-boats thereby compromised. Only a great deal of luck in the way of almost incredible slowness on the part of the Germans, together with some skilful deception, thereafter enabled us to use it successfully against the U-boats.[2]

In his autobiography Watson-Watt says of H₂S: ". . . its indisputable father is Philip Ivor Dee," and this provides another good example of Prof's influence in the war. He convinced the Prime Minister that it was a good idea, and, because Churchill trusted him, he used all his powerful authority

[1] Professor R. V. Jones to author.
[2] *The Times*, April 8, 1961.

to force H₂S through many frustrations and difficulties. In Churchill's words: "It revolutionised the Radio War both on land and sea."

A letter from Philip Ivor Dee in June 1946 to Prof, thanking him for congratulations on receiving an honor, affords further confirmation of Prof's support:

> I wish to thank you for the congratulations conveyed in your telegram. It was particularly gratifying for me to hear from you on this occasion, since I suspect that you were probably responsible for my appearance in the list, and I am given the opportunity of thanking you. I am also very conscious of having stupidly misunderstood you on your first contact with H_2S in the war, and for a long time now I have realised the enormous part you played in furthering the project on its initiation. But for your bold policy of driving for production before the experiment was fully developed, I am sure it would never have been ready for the crises when they occurred. I therefore feel very strongly that you not only supported me when I was weak and wavering but that you then obtained some recognition for me for what you largely effected!
>
> I hope that you will not be embarrassed by such wordy gratitude, but I am obliged to give it my sincere expression.[1]

The Prof's work for microwave radar was not confined to talk. A man who had always pined for action was now in a position to enforce it. In the Clarendon Laboratory Dr. J. H. E. Griffiths and his colleagues, all former pupils of Prof's, succeeded in producing a reliable and stable crystal detector, essential to the production of microwave receivers suitable for operating radar, since the only detector which could be used at these short wavelengths was the crystal detector, which, up till then, had been far too unstable and temperamental to be used for radar.

[1] Cherwell archives.

This account of the importance of microwave radar, and the extent to which we owe its successful development to the drive and conviction of the Prof, has been given because few know how much England owed to it, and even fewer how much she owes to him that we had it.

Another successful operation which was due to the inspiration of the Prof was the jamming of the German radar, used for controlling their night fighters and for laying their anti-aircraft guns, by a device known by the code name Window. Churchill describes the obstacles which had to be surmounted:

> But we still had to deal with enemy night fighters, which accounted for about three-quarters of our bomber losses. Each German fighter was confined to a narrow area of the sky and was controlled by a separate ground station. These ground stations had originally formed a line across Europe, called the Kammhuber Line, after the name of the German general who built it. As we attempted to pierce or outflank it, so the enemy extended and deepened it. Nearly 750 of these stations spread across Europe ivy fashion from Berlin westwards to Ostend, northwards to the Skagerrak, and southwards to Marseilles. We found all but six of them, but there were too many to destroy by bombing. If they were permitted to stay in operation our bombers would have to drive their way through many hundred miles of night fighter "boxes" stretching from the North Sea to the target. Although the losses in each "box" would rarely be high, they would rarely be nothing; and in time they might cripple our bomber offensive. A cheap and wholesale method of jamming the entire system was urgently needed.
>
> As early as 1937 Professor Lindemann had prompted me to make a very simple suggestion to the Air Defence Research Committee. This was to scatter from the air packets of tinfoil strips or other conducting material cut to a special length so as to simulate a bomber on the enemy's Radar screens. If a cloud of these were dropped by our aircraft the enemy

fighters would not be able to tell which were our bombers and which were our tin-foil strips.[1]

In the early days of the war Prof had discussed with the physicists operating the long-wave warning station at Pevensey the possibility of jamming radar by means of what were called dipoles tuned to the wavelength of radar. These dipoles can be made from narrow strips of metal, with a length a little less than half of the wavelength of the radar. The group of workers at T.R.E. (Telecommunications Research Establishment) at Malvern[2] had produced propaganda pamphlets covered with tin-foil, later aluminum, to drop from aircraft to jam the German 50-centimeter wavelength radar. The efficiency of these pamphlets was less than one-tenth of that of strips made in the form of dipoles, a very serious shortcoming since aluminum foil was in desperately short supply.

The question was first brought to the attention of the Prof in April 1942 at the request of the Commander-in-Chief, Fighter Command, who was anxious lest this new form of jamming, if proven, might be used by the enemy to jam our own Fighter Command's radar. The Commander-in-Chief was unconvinced by the report from T.R.E. that the metalized pamphlets did not affect radar operating on the wavelengths used by Fighter Command, and demanded a more thorough investigation of the vulnerability of his command to this form of jamming.

The Prof wasted no time in the matter, and his first action was to send for his friend Derek Jackson,[3] then an officer in the R.A.F., on the staff of Sholto Douglas, C.-in-C. Fighter Command, and he was eventually put in charge of the operational trials of Window. There was also a great deal of staff work done at the Air Ministry both before and after he was

[1] Sir Winston Churchill, *The Second World War,* Vol. 4, pages 256–257.
[2] The scientific establishment in charge of the radio war.
[3] Professor of Spectroscopy at Oxford from 1934 to 1947.

making his contribution. Watson-Watt wrote of the arrival of Jackson to conduct these experiments:

> For the carrying out of these trials there was attached to T.R.E. Wing Commander Derek Ainslie Jackson, O.B.E., D.F.C., A.F.C., D.Sc. (Oxon), F.R.S. Derek is an Oxford don who, as a distinguished Professor of spectroscopy, was one of the world's greatest authorities on dipoles of sub-microscopic dimensions, had ridden in the Grand National, was one of our two most outstanding night fighter AI-observers, and had an irresistibly endearing explosiveness all about him. . . . Derek did a first class job on the secret trials of Window, adding to the strength of old adages about poachers turned gamekeepers, one about setting a night-fighter to fox a night-fighter.[1]

Jackson wrote of his trials:

> As a result of this, trials were carried out by me of the effects tuned dipoles both on the Fighter Command Controlled Interception Radar and on Air Interception Radar. The trials showed that both of these radars were very easily jammed, and the Prof called a meeting consisting of the Chief of Air Staff, the C.-in-C. Fighter Command, and his Chief Signals Officer (Radar), the Prof and myself. Before the meeting I had worked out in detail, at the request of the Prof, how this form of jamming could be used most effectively against the German radar, and what steps could be taken to render our own radar less vulnerable to it. I had already explained my plans to the Prof; he was entirely in favour of them and assured me he would give me all the support he could to get them adopted by the Chief of Air Staff. These plans consisted first in producing the "Window" in sufficient quantity for the aircraft of Bomber Command in their operations over Germany and German territory to drop enough of these dipoles to make the German radar virtually useless — to such an extent that ground controlled interception of the R.A.F. bombers by German night fighters, and radar controlled gunlaying by

[1] Sir Robert Watson-Watt, *Three Steps to Victory*, page 417.

the German anti-aircraft guns would no longer be feasible; they also included plans for introducing at an early date a new form of American radar, operating on the microwave system — so strongly advocated by the Prof — for our night fighters, which would be free from jamming by "Window," even if this were modified to be tuned for the wavelength, 10 cm., of this microwave radar.

The meeting took place; both the C.A.S. (Portal) and the C.-in-C. Fighter Command were entirely favourably disposed to the Prof, so much so that the C.A.S. asked me to explain the whole plan to him, as if I were "at Oxford giving a lecture to my undergraduates." The C.A.S. was satisfied with my proposals; he agreed with the Prof that I should be put in charge of the whole project of jamming the German radar with "Window," and that I should also be responsible for making the Fighter Command radar invulnerable to jamming by "Window" at as early a date as possible; he also agreed to C.-in-C. Fighter Command's request that "Window" should not be used until his radar would be sufficiently invulnerable to jamming by "Window" for Fighter Command's night fighters to be able to render a fairly effective defence. It was also agreed that, under the Ministry of Aircraft Production, a "Window" panel should be formed, of which I was to be Chairman, which should be responsible for the development and production of "Window." This was a great achievement on the part of the Prof, and it was fully justified by the subsequent developments.[1]

By the end of August, or the beginning of September 1942, the tests on how "Window" should be used were complete, and it had been agreed in what form the strips of aluminum foil should be dropped from the bombers, and at what rate the dropping should take place. As a result of the Prof's influence these detailed plans were approved, and stocks of Window accumulated with the machinery necessary for keeping

[1] Professor Derek Jackson, F.R.S., to author.

up production supplied by the Ministry of Aircraft Production. Three separate bodies were officially ordered by Portal to work out the amount of Window that would need to be used. One was Dr. Dickins of the Operational Research Section of Bomber Command, the second was Derek Jackson of Fighter Command, and the third, R. V. Jones of Air Intelligence. They produced three separate answers, Jackson's being the largest and Jones's the smallest.

Meanwhile the new American microwave radar was installed in a Mosquito and put through its operational tests. It was entirely in accordance with what the Prof had expected from microwave radar that it proved highly effective both when operated without jamming and when subjected to intense jamming efforts by Window. These tests were completed by May 1943, and at last the C.-in-C. Fighter Command, Air Marshal Leigh Mallory, was satisfied, after suitable assurances, that his objections to retaliation on his own airplanes by Germans using Window had been met. A meeting early in June 1943, at which the three estimates of the amount of Window to be used were presented, marked the occasion when Portal decided to ask the Prime Minister for permission to use Window. Jackson was not present at the meeting with the Prime Minister, but Portal took Jones with him as his expert witness, and Watson-Watt attended to express his opposition. Thus it was at last decided to use Window, and the chosen target was Hamburg, notorious for the heavy losses inflicted there on our bombers by German night fighters and flak, both radar-controlled. The results were admirable, the losses being about ½ per cent as compared with 5 per cent before the use of Window. On this Jackson wrote:

This success of Window is described in Winston Churchill's book The Hinge of Fate, where he describes its success as having "greatly exceeded our expectations," and is very kind to me about it, but fails to say that it was at the Prof's instigation that I worked out the whole scheme.[1]

Some, including Professor R. V. Jones, Chief of Scientific Air Intelligence throughout the radio war, thought that the wrong tactical use had been made of the weapon. Jones had, after its successful trials, pressed for its immediate use against Germany, but found that Prof had been persuaded that by using it prematurely we could do more harm to ourselves than to the enemy.

> This issue [said Jones] should never have been in doubt, because all the best Intelligence showed that the German Air Force was wasting away, inextricably committed in Russia, so that at any time after the middle of 1942 we should be able to exert a bigger bomber effort against the Germans than they could against us.[2]

.   .   .

The time had at last arrived for the employment of "Window." Its antagonists fought to the last ditch, but events were against them. Finally, at a Staff Conference on 23rd June 1943, the Chief of the Air Staff took the case to the Prime Minister, who gave permission for "Window" to be used. There was still a little more delay, however, until the invasion of Sicily was successfully launched, in case the Germans might retaliate immediately with their own Window. With the Sicilian operation well advanced, Window was used for the first time in the Hamburg raid of 24/25th July 1943. Let the Germans give the verdict: "Since July 25, the enemy, first at night — in isolated cases in daylight too — combined with the raids into Reich territory, the dropping of 'Hamburg bodies.' The technical success of this action must be designated as complete . . . By this means the enemy has delivered the

---

[1] Professor Jackson to author.
[2] Professor R. V. Jones, *The Radio War.*

long awaited blow against our decimetre radar sets both on land and in the air." [1]

After the fall of France, and before the entry of America into the war, the major strategic decision was taken to concentrate the main effort on bombing Germany. If it is admitted that England could not alone have invaded Europe, this was the only form of attack open to her. It was a policy that wholly suited Prof's temperament. After the ghastly suffering that Germany had inflicted upon the world, and the savage assaults on British cities, he shared the intense desire felt by millions of others for that country to feel the severity of war on her own soil. His desire to bomb Germany led him to constant efforts to prevent the Army, Navy, Coastal and Fighter Commands from claiming what he regarded as an excessive share of the national resources, and to increase the effectiveness of bombing.

He continually argued that the two older services demanded an extravagant amount of stores and shipping, and it was with zest that he calculated that the naval shell requirements were sufficient to fight the battle of Jutland continuously, all the year round. Hence, too, his struggles to get Middle East vehicle requirements limited, and the vehicles sent, with a vast economy in shipping space, broken down and boxed up. He indulged in a long and embittered complaint about Coastal Command demands for aircraft and radar equipment. One of his colleagues remembers him arguing, when there was a requirement for antisubmarine radar for merchant ships, that since the ship could see the U-boat's periscope as soon as the U-boat could see the ship, a sharp lookout with good binoculars was worth any expensive wireless apparatus. This point was proved when he discovered that fast merchant ships traveling out of convoy were virtually never sunk if they saw a periscope before a torpedo was fired.

[1] *Ibid.*

Such controversies were essentially subordinate to his direct efforts to increase the size and effectiveness of the bombing force during the period of mid-1940 to mid-1942, and part of 1943. In view of his suspicions of the results of our bombing, and the successful inquiry he instituted into that subject, the charges of Sir Charles Snow must be regarded with particular reserve, although it can be argued that Prof's inflexible desire to pulverize Germany led him into underestimating other targets such as U-boats and naval warfare in general, or the possibility that the resources devoted to it could have been better used to increase the invasion forces and accelerate their effort.

When we consider the accusations often made today, after the event, that the bombing effort was a mistake, it should be remembered that at the time it was the only available method of hitting Germany hard, and that this was the ardent desire of all. It has often been pointed out that German military output actually rose until the end of the war in spite of the deluge of high explosive, but this is an inconclusive argument which takes no account of the extent to which it would have risen yet further without bombing. As to the claim that German morale remained unbroken, who can assess to what degree the terrible punishment impaired their war effort? The whole question of the strategic bombing offensive is still *sub judice*. We await the publication of the great official work on which Sir Charles Webster and Dr. Frankland have been engaged for the last ten years. It can be said that the conclusion of the authors will be that the offensive rendered a major contribution to the victory of the Grand Alliance in 1945, and that Prof played an important role in it at a critical time, and that if their views are accepted he is entitled to credit for the stand which he made.[1] It was obvious that bombing was the only available policy when this country stood alone, and this

[1] Sir Charles Webster to author.

situation remained until it was clear that the Russians would not be defeated and would not sue for peace. One who had observed the carnage of the First World War had also the right to doubt whether a frontal assault on the enemy in France would then have been a quicker or less bloody method of settling the issue.

To these considerations must be added some weighty opinions which prove that the differences between Prof and Tizard on strategic bombing were by no means so wide as Sir Charles Snow would have us believe. As Snow thought, quite wrongly, that Lindemann had a sadistic streak, it was perhaps natural that he should represent him as elated at the prospect of destroying working-class dwellings and killing thousands of women and children. In R. V. Jones's words:

> Viewed from a background of peace, the decision to attempt to break the spirit of the German people by destroying their houses was a horrible one and a reversal of previously declared policy, but it must be judged against the spirit of the time. We ourselves and our Allies had suffered much from the German Air Force, and bombing then appeared the only way in which we could hit back. Given the inaccuracy of our attacks, as then established, it was considered that selective bombing of special targets such as oil installations was impracticable. We had earlier tried to attack such targets without success. Actually our accuracy had improved quite rapidly, thanks to radio aids, and we might have been able to carry out a very effective programme of selective raids in 1943 had we realized by then how much our bombing had improved. But this was not foreseen in 1942, discouraged as we then were by our previous imprecision. Lindemann calculated that by the middle of 1943 about one-third of the total population of Germany could be deprived of housing. Tizard, who since 1940 had been at the Ministry of Aircraft Production, gave substantial reasons for believing that Lindemann's estimate was about four times too optimistic.

Lindemann did not intend his figures, as the official record will probably show, to be taken too literally but he was convinced that the effect of the bombing would be catastrophic. Tizard did not deny this but doubted whether it would be decisive. He was not, he wrote, fundamentally against the bombing policy, but he was afraid that the bombing, even on the heaviest scale that we could achieve, would be indecisive, and that in the meantime we should have diverted vital efforts from other air tasks, such as the anti-U-boat campaign.[1]

Sir Charles Webster considered that Snow gave "a very distorted" picture of this issue:

It was concerned with the strategy of the R.A.F. in 1942. That year was critical for Bomber Command. It had little to show for its heroic efforts in the first years of the war; it was able to demonstrate its potentialities in 1942 because of the courage, energy and imagination of Sir Arthur Harris. But meanwhile the prosecution of the strategic offensive was under heavy attack and Bomber Command might well have been deprived of the opportunity to re-establish itself. The other two services wished to divert its aircraft to their own purposes, the Admiralty pressing hard that they should be used for the defence of the Atlantic.

Lord Cherwell, who had himself exposed the defects of Bomber Command in 1941, strongly advocated a strategic offensive in a minute which sought to show, by simple arithmetical calculations suitable to the comprehension of the Prime Minister, that, if Bomber Command were given the necessary aircraft and more scientifically handled, it could destroy half the housing of fifty-eight large German towns, something which the German people would be unable to bear. Tizard was immediately able to point out that the assumption and calculations of the minute could not be sustained, and Blackett at the Admiralty naturally made a similar criticism. These criticisms were true enough, and Lord Cherwell ad-

[1] Professor R. V. Jones, *The Times,* April 8, 1961.

mitted them, but he pointed out that all his calculations were
intended to show was that a great deal of damage could be
done by bombing built-up areas. Tizard then stated that
he did not disagree fundamentally with that policy, but wished
to show that it could not be decisive in 1943, as Lord Cherwell
had suggested, and that meanwhile the war might be lost —
by which he meant failure to cope with the U-boats. The question at issue was whether the emphasis in air strategy was to be
offence or defence.

Sir Charles ignores or is ignorant of this part of the discussion and even suggests that the issue was settled in an
hysterical atmosphere. Anyone less hysterical than Lord Portal,
who played a major part in it, it is difficult to imagine. But it
was certainly a fateful decision, for on it hung a good deal
of the future of the war.[1]

The following is the minute referred to by Webster which
was submitted by Prof to the Prime Minister on March 30, 1942:

The following seems a simple method of estimating what
we could do by bombing Germany.

Careful analysis of the effects of raids on Birmingham, Hull
and elsewhere have shown that on the average one ton of
bombs dropped on a built-up area demolishes 20–40 dwellings
and turns 100–200 people out of house and home.

We know from our experience that we can count on nearly
14 operational sorties per bomber produced. The average
lift of the bombers we are going to produce over the next 15
months will be about 3 tons. It follows that each of these
bombers will in its lifetime drop about 40 tons of bombs. If
these are dropped on built-up areas they will make 4,000–
8,000 people homeless.

In 1938 over 22 million Germans lived in 58 towns of over
100,000 inhabitants, which, with modern equipment, should
be easy to find and hit. Our forecast output of heavy bombers
(including Wellingtons) between now and the middle of

[1] *Sunday Times,* April 9, 1961.

1943 is about 10,000. If even half the total load of 10,000 bombers were dropped on the built-up areas of these 58 German towns the great majority of their inhabitants (about one-third of the German population) would be turned out of house and home.

Investigation seems to show that having one's house demolished is most damaging to morale. People seem to mind it more than having their friends or even relatives killed. At Hull signs of strain were evident though only one-tenth of the houses were demolished. On the above figures we should be able to do ten times as much harm to each of the 58 principal German towns. There seems little doubt that this would break the spirit of the people.

Our calculation assumes, of course, that we really get one-half of our bombs into built-up areas. On the other hand no account is taken of the large promised American production (6,000 heavy bombers in the period in question). Nor has regard been paid to the inevitable damage to factories, communications, etc. in these towns and the damage by fire, probably accentuated by break-down of public services.

The following letters also emphasize that there was far less difference between the views of Prof and Tizard on strategic bombing than Snow would have us believe, and that Prof never assigned a time limit for the results to be achieved.

Sir Henry Tizard to Sir Archibald Sinclair,
Secretary of State for Air.

Ministry of Aircraft Production,
Millbank, S.W.1.
20th April 1942.

SECRET

My dear Secretary of State,

Thanks for your letter, I enclose a copy of a note that I have sent to Cherwell.

You will see that I think Cherwell has overestimated the probable effect of using the whole of our heavy bombers and most of our Wellingtons on Germany by a factor of at least 4, and probably by a factor of 6 or over, in view of the remarks in my paragraph 7.

I should like to make it clear that I don't disagree fundamentally with the bombing policy, but I do think that it is only likely to be decisive if carried out on the scale envisaged by the Air Staff, which, if I remember rightly, contemplated a front line strength of 4,000 aircraft and a rate of reinforcement of something of the order of 1,000 heavy bombers a month.

We cannot achieve this, this year, or even until next year so if we try to carry out the policy with a much smaller force it will not be decisive, and we may lose the war in other ways.

You know that I am very keen about the greater and better use of the Air Force against enemy ships of war as well as of merchant shipping. If such a policy is adopted it must be adopted on a pretty large scale: it is no good attacking one warship with one bomber. If we say that no heavy bombers will be diverted for the object of keeping command of the seas, are we not running a grave risk without getting enough dividends elsewhere?

I know that these are complicated questions, and that I have not sufficient access to information to enable me to form a really good judgment, and I have often felt that I should like to hear the strategic policy discussed by the Air Council; but we never have such discussions — perhaps for good reasons. I have hesitated to talk things over with Portal because he is so pressed and has such a heavy responsibility on him. I do not feel I can demand any of his time unless he himself wants this.

Yours sincerely,
(Signed) H. T. TIZARD

Lord Cherwell to Sir Henry Tizard.

22nd April 1942.

MY DEAR TIZARD,

Thank you for your letter and enclosure. I am glad to see that we do not differ in arithmetic, or even in our general conclusion.

My paper was intended to show that we really can do a lot of damage by bombing built-up areas with the sort of air force which should be available. I used the round figure of 10,000 partly because I wrote my note in March, and partly to save the Prime Minister the trouble of making arithmetical calculations.

M.A.P.'s[1] promise was originally much higher and I think the lowest figure the Prime Minister would recognise is in this neighbourhood. The exact date of "midsummer," of course, gives you some latitude. I must say I am horrified that you think even their latest programme is an overestimate. It has been written down many times, and we were assured that it was now entirely realistic. I still hope that you are pessimistic in thinking they are likely to be about 1,500 short.

You say that 689 Wellingtons are earmarked for Coastal Command, and should therefore be subtracted. This is a matter of policy, which may, and probably should, be decided in that sense.

I have made no assumptions about the date at which the bombing is to be completed. The Air Ministry have made arrangements to absorb all the bombers promised (not only 85%). No doubt some of the bombers delivered in June 1943 will still be operating some months after, but sooner or later I trust their bombs will be dropped.

I am not building upon the use of Gee next winter, but on the new equipment which in my view should be installed by then. It is most disheartening to hear that you do not expect it to be ready for use till the Spring. I cannot conceive that it is impossible to produce it six months earlier if sufficient

[1] Ministry of Aircraft Production.

drive is put behind it. With this equipment 50% should be well within the reach of our bombers.

Even on your figures the weight of attack on all the principal German cities would be three or four times as great as on Birmingham and Hull. From those who have studied the effects on these towns I gather that even this intensity of bombing spread over the whole country would be catastrophic. But of course I regard your figure as too low.

My argument naturally assumes that we use the right kind of bombs. I am shocked to hear that the M.C. bomb is not yet in production. It was asked for over a year ago, and I cannot see why there should have been all this delay in getting it into production.

The whole point of my note was to show what damage would be possible with a given number of bombers devoted to attack on the large German cities. I did not say that we could carry out the desired devastation by a given date, nor did I say that we should necessarily devote all our bombers to this purpose. But perhaps it is relevant to mention that I took no credit for the fact that considerably more damage is done in densely built-up areas than I have assumed, nor for any bombing done by American aeroplanes, which we must expect in increasing numbers in due course.

I trust that this will show that there is not much difference between us, and remain,

As ever,
Yours
(Signed) CHERWELL

The misconceptions caused by Snow's misleading account of the parts played by Prof and Tizard in the matter of bombing policy is summed up with admirable lucidity in a review in the *Times Literary Supplement* on April 14, 1961.

There was also, though this is not mentioned by C. P. Snow, a Committee for the Scientific Survey of Air Offence of which Sir Henry Tizard was the chairman. It achieved little or nothing and Bomber Command entered the war without any of the radar equipment which was needed for accurate bombing. This failure, for which there were many extenuating reasons, weighed heavily upon Sir Henry Tizard's mind for he was not against bombing in the way suggested by C. P. Snow. It is possible that Lord Cherwell might have driven this side of the work through with greater vigour but, however that may be, the thrust which did eventually produce the aids to navigation and bomb aiming needed by Bomber Command did, in essence, come from Lord Cherwell, as also did the scientific investigations, or operational research, which showed the need for them. What Sir Henry Tizard did for Fighter Command Lord Cherwell later did for Bomber Command. Both achievements were of immense importance and of much greater historic interest than the disputes between the architects.

But because of the different view which he takes, C. P. Snow follows these disputes through to the great bombing debates of 1942 when Cherwell and Tizard had their arguments about the statistics of the damage which would be caused by Bomber Command. His analysis, however, is of little value because in this matter C. P. Snow loses sight of, or does not know, the facts. The bombing policy being attacked or defended was not Lord Cherwell's. It was not attacked by Sir Henry Tizard and it was not the policy described by C. P. Snow. Nor was any policy of strategic bombing ever, as it is asserted on page 51,[1] "put into action with every effort the country could make." Neither Lord Cherwell nor Sir Henry Tizard, nor Sir Winston Churchill nor any of the Chiefs of Staff, including the Air Force one, Lord Portal, believed the war could be won by bombing alone. But equally no one in authority believed that it could be won without bombing. Some who were not very highly informed believed that Bomber Command would do better if it attacked targets which it could not hit than if it struck at larger targets which were more or less within its operational capacity. Sir Henry Tizard was

[1] C. P. Snow, *Science and Government*.

not among these. He merely believed that Lord Cherwell was being over-optimistic about the consequences of attacking city centres with the forces available.

Sir Henry Tizard's note of caution was well-founded but it was not important because the issue did not concern the number of houses which would or would not be destroyed. It concerned the question of whether Bomber Command was to be developed as the medium of a major offensive against Germany or not. With many qualifications, Sir Winston Churchill, who was certainly more sceptical of bombing results than Sir Henry Tizard, decided that it should. This decision was justified by subsequent events. Drawing its inspiration from the incomparable leadership of one of the great commanders of the war, Marshal of the Royal Air Force Sir Arthur Harris, nourished by the resources of British science and aided by its great ally, the United States Eighth Air Force, Bomber Command gradually surmounted difficulties which proved far more formidable than any foreseen by Lord Cherwell or Sir Henry Tizard and rendered a major contribution to the victory of the Grand Alliance in 1945.

It is to be hoped that C. P. Snow's brilliantly written and characteristically incisive lectures will stimulate and even accelerate the production of the historical record of the great events which were influenced by Sir Henry Tizard and Lord Cherwell. But it is also to be hoped that no one will read these lectures as that historical record.[1]

In the course of this sustained and nerve-racking work the circumstances of Prof's personal life were bad for his health and allowed little, if any, relaxation.

When Churchill became Prime Minister the Section migrated from the Admiralty to Richmond Terrace, and at the end of 1940 to Great George Street, where their quarters were directly above the Prime Minister's. Their night quarters were in a noisome hole in a basement in Scotland Yard. The

[1] The *Times Literary Supplement*, April 15, 1961.

period of the blitz was a trying one for the Prof, who was now working harder than he had ever done in his life.

He found himself faced by a long hiatus in the evenings. When his colleagues had dispersed for the night, he had to wait in maddening inaction and loneliness in a cellar for his meeting with Churchill in the small hours. He began to look drawn and ill, and it is possible that his heart was already giving him secret alarm. He lived at the Carlton Hotel, a home from home amid the squalor and desolation, until it was destroyed by a bomb. Occasionally he slept in the shelters of No. 10 and at the Cabinet Office in Great George Street. His difficulties of diet had not yet become serious, and at his many meals with the Churchills their cook, Mrs. Landemore, would tempt him with such delicacies as *risotto* with tomato sauce or *gnocchi romaine* with globe artichokes, and hot asparagus with the hollandaise sauce he loved. Later, when the severe shortages came, he was to exist on a semistarvation diet, deleterious to health and vigor.

The faithful Harvey was ever at hand in the nights of blitz to minister to the Prof's many needs. Prof never showed the slightest concern about air raids, V-1 or V-2, except on Harvey's account.

> During the war in air raids I never missed an opportunity of being with him for I felt so much braver in his presence. No matter what dangers were ahead or how severe an air raid, the Professor never allowed his routine to be altered in the slightest. I have strolled down Whitehall with him in heavy raids with the inevitable bowler hat on his head and helmet in his hand. On one occasion, being anxious not to show my desire to run, I carefully did not keep quite abreast of him. He noticed this, however, and said: "There is no point in loitering, Harvey." One night during the Professor's stay at Marsham Court when I was sleeping in my office in Great George Street there was a particularly heavy air raid, and many fires were

started in the Marsham Court area. When things had quietened down I went to see if Marsham Court had escaped. I found it had, and the Professor in bed reading a P. G. Wodehouse book. He asked: "Is there anything wrong, Harvey?" He never allowed me to run any risks that could be avoided, and would not allow me to fire-watch.[1]

When the blitz made the work of his section in London impossible, a suitable house was found in Marlow, which by a strange coincidence adjoined that once occupied by his father. When he left Marlow he returned to London and took a flat in Marsham Court.

At 5.30 one evening the Statistical Section moved into the house at Marlow — a motley collection with piles of Cabinet boxes stuffed into three or four cars provided by the Women's Voluntary Services, Prof's fury at their two male servants at Marlow being called up to rot in the tail of the army instead of ministering to his comfort being only appeased by the news that the male staff at Buckingham Palace had been called up as well. There was no leisure at Marlow after nightfall. When they arrived there each evening they settled down again to the dreary grind, laboring on the papers they had brought with them, and, after a communal dinner, disputing with the Prof into the small hours of the morning. In this monastic existence, in spite of his awkward temperament and surly moods, he won golden opinions from subordinates who had not known him before and were intimidated by the aura of greatness that surrounded him:

He displayed admirable tact and could be a most fascinating companion. That he could be and often was intolerably grumpy, spoilt, unjust etc. cannot possibly be denied — too many who only met him once or twice saw nothing else. But if all was well he could be entrancingly funny, understanding

[1] James Harvey to author.

and kind. He was admirably loyal to his staff, defending them after their blunders, finding them jobs when his Branch was wound up far beyond the mere line of duty. He used, in his off-moments, to drive us all dizzy with irritation, but I do not think that any of us failed to perceive that he had a real scale and greatness in the depth, clarity, speed and severe simplicity of his thought. Certainly in my own experience he can be compared only with Keynes. Perhaps there was an interval between them, but there was a larger one between this pair and the rest of the world.[1]

Prof was, by this time, a completely dedicated man. He ignored such hospitality as existed, as at parties he was cut off from all serious discussion by the secrets he kept so stoutly locked in his bosom. He had no recreations apart from an attempt to return to his old love prime numbers, and in consultation with Champernowne to develop a theory for relating the distribution of prime numbers to general probability principles. He sought no fresh air, and took no exercise, apart from a daily walk back and forth down a trodden path in the garden, as his doctor had warned him that the confined life he was leading was impairing his eyesight.

It is delightful to realize that amid all these stresses and the unnatural tempo at which he was living, his habitual courtesy and kindness to women and servants remained constant and charming. Mrs. Cross, his housekeeper and cook at Marlow, remembered him with an abiding affection:

> His main characteristics so far as I was concerned were his very great kindness and courteous good manners. Whenever I had occasion to see him, I would always be asked to sit down while he stood . . . he loved chocolates and would take them to bed with him when they were obtainable. He would take his white-of-egg sandwiches to public lunches etc., and the eggs

[1] D. M. B. Butt.

had to be unfertile from his own chickens. He was supposed to dislike women, but was always most kind to me and very reassuring at a time when I was intensely worried about my husband overseas. He was a very kind-hearted gentleman in the true sense of the words, and I should like to feel that I have perhaps been able to help, although in such a tiny way, in the perpetuation of his memory.[1]

Prof was criticized by Dr. Crow,[2] the English rocket expert, and by other scientists for the obstinacy with which he refused to believe in a German rocket attack, and it cannot be denied that he seriously underestimated the German preparations for the V-2 rocket, and advised the Prime Minister that its construction would be so difficult that it was almost inconceivable that the Germans would divert precious manpower and material from the manufacture of bombers which were infinitely more effective than any rocket, and could plant their bombs with far greater accuracy.

It should be remembered in his favor that in his minutes to the Prime Minister he never stated that it was impossible that the Germans were making the rockets, or that they could not be made, but that in view of the overwhelming technical difficulties, and the comparatively meager results to be expected, it was highly improbable that they would be so foolish.

Nor was he alone in this opinion. The German Minister of Munitions, Dr. Speer, ablest of Nazi leaders, deplored the effort that had been put into the making of rockets. Each one, he said, cost as many man-hours to produce as six or seven fighters, and twenty flying bombs could have been made for the cost of one rocket.

Prof also differed from Sandys, Joint Parliamentary Secretary to the Minister of Supply, and his advisers as to the size

[1] Mrs. L. W. S. Cross to author.
[2] Sir Alwyn Crow to author.

of the warhead that such a missile would carry. Their forecast was that it would be ten to twelve tons, and his, one to two tons, if it ever appeared, and here he was proved right. He also rejected the panic-stricken estimates of the scale of the attack and the damage it would cause, which he thought grossly overrated, and in this also he was completely justified.

When Intelligence reports of an enormous rocket with a ten-to-twenty-ton warhead reached his office, he ridiculed the idea from the start, on the grounds that the ratio of the fuel weight to the total weight would have to be so high to achieve the required range that its structure would not be strong enough to withstand its own acceleration. He based his argument on various assumptions; the total weight of the rocket, the calorific value of the fuels used, the temperature which the materials could withstand, and from this position he refused to budge.

Given the two protagonists, Mr. Duncan Sandys and Prof, it was inevitable that the controversy would become partisan. In the Prof's circle what "they" were doing with "their" rocket referred not to the Germans but to Sandys and his Ministry. At a meeting convened by Prof of such important men as G. P. Thomson, he was led into overstating his case by his rivalry with Sandys for the Prime Minister's ear.

His obstinacy about rockets did not prevent him from making a clear prediction of the flying bombs which preceded them long before the photographs of them were taken at Peenemunde, and when the first V-1 attacks began he was fortified in his belief that the rocket was a fantasy.[1] R. V. Jones gave one of Prof's colleagues a serious warning not to let him go too far, as in his opinion the Germans undoubtedly had a long-range rocket; but by this time nothing could alter the Prof's *idée fixe* except the arrival of the missile itself. On April 22, 1943, he still doubted whether such rockets would be used,

---

[1] For the accuracy of Cherwell's predictions on the V.1., see Appendix III.

which, if they were, would probably be equivalent, at most, to a 2000-pound bomb.

Terrible shocks were however, given to Ministers in May and June, when they were told that the weapon would probably have a ten-ton warhead and a range of 100 to 115 miles, that they must reckon upon 600 casualties, 150 fatal, per bomb falling on London, that the bombardment might begin in a few months, and, assuming one rocket per hour, this would imply 108,000 fatal casualties and 300,000 wounded a month. Consternation seized the Ministers present, and Herbert Morrison, the Home Secretary, spoke of the evacuation of a large part of the population from London, and of putting the center of government underground, if indeed it should be left in the capital at all.

Prof remained calm, and opposed all these steps. He did not believe that warheads anything like as great as ten tons could be used on such rockets. Nor did he accept the figure of killed and wounded which had been quoted. Disdainfully he said that it was far too early to make plans for mass evacuation. He persisted in his view that flying bombs were the real danger. On October 24th it was reported that rockets with a range of 130 to 300 miles were to be expected with warheads of ten to twenty tons, and on November 3rd the Minister of Aircraft Production asked his department to plan on the assumption that all production in London would be lost. Prof remained unconvinced in spite of the acquiescence of some scientists in this forecast.

In spite of the comparative failure of the V-1, which Prof had accurately forecast, anxiety about the rocket attack remained acute, and in the second half of July 1944, the experts at Farnborough succeeded in reconstructing the remnants of one that had fallen in Sweden. At meetings on July 25th and August 10th the usual difference between the two schools of thought reappeared, Prof and R. V. Jones maintaining that the warhead would weigh about one ton, against the official view. On July 27th the Cabinet discussed the evacuation of London, and Morrison proposed that plans should be made to send away a million people.

The first rocket fell at Chiswick on September 8, 1944. It was a wonderful technical achievement which astounded the English experts. The fuel consisted mainly of methyl alcohol and liquid oxygen. Each rocket contained a 1000-horse-power turbo-compressor which forced the fuel into the combustion chamber during the few seconds required. The warhead, about which there had been so much controversy, weighed just under one ton, and the damage inflicted by each rocket was thus similar to that produced by each flying bomb.

Indeed the rocket proved the smaller menace. Of the thousand odd launched, only about five hundred reached the seven-hundred square miles of Greater London. Instead of the 108,000 fatal casualties per month which had been forecast, deaths from these weapons amounted to 1500 during the period when the country was under fire. What was the Prof's record in this matter? Without completely discounting the rockets, he had in the strongest terms and up to a late date denied the likelihood of their being produced. On the other hand, assuming that they were, he had consistently estimated the warhead at one to two tons, and held that the ghastly destruction anticipated by others was grossly overestimated. These facts, in his view, entirely vindicated all he had said and done on the subject.

8

The Economic Background

IN THE SUMMER of 1941, before the Americans were involved in the war, there was a dramatic meeting of the Prime Minister and President, which resulted in what was known as "The Atlantic Charter." By this it was provided that the United States and Britain should co-operate to produce better order in the world, both in the field of politics and in that of economics. This gave rise to the question whether thought should be given to the means for implementing this undertaking before the war was over.

There was another more impelling reason for the pooling of ideas on the economic side. Earlier in 1941 President Roosevelt had proposed a scheme for "lending" and "leasing" supplies to Britain for the waging of war, since her fund of dollars for purchasing from the United States was almost exhausted. What is "lent" or "leased" presumably has to be restored. In what form would expendable aircraft and other weapons of war, or indeed supplies for maintaining the civilian population, be restored?

During the course of 1941 it was generally agreed that the restoration should not be in the form of money, since the repayment of wartime debt had burdened the world economy so heavily after the First World War, and was held by some to have caused the great world depression, which was to be avoided in future at all costs. Repayment in kind did not seem very feasible. Why should not the Americans waive all forms of material repayment in consideration for an undertaking by Britain that she would co-operate on certain lines in securing the economic objectives of the Atlantic Charter? A document was drawn up which was for some time known as "the Consideration" and later became Article VII of the Mutual Aid Agreement. The waiving of repayment was expressed in somewhat vague words: "In the final determination of the benefits to be provided to the U.S. by the British government in return for lease-lend aid, the terms and conditions thereof shall be such as not to burden commerce between the two countries but to promote mutual advantageous economic relations between them and the betterment of world-wide economic relations." These were to include agreed action "directed to the expansion . . . of production, employment, and the exchange and consumption of goods . . . and the elimination of all forms of discriminatory treatment in international commerce and to the reduction of tariffs and other trade barriers . . . Conversations shall be begun between the two governments with a view to determine . . . the best means."

If this was signed, Britain would be obliged to enter upon such conversations in return for the material assistance she was receiving. Later in the year there was an unofficial visit by Professor Hansen and Mr. Gulick of the State Department, who suggested the creation of a world investment bank by the United States and Britain. These visitors were held to represent the thinking of "New Dealers" in the United States. At the same time it was made plain that the State Department, under the influence of Cordell Hull, would attach great importance to the "elimination" of "discrimination" and the reduction of trade barriers.

The British Government immediately began giving thought to these problems, under the leadership of Sir Richard Hopkins, the Head of the British Treasury. Lengthy documents were produced and there was much interdepartmental discussion and committee work. It at once appeared that there were two views about this matter. One view, most fervently put forward by Sir Hubert Henderson, then in the Treasury, was that Britain should be extremely cautious in committing herself. He believed that it would not be possible for the country to survive on the basis of open multilateral trade, owing to the prospective balance-of-trade difficulties, and held that the continuance of the wartime system of bilateral agreements and blocked currencies would be necessary for an indefinite period.

This of course went dead against American ideas, so he proposed that we should do our best to postpone or at least to circumscribe the scope of discussions, and in any talks that took place should put in the forefront the grievous nature of our prospective balance-of-payments difficulties.

The other school, of which Lord Keynes eventually took the lead, while holding that we must make sufficient safeguards for a "transitional" period, thought that it was in our interest to go forward with discussions for plans on bolder lines, taking advantage in particular of the known views of the "New Dealers," which were by no means confined to the mere elimination of "discrimination" in commerce. Already, on August 9, 1941, he had drafted a few pages, sketching what was to become his plan for an International Clearing Union. In the following months the volume of paper mounted quickly. Sir Richard Hopkins, trying to formulate the views of both parties, looked with some favor on the more optimistic ideas of Keynes. Prof inclined to the second view, namely that we should proceed with plans along the lines desired by the Americans.

In December the issue was further pointed by the arrival of Mr. Redvers Opie from Washington, presenting a reasoned document by Mr. Leo Pasvolsky of the State Department, which not only stressed the benefits of greater freedom of trade, but also contained a sort of implicit threat that, if the British refused to agree, the Americans would be in a position to embark on a bilateralist policy themselves with much greater effect than Britain, and to her grave detriment.

Two issues were at stake at this time, the actual signature of the "Consideration," on which the continued flow of lend-lease supplies depended, and the promotion of conversations.

Prof was emphatic that the document should be signed at the earliest possible date, subject to some negotiations on verbal points and an understanding that the "elimination" of discrimination could only mean the end of Commonwealth Preferences if great concessions were made in the way of tariff reductions by the Americans in return. He urged the Prime Minister to settle the matter with the President on his historic visit to Washington after Pearl Harbor. This did not happen. But after a further interchange of correspondence the Mutual Aid Agreement was signed on February 23, 1942.

When Pearl Harbor occurred there were high hopes in the Henderson school that the Americans would be too busy to wish to proceed with immediate discussions, and Prof was not altogether averse from this view. There were, in fact, some delays, but those responsible for such matters in the United States continued with the work of formulating their own plans, in parallel with the work that was proceeding in the British Treasury. It soon became evident that the conversations would have to take place.

Prof was favorable to co-operation with the Americans on those lines. He was generally inclined to be favorable to the idea of freedom of trade. He was not impressed by the arguments of the "bilateralists" who held that we should be in a strong bargaining position because we afforded such a good market for other countries. He often ridiculed this view by the analogy of a man going into the Ritz Hotel and pleading that he was in a strong bargaining position because he was so hungry — quite regardless of his means for paying for what he wanted.

Accordingly he encouraged those who were working for him to take an active part in the Treasury discussions for wider schemes for international co-operation, such as that being proposed by Keynes for an International Clearing Union, and one on which Keynes was also working for international buffer stocks to even out oscillations in commodity prices, and he advised the Prime Minister in this sense. He was eager to learn about the progress of the discussions and allowed his representatives to declare themselves on the side of full co-operation with the Americans in their wider schemes.

Prof continued to hold these opinions throughout the war. Apart from the wider questions, he became more and more impressed with the financial difficulties that would arise when the war was over, and the need for American goodwill to tide us over, a point that was proved in the event. We had incurred huge debts to other countries; we had sold many of our overseas investments; we had cut our exports to a fraction of what was needed to pay for our imports. When the war was over we should not be able to survive without large-scale assistance from the United States until we had raised our exports to many times the wartime level and perhaps more than 50 per cent above the prewar level. It was essential, he thought, to make a start on this task in Stage II, between the end of the German and Japanese wars, and he felt that it would be difficult to get United States "permission" to do this — in competition with their exports — while they were still giving us aid. He was to negotiate with the Americans on this matter in Quebec and Washington in the autumn of 1944. United States co-operation would also be of great assistance if there was to be a scaling-down of wartime debts, and on this Prof took an extreme view, holding that the Indians, Egyptians and others had defrauded us.

In all these ways we should be dependent on the United States. But this was not the only reason why Prof supported the continuation of discussions with the United States on the International Monetary Fund, on commercial and commodity policy and all the other issues. He thought the proposals were, by and large, in our interest. He was not a doctrinaire free trader, but he was attracted by international arrangements that would oblige countries without balance-of-payments difficulties to pursue liberal trade policies while permitting countries with such difficulties — and we were likely to be one of these for a considerable time — to restrict their imports, maintain exchange control and even discriminate against the United States. Likewise, the I.M.F.[1] would allow us to devalue the pound if this was necessary to improve our competitive power, while preventing competitive devaluation by other countries more fortunately placed, as had happened in the thirties.

Prof spent a great deal of time refuting the arguments of Beaverbrook, Amery and Hudson in particular, who bombarded the Prime Minister and the Cabinet with papers denouncing the proposals. Prof mainly argued that they misrepresented the schemes proposed. Churchill naturally had little time to think about these matters and, with so much criticism coming in from influential Conservatives, as well as from Labour, he must have been very tempted to agree with those who wished to postpone the discussions; but the Americans were set on pursuing them vigorously.

Beaverbrook was at heart against any limitation of Imperial Preference but realized that it was no use arguing on these lines with an old Liberal like the Prime Minister. He therefore argued that the schemes involved a return to the old gold

[1] International Monetary Fund.

standard, remembering that he had been one of the few people to warn Churchill in 1925 against a return to gold at the 1914 parity — a matter about which Churchill was sensitive. Prof pointed out again and again that this was a travesty of the facts; for the proposed Monetary Fund would be far more flexible than the old gold standard.

On Imperial Preference, Prof argued that, under Article VII, we were obliged to reduce margins only in return for a substantial reduction in tariffs and other trade barriers by the United States and other countries; that the Dominions were not so wedded to Imperial Preference as we might wish and were already whittling it away; and that in any case we had committed ourselves on Imperial Preference by signing Article VII. He was also skeptical about our ability to build up an Empire, or a non-dollar, trading bloc, in opposition to the United States.

On agriculture, Prof argued that the proposed agreements left a good deal of scope for assisting British farmers, and that it would be foolish to throw away a number of other advantages simply to safeguard the power to protect a few growers of tomatoes and snowdrops.

The discussions between the British and Americans led to the adoption at Bretton Woods in July 1944 of the Articles of Agreement of the International Monetary Fund and the International Bank for Reconstruction and Development.

In general, Prof was always pointing out that one could not expect a world system in which we were free to do whatever we liked, while other countries were obliged to behave like good free-traders. If there were no international code of rules, there would be international anarchy; and this would be disastrous for a nation that depended as much as we did on foreign trade.

Prof held firm views on reparations. In 1944 he led the British mission to Quebec to discuss Stage II negotiations. Later

Keynes went out and took charge. It was at one of these meetings that Morgenthau produced his plan for the pastoralization of Germany. Lord Brand gained the impression that Prof was in favor of these impractical proposals,[1] but it must be pointed out that this was not so. Although he was in favor of depriving Germany of her capital industrial machinery so that she would not be in a position to start another war, he considered that the Morgenthau plan went much too far and could only result in our having to support Germany. But he did feel very strongly that after the war we should discourage the rebuilding of German industry, especially heavy industry, and should make an all-out effort to capture the German export market, which was far more important than seeking reparations from Germany in the form of manufactured goods.

[1] *The Observer,* January 8, 1961.

9

Out of Office: 1945–1951

AFTER THE CRUSHING Conservative defeat in 1945, the Prof returned with relief to Christ Church. In the following October there was a faintly comic exchange of letters about his demission of ministerial office. Like other Ministers he had been asked by Churchill, when the results of the election were known, to continue to discharge the duties of his office until they were taken over by his successor. But Attlee, when he formed his Government, did not fill the office of Paymaster General; and in October it occurred to the Prime Minister's private secretary that the Prof, not having been relieved, might consider that he was still under some obligation to fulfill the duties of his old post. He thus received a letter from 10 Downing Street stating that the Prime Minister wished it to be put formally on record that he had ceased to discharge the functions of his former office. To this curious message Prof replied in a note of happy flippancy:

> Your letter raises most important and difficult philosophical questions. If a man has no duties and does nothing, he is carrying out his duties to perfection. The Schoolmen, I agree, might argue the point, but I as a plain blunt physicist find it difficult to see how anyone can do less than nothing. I must, therefore, repel the suggestion, however formal, that I have failed in my duty to do nothing by doing nothing.

He became a member of Churchill's Shadow Cabinet, from which he offered to resign in the spring of 1950, on the grounds of its size, and that he was probably the oldest member, and almost certainly one who would not be able to take office in any Government which Churchill might form.

Churchill did not wish to release him and wrote briefly that he expected to see him in his place as usual. He was thus not allowed to abandon politics altogether, and remained a member of the Conservative Shadow Cabinet until the Party returned to office in the autumn of 1951.

He had been at the heart of policy for so long that it is unlikely that he was now willing to relinquish all contact with great affairs, and he made brilliant contributions to the House of Lords, mainly on economic and scientific matters when he acted as Opposition spokesman, and delivered an annual speech on the Economic White Paper.

Like his old Oxford lectures, these speeches were often inaudible, and it was necessary to consult Hansard to appreciate the quality of their arguments and their sardonic wit. On March 26, 1946, he became Consultant to the Ministry of Supply on atomic energy questions, and a member of Lord Portal's Technical Committee.

Complete worldly success and a placid consciousness that he was approaching the evening of life mellowed the harsh side of his character to a remarkable extent, and he became more willing to admit strangers to the anteroom of his mind. The expression of emotion was to him still so difficult as to be almost impossible. Sometimes, but very seldom, a shaft pierced his shyness with a visible effort, as when he came to the hospital where I lay sick, bringing a book by Dornford Yates as a timid offering, and, on departure, said in a strangely altered voice: "Goodbye, old chap," and this phrase, so alien to his ordinary speech, was a revelation of suppressed affection. There came, too, a gentle physical rallentando. When climbing to his first-floor rooms, he would pause for an appreciable time on the landing. His entertaining became less frequent, and although he liked to visit his friends in London as before, he spent more time at Christ Church, often strolling in the Meadow, one of the few peaceful open spaces left unpolluted in Oxford.

Sometimes he felt quivers of apprehension that the day might come when he would have to leave his rooms, where he had struck deep roots, and which were to him the loved home and sanctuary he had not known since boyhood. In spite of the gradual slowing-down of the tempo of life and the mellowing of disposition, the mind remained keen as a razor's edge, and, paradoxically, more provocative than ever in inducing controversy. Convinced as always that our main hope of survival lay in the deterrent of the atom bomb, he had protested strongly against the proposals to ban further trials. He wrote a series of letters, mainly to the *Times* and *Daily Telegraph*, as blistering as caustic soda, and his article later in the *News of the World* on the H-bomb fallout brought such a mass of venomous replies that Harvey was forced to open a new file. He read these outpourings with childish pleasure, often asking plaintively, "Aren't there any more, Harvey?" and particularly appreciating those expressing the hope that he would die of bone cancer or be sent to Christmas Island.

In the Clarendon Laboratory they were experimenting with radio techniques and his first love, low-temperature research. But he was now little more than the creator and titular head of the great new Clarendon, which had risen, phoenix-like, from the ashes of its dead self, and where the work was carried on by the men he had so wisely chosen.

He began to appreciate more and more those quiet evenings in his rooms looking at television. He had long delayed before buying his set, awaiting improvements in technique. He and Harvey enjoyed the same programs, and Prof often invited his servant to watch the screen with him. His favorite programs were as lowbrow as his taste in fiction — "Double Your

Money," "Burns and Allen," "I Married Joan" and the news.

Knowing Harvey's love of boxing, he would remind him days ahead of a fight in the program, and they would watch it together, with Harvey in high excitement trying to emulate Prof's detachment. Thoughtful as always for others, if the telephone rang he would answer it himself, telling Harvey not to miss any of the program. On such evenings he would go to bed earlier than had been his habit for a lifetime, and read himself to sleep with one of the Dornford Yates or Wodehouse novels that surrounded his bedhead.

There is something pure and moving about the life led by this great man in his last decade; something noble too in his unbreakable union with the loyal and chivalrous Harvey. Well might the servant exclaim from the heart:

> I lived so closely to the Professor for so long, whether we were abroad or in the privacy of his rooms, and all through these odd thirty years to the very end his behaviour and way of life were as exemplary in every possible manner in the privacy of his rooms as when he was in public.[1]

His love of animals and his gentleness to them also grew upon him in these last years, and he made little distinction between domestic animals and those commonly regarded as pests, finding a quiet pleasure in feeding the squirrels in the Meadow. Animals were an important element in his still unsatisfied yearning to bestow affection. He abominated any form of cruelty to the humblest creature, and, seeing a mouse in his rooms, told Harvey at once to get a repellent, saying that he would have no trap set, and forbidding him to switch off the light if the cat was in the room. His constant companion in his rooms and on his walks, until her death soon after the war, was the gray Cairn terrier bitch, Dinah, given to him by his friend Birkenhead.

[1] James Harvey to author.

This was also the period when he devoted most time to surreptitious kindness, and there are many examples in his papers of moments when he was touched by the misfortunes of others and gave all his patience and sympathy to their succor. Many of these beneficiaries were humble people who could have yielded no possible advantage to him. About all these transactions he kept the silence of the grave, and surrounded them with a pall of secrecy, as though committing some disgraceful action.

When he heard about his old nurse, Mrs. Beard, a pathetic figure, described by the Charity Organisation Society as "a frail old lady who fell upon evil days," the compassionate side of his nature was at once touched. He arranged to pay a pension to her for life to relieve her anxieties, bringing tranquillity into her last years.

The extraordinary persistence he gave to these hard cases is shown by his correspondence with the authorities about Siegfried von Ilsemann, a German boy whose father had been A.D.C. to the Kaiser, whom he followed into exile in Holland. When the Germans overran that country in the Second World War, Siegfried was taken to Germany and forced to join the German army. He was taken prisoner by the Canadians and interned in a P.O.W. camp in England where he acted as interpreter.

From there he made contact with Prof, who had not seen him since he was a boy. Ilsemann finally arrived at a Y.M.C.A. hostel at Hereford where he worked as a warden. He could not bear the thought, when the time came, of returning to Germany and longed to become a naturalized Englishman. In Holland he would be considered a German, and the last thing he wished was to live in Germany.

The Prof's papers tell the story of his battle to get extension of leave for the young man to stay in England, employment, and finally, naturalization. This was at last granted to him, after a long struggle, in April 1954. Reading these papers one is astonished at the way in which Prof exerted himself on behalf of this young man who could mean little or nothing to him.

Throughout these years he worked on Ilsemann's behalf as though he had been his own son, and befriended him in every possible way. He did not hesitate to write to Lord Pakenham and to Lord Henderson, then Ministers at the Foreign Office, and to interview both of them personally, as well as Sir Godfrey Ince at the Ministry of Labour, and it was entirely due to his efforts that Ilsemann was allowed to stay in England.

How typical of so many other cases of his unobtrusive, almost clandestine kindness is this letter from a worker in his laboratory:

> DEAR LORD CHERWELL,
> The almoner of the Radcliffe Infirmary has written to me, explaining that at your request my account for the period during which I was in the Infirmary was sent to you. I should like to thank you very much for this, and for all your help since my accident.

It is no exaggeration to say that in this secret enclave of his life he was filled with the milk of human kindness. To the children of his servants or his friends he sent gifts at Christmas and on their birthdays. By nature careful with money, he opened his purse again and again ungrudgingly to those in evil case, his only doubt being a perverse terror of this tenderness of heart being discovered.

In spite of his contempt for socialism, he was willing, when expedient, to work with Socialist Ministers in perfect harmony when he considered some measure necessary. He displayed this unexpected adaptability in 1948 during the passage of the Radio-active Substances Bill, which is of interest here in showing Prof co-operating, without political bias, with

Socialist Ministers in order to get through a bill in which he believed. He conducted himself in such a conciliatory manner that Aneurin Bevan thanked him for his co-operation, and later invited him to join the Advisory Committee under Sir Henry Dale, to advise Ministers on their functions under the Act, an offer he gladly accepted.

On October 16, 1945, Prof made an effective intervention in the debate raised by Lord Darnley on Co-operation for Peace. In his speech he sought to expose some of the loose thinking and catch phrases that so bedeviled calm discussion of the question of nuclear energy. He first argued that the larger claims made on behalf of its peaceful application were, in his opinion, grotesque, a view which he afterward abandoned; he then showed how unrealistic was the suggestion that nuclear power could be handed over to the United Nations like the plans of a fortress in a spy story.

The speech was certainly more critical than constructive, and it would not have been popular if he had expressed his real opinion that the bomb was the only true deterrent to the Russian conquest of Europe, and in the interests of the Western world should be concentrated for as long as possible in the hands of America. He was moved to unusual eloquence in his conclusion:

Man is indeed a strange mass of contradictions. Here we are, microscopic creatures scuttling about on the surface of a planet circling round a second-rate star in one of half a million galaxies. In some ways our minds are so capacious and penetrating. We can judge the weight and composition of the stars whose light started before man appeared on this earth. We can unveil the secrets of the nuclei which are so small that if we could put together as many of them as there are drops of water in the ocean they would together scarcely form a particle visible with a microscope. Yet we seem to be unable to order our own affairs so as to avoid exterminating one another. Perhaps the threat of this new weapon may in the end bring home to the various nations the overriding need of finding means, at no matter what cost and sacrifice, of reaching agreement without resort to force. We must pray that this will be achieved in time, for if it is not then the end of civilised life on this planet is at hand.

It was in his correspondence with his brother, with whom he was always so intimate, that Prof expressed himself about the contemporary scene and private matters with most freedom; discussing his will with Charles, to whom he then intended to leave everything, he described the dispiriting atmosphere of England in 1946, drawing a particularly freakish conclusion:

. . . People are so listless and depressed they will put up with anything. I attribute it largely to the bread which is bleached with NC13. It has been shown that dogs fed on it become slack and finally hysterical & I cannot help thinking that socialist victories in the by-elections show that people are affected in much the same way.

Another depressed letter reported a somber warning from his doctor, Frank, and described how things in Britain were "going from bad to worse. Naturally after twenty years of Socialist propaganda people think that they can slack off under a Labour Government. I shudder to think what will happen when the American Loan is exhausted."

Prof's foreboding under the Labour Government had become obsessive, and he discussed with Charles the possibility of finding some temperate refuge to which they could escape from the fogs and misery of winter England. It was also now necessary for him to watch his health more carefully as his doctor had found a tendency toward angina. Strong in these letters is the yearning for some tropical refuge in the sun, man's ally against cold and sterility and everything that made life repulsive to him, until the sap returned to trees and hedges — perhaps some island,

> Where the sea egg flames on the coral and the long-backed
> breakers croon
> Their endless ocean legends to the lazy locked lagoon.

The only serpents in such an earthly paradise were, to him, the Negroes who happened to live there in large numbers and who, he had heard, "were becoming a little cheeky, which would be a nuisance."

By November 1950 Prof's health was causing him intense gloom, and we find him writing to Charles that a new enemy was now shaking his distempered body:

> I have been suffering for six weeks from what is rudely called neurotic odoema (probably spelt wrong). If you saw me in the evening you would probably only give me six days to live. Nobody can suggest a cure so I suppose it is the beginning of the end.

10

In Office Again: 1951–1953

ON ONE MATTER he had made up his mind. If a Conservative
Government was again elected, he had no desire to return to
office. But such was his loyalty and subjection to his master's
wishes that he could always be overpersuaded while the
breath of life was in him, until the final prohibition of his doctor. When Churchill was forming the new Conservative Government in October 1951, Prof thus set out to him his reasons
for not wishing to join the Ministry:

I hope you will not take it amiss if I try to clarify my position
in the matter we discussed yesterday.

As you know, I intended to resign in 1945 had we won the
election. The arguments against switching now at the age of
sixty-five from the peace of Oxford to the hurly burly of political life are even stronger. I am sure I am quite unsuited to it;
not only should I never be much good at it, but I am not avid
for its prizes and I dislike publicity.

Here in Oxford I have a job which I understand and can do.
The Physics School which I have built up in the course of 30
years is now coming into its own and I may still be able to
produce work of permanent value. Furthermore my professorship is a life apointment and my rooms in Christ Church —
the only home I have had for thirty years — go with it. I hope
you will forgive me, therefore, if I decide not to sacrifice all
this.

In the circumstances I hope you will forgive me if I say

quite definitely that I must stick to my post in the University. As I have said, I believe I could be just as useful outside the Cabinet as in, and naturally I would be more than pleased to do all in my power to make myself useful in any way you wished. If you are convinced that I would be wanted full-time for six months or so, the University might possibly be prepared to give me leave of absence, though it is doubtful whether this would be granted in peacetime. But I hope you may agree that I could do just as much work part-time as your personal assistant as I did in the first half of the war.[1]

Churchill swept away Prof's reluctance and persuaded him to serve again. His hand was strengthened by the fact that one of the last ambitions of Prof's life remained unfulfilled — the establishment of an independent atomic energy authority safely removed from the control of the Civil Service.

The Prime Minister wrote to the Vice-Chancellor of Oxford University asking him to release Prof from Oxford for one year in order to help him deploy the country's scientific resources in the emergency period of rearmament, and to supervise the organization of atomic energy. The value Churchill placed upon the wartime Statistical Department as an adjunct to government is evident from the fact that he also explained to the Vice-Chancellor that part of Prof's duties would be to rebuild this Department on which the Prime Minister relied for his general outlook.

Thus a crack of the whip accompanied by an appeal *ad misericordiam* sufficed to bring the reluctant Prof to heel, and to shatter his dreams of cloistered peace. On October 29, 1951, he gave way:

Thank you for letting me have a copy of the letter which you sent to the Vice-Chancellor which was phrased in such very kind terms.

[1] Cherwell archives.

In the first place I should like to say how very grateful I am for this mark of confidence. It seems to me quite likely that the University will give me leave of absence for one year and I need hardly say that I shall enjoy very much working for you once more. As I told you, I believe that I could be just as useful as your personal assistant, but if you consider it better for me to be a member of the Cabinet I will of course defer to your judgment.

In whichever capacity I may act I would like to make it plain that I do not propose to accept any salary.

This supine attitude shows that it was almost *lèse-majesté* for Prof to disobey his master's orders, even when contrary to his own personal interests. He clearly felt that his behavior in this matter had been weak and he sought to explain his conduct to his brother in an unconvincing piece of special pleading:

My dear Charles,

Just a line to explain my apparent feebleness, of which you may have read. Great pressure was put upon me to join the Government, appeals to old friendship, to duty and so on which culminated in a letter from the P.M. to the University asking them to give me a year's leave of absence. As the Oxford people were also very keen on my going to London for a year I have had to accept on the clear understanding that I shall return here. I wish it had not happened but it was very difficult to refuse.

It is true that he made further attempts to escape, but they were not pressed with vigor and were easily overruled. On July 15, 1952, Prof wrote again to the Prime Minister saying that his doctor had definitely advised him to give up his ministerial appointment, and that in any case he did not think that the University would extend his leave of absence.

This letter was written at a moment of intense depression

when Prof believed that he had finally lost the battle for the independent soul of atomic energy. Churchill persuaded the University to extend his leave of absence for another year, and again he limply acquiesced. The incessant toil began to tell on him, and he confided to his brother in November 1952 that he was longing to escape. The work was overwhelming; the day before, lasting from before 10 A.M. to midnight, and a series of enervating squabbles on committees. He knew that this senseless grind was shortening his life, but he was too loyal or too weak to send Churchill a plain "Go to Hell." In fairness to him it should be insisted that loyalty and a sense of duty were uppermost in his mind, for in spite of his veneration he had never been afraid of Churchill.[1] It had long been his habit to argue with him forcefully on every point where he considered the Prime Minister to be wrong, but when a personal favor was asked of him with all the devastating artistry at Churchill's command he could not bring himself to refuse.

During this second administration Prof was the only member of the small group of intimate friends to maintain close contact with the Prime Minister. Bracken and Beaverbrook were no longer continually in his presence, but Prof was still a regular visitor at Chequers, spending almost every other week end there with his friend. During this administration he gave balanced and excellent advice to Churchill, particularly on economic questions. To the Prime Minister, never at ease in such matters, he lent his wonderful power to interpreting complicated fiscal problems, and translating the jargon in which they were wrapped. While Prof discoursed after dinner, sipping the thirty-two cubic centimeters of brandy which he allowed himself on Churchill's orders, the Prime Minister would often murmur with a happy smile, "Prof has a beautiful mind." When Churchill required elucidation of an economic issue he would mark the document "Prof," and Prof would produce a

[1] Lady Churchill to author.

compact précis making scrupulously clear which parts of the answer were his own comments.[1]

On returning to office in 1951 Prof went to live during the week on the top floors of No. 11 Downing Street, the official London home of the Chancellor of the Exchequer. R. A. Butler, who was Chancellor in the Conservative Government, from 1951 to 1955, continued to live in his own house in Westminster, and agreed that Prof should have the use of rooms for himself and Harvey at No. 11. This was a convenient arrangement, for when summoned in the small hours by the Prime Minister, he had merely to walk through one of the communicating doors into No. 10. The fatal drawback was that, as there was no lift in the house, he had to climb the long steep staircase several times a day. Nothing could have been worse for his heart, and it is probable that this exertion did much to shorten his life. After his retirement in 1953 he kept his rooms at No. 11 for use on his visits to London until December 1955, when Macmillan became Chancellor of the Exchequer and went himself to occupy them in the New Year.

Although Churchill was unwilling to do without him, and forced him to accept office against his will, there was in fact less scope in a peacetime Government for the kind of help and advice which the Prof had given to him during the war. First, there was little occasion for the kind of guidance which the Prof could give on scientific questions, and there were no opportunities to match his wartime work of weapons production. Apart from the great question of where the control of atomic energy should reside, in which we shall later see him playing a vital part, there was far less necessity for scientific advice in 1951–53 than there had been during the war.

Secondly, there was a smaller field for the application of his analytical and statistical methods in the realm of policy, mainly because the Government were no longer operating a

[1] John Colville to author.

controlled economy. Those methods which had matured from
tentative beginnings had been of particular relevance in the
wartime days when it was a primary object of the Government's
policy to mobilize the whole of the nation's resources for war.
When the Conservative Government was returned to office at
the end of 1951 it was more concerned to free the national
economy from the controls and planning in which it had been
blanketed by the Labour Government. It was a resolve fully
in tune with the Prof's political philosophy, but it was inevitable
that there were fewer opportunities for him to deploy that
special statistical technique which he had developed during the
war as an aid to the formulation of policy.

Thirdly, Churchill himself had become a less dominating
figure in the reaction that followed his prodigious efforts. Always more adept in the arts of war than in those of peace, he
sometimes found tedious and indeed baffling the process of
beating swords into plowshares. His methods of administration
became less highly personal. More responsibility was left to
departmental Ministers, more scope was given for the exercise
of collective responsibility by the Cabinet as a whole. Although the Prime Minister continued to dominate his colleagues by the force of his personality, he did less on his own
and through small groups of Ministers and intimate advisers,
and more through the medium of the full Cabinet itself. On
the complex problems of peace and reconstruction his personal
touch was less sure, and his interest far less deeply engaged
than it had been on the problems of war strategy which he
understood so well. Many of the new problems which now
clamored for solution were to him not only tedious, but difficult to follow, and he wandered uneasily in the jungle of economics.

The Prof was now a Minister from the outset, and to a far
greater extent than had ever been demanded during the war
was required to make his contribution *in propria persona* in

Cabinet discussions among ministerial equals. He had ceased to be a guarded flame. It was a disagreeable change to one reluctant to be serving at all, and he often sighed for the days of freedom when as an *éminence grise* he had exercised power without responsibility behind the scenes. As the range of his work was reduced there was less reason for him to create a special staff of assistants to help him. The loyal and indispensable MacDougall had indeed re-enlisted, but there were few others to help him.

His health was now giving ominous reminders of the toll which the war had levied upon it, and although his interest in every aspect of world affairs was unabated, he yearned for the sanctuary of Oxford. He had accepted his last appointment reluctantly and out of loyalty, but he was now living on his nerves and driving his jaded body into discharging its duties. He was growing old. Even so, he remained ever at hand, trusty counsellor and obedient friend, and Churchill continued to turn to him for advice. When necessary he could still muster great energy. In these last two years of office he concentrated most of his thought and effort on three questions: development of the atomic energy project, the expansion of technological education and the major aspects of economic policy. His mind was haunted by the fear that the atomic energy project would be allowed to become petrified in the hands of the Civil Service, and by the belief that if a considerable number of technological institutions were not soon put in hand England might decline into one of the submerged countries of history. His interest in economic policy culminated in the 1952 discussions about the convertibility of sterling.

When the Conservative Party returned to office in the autumn of 1951, the gold and dollar reserves were falling at an alarming rate and the outlook for the balance of payments was frightening. The reserves, at about $3000 million, were draining away at a rate of about $300 million per month, and seemed to be plunging rapidly toward the level of $1340 million, at which Cripps had devalued in 1949.

Both the United Kingdom and the rest of the sterling area were in heavy deficit in their international accounts. British exports of engineering products were held up by shortage of steel and by the diversion of capacity to the rapidly growing rearmament program, while textiles were suffering from a recession in world demand. Imports had risen greatly since 1950, both in price and in quantity, and the position was further aggravated by strategic stockpiling of certain imported commodities and by a loss of income from oil owing to the abandonment of Abadan. The other countries of the sterling area were suffering a sharp contraction of their export earnings following the bursting of the post-Korean boom, while they were still importing heavily out of the high incomes earned during that boom.

The new Government quickly took action to reduce the deficit. Imports were cut in November and again in February. Measures were taken to divert capacity and materials from armaments, investment and consumption to exports. When the Prime Minister visited Washington early in 1952, the Prof played an important part in obtaining from the Americans a million tons of steel, which was scarce throughout the world and a vital material for our exports; the Americans were also pressed to speed the financial assistance they had promised for our rearmament program. The Finance Ministers of the Commonwealth were invited to a meeting in London in January at which the other sterling area countries agreed to cut their imports and to pursue anti-inflationary policies so as to help reduce the sterling area's deficit. It was decided to have an early Budget on March 4th (later postponed to March 11th) and to make it a stern one; among other things, the food subsidies were to be greatly reduced.

As a result of all these precautions it was hoped that the

sterling area's accounts would be restored to balance in the second half of 1952. Since, however, the various measures would take time to produce results, the reserves were expected to continue falling until about the middle of the year, but they would then stabilize — admittedly at a low level, but not at a dangerously low one. This, at least, was the plan agreed at the Commonwealth Finance Ministers' Meeting.

Meanwhile, however, the view had been forming in some quarters, both in Whitehall and Threadneedle Street, that a more radical approach to the external financial situation was needed. A plan was devised to make sterling substantially convertible with a floating rate with the object of taking the strain off the reserves of gold and dollars and transferring it to the rate of exchange.

The scheme was known dramatically as Operation Robot, and this code name was shrouded in the deepest secrecy. It was early in 1952, soon after the Conservatives had taken office, that the startling solution to England's financial difficulties was suggested. The main features of the proposals were first a floating (fluctuating) rate of exchange for the pound, which had hitherto been fixed at £=$2.80 since September 1949. To support this rate, when the demand for dollars exceeded the supply, the Government had to supply dollars out of its reserves as it had been doing on a vast scale for a good many months. The simple idea now propounded was to husband the reserves, refuse to pay out, and allow the price of the pound in terms of dollars to drop, until the demand for pounds and the supply of them were brought into equality. The new policy, it was claimed, would thus "take the strain off the reserves and put it on to the rate of exchange," a phrase which Prof repeatedly castigated as a grossly misleading oversimplification.

Secondly, it was proposed that sterling held by all nonresidents of the sterling area was to be made convertible into dollars — which it had not been since wartime, apart from a brief period during the ill-fated experiment of 1947 — on the argument that convertibility was an inescapable concomitant of a floating rate, since it was held that no one would hold a currency that suffered from the two disadvantages of inconvertibility and a fluctuating dollar value.

However, 90 per cent of the existing sterling balances held by nonresidents of the sterling area other than the dollar countries were to be blocked and, despite the convertibility of the remainder, and of future earnings, granted to nonresidents, residents in the sterling area, including Britain, would be no freer to convert their money into foreign currency than before. Indeed, a large part of the sterling held by central banks in the rest of the sterling area was to be blocked. In Britain exchange control would be retained, as would quantitative restrictions on imports.

The advocates of this plan contemplated that it should be launched as an emergency operation, with the minimum period of warning to the United States, the members of the sterling area and other interested parties. It seems almost inconceivable that proposals raising such enormous problems should so nearly have slipped through, when they were mooted, with virtually no discussion. But it is almost certain that they would have done so but for Prof. Among expert advisers in Whitehall widely differing opinions came to be held about this plan. From the first Prof opposed it with all his strength, fearlessly challenging the views of great institutions, and in the end his opinions prevailed, but not before a mighty battle had been fought, the full details of which cannot, unfortunately, yet be told. Had he lost, he would almost certainly have resigned.

He felt that too gloomy a view of the prospects for the reserves had been taken by those who proposed this drastic remedy, and that most of the measures taken to improve the balance of payments had not yet had time to bear fruit. These included the November and February import cuts, the agreement by the Commonwealth Finance Ministers, some of whom had barely reached home, to cut imports, and the measures taken to switch production from defense, home investment and consumption to exports. Prof bore in mind the fact that the Commonwealth Finance Ministers had reached agreement on measures which it was hoped would balance the sterling area's trade with the non-sterling area in the second half of the year. Meanwhile, it was calculated that, though Britain's reserves would fall to about $1400 million by the middle of the year, they would remain constant thereafter. Presumably, at the time of the Finance Ministers' Conference this had been regarded as a reasonable plan. It therefore appeared unreasonable to adopt a completely different plan, with revolutionary aspects, when nothing much had happened to make the outlook worse, and when Commonwealth governments had not even had time to put their agreed measures into effect. In fact the reserves at the middle of the year were $1685 million, and at the end of the year $1846 million. In fact, too, the Australians and other Commonwealth countries shortly afterward took extremely drastic measures to curtail imports, although the advocates of Robot were arguing that they would do hardly anything.

It seemed to Prof that even if the official forecasts were right, this was no argument for Robot. He was certainly not against freeing the pound in any circumstances. He was as anxious as anyone to get rid of controls, and he would have been happy to see the pound free and made convertible from a position of strength, when reserves were large and the balance of payments favorable. But to do this from a position of weakness would, he believed, be reckless and dangerous to a degree. He was convinced that Robot, far from reducing our deficit, would increase it. The foreign-exchange earnings from our exports would fall as the rate fell, particularly as a large part of our exports was still limited by supply rather than by demand.

This loss of exports would, he believed, be intensified by convertibility which would throw our exports wide open to American competition and give countries an incentive to cut imports from Britain to earn dollars. It was most unlikely that the import bill would be significantly reduced by a fall in the pound, at least in the short run.

All these considerations led him to conclude that either the rate for the pound would fall disastrously low or, if it were supported, the reserves would go down more than they otherwise would, and not less, and that there would be serious repercussions at home and abroad. At home it would mean a rise in the cost of living, the danger of a wage-price spiral, and growing unemployment. This was the way it was proposed to correct the trade deficit. This to Prof was the plain English for the grandiose talk of "taking the strain off the reserves and putting it on the rate of exchange."

Abroad, the repercussions would be equally serious. It was admitted that the plan would mean the end of the European Payments Union, from which we had just borrowed large amounts of money, and a serious setback to O.E.E.C.[1] trade liberalization. This, apart from the obvious effects on our relations with Europe, would antagonize the United States, the originators of the Marshall Plan. America would also regard the gold market and floating rate with extreme dislike. As regards the Commonwealth, it was admitted that many countries might leave the sterling area. They would also resent strongly the receipt of an ultimatum demanding acceptance of a plan about which they had been told nothing at the Finance Ministers' Conference only a month before, almost as soon as the Ministers reached home.

Nor was Prof's opposition to Robot a purely destructive one. He believed that, if the outlook was as serious as the advocates of Robot claimed, which he doubted, an entirely dif-

[1] Organisation for European Economic Co-operation.

ferent policy should be adopted. We should impose more severe import cuts, and we should borrow from the International Monetary Fund where the sterling area quotas of some $2 billion entitled the area to draw $500 million in any one year, and on the strength of the $500 million of American securities held by the Treasury; and possibly of the aid we had been promised by the United States Government. We should raise Bank Rate and take such budgetary action as we could to prevent a fall in confidence abroad, and press for the rest of the sterling area to cut their imports quickly and even more severely than they had agreed.

From these considerations Prof inferred that there was no need for panic, but that if the situation was as serious as had been claimed, Robot was a bad plan, and not the one with which to meet it. His logical mind recoiled from what he thought to be a piece of financial legerdemain, and saw the only solution in a return to fundamentals. The plan, he thought, was based on the hope that some financial jugglery, some economic magic would enable Britain to escape from her predicament without toil or sweat. The proposals would mean the complete reversal of the policies of the last twelve years. Moreover, it was impossible to predict what the consequences would be beyond the certainty that the attempt to maintain full employment and price stability would have to be abandoned, and that the pressure would fall particularly on the cost of living. "Let us," he argued, "return to the fundamental verities. Unless we can export more by volume or at higher prices, or in the form of invisibles, we shall have to reduce our imports and therewith our standards of life. Nothing in the world can alter this, and it is to this end that we should bend our efforts."[1]

The Prof used all his dogged persistence, sustained by a conviction of rectitude, in pressing his views on the Prime Minister

[1] Cherwell archives.

and on his ministerial colleagues, and the plan was rejected. This was at the end of February. Churchill, however, appeared still to be hankering after Robot. Thus a minute sent by Prof to the Prime Minister on March 18, 1952, begins:

> I have been rather anxious about your remarks last week that you looked forward to the day when we could "free the pound" which the Cabinet decided against a fortnight ago.

The minute continued to explain in simple language the essence of the problem, emphasizing particularly the internal political implications. It appeared from later remarks of the Prime Minister that this minute bore fruit — that Churchill gradually got its arguments into his mind and began to use them in conversation and discussion. After the Budget, which, with a simultaneous increase in Bank Rate from 2½ per cent to 4 per cent, did much to restore confidence in the pound, the reserves pulled out of their alarming dive and leveled off, remaining roughly constant for about six months and beginning to rise markedly in the autumn. Thus were the gloomy forecasts proved wrong and the Prof right. Although it had been agreed to reconsider Robot in April, the Chancellor did not raise the matter, and the plan was, at least temporarily, shelved.

But Prof felt in his bones that the Treasury and the Bank had not yet shot their bolt, and in June 1952 the project was indeed revived in a somewhat different form, but again rejected. By then arrangements had already been made for a special meeting of Commonwealth Prime Ministers on economic affairs to be held in November. This was a blow to the advocates of Robot, which was essentially a financial *coup d'état* which could only be achieved in an atmosphere of panic, crisis and extreme secrecy. It could not be put forward in cold blood to the Commonwealth — they would never accept anything so drastic — and it could not be made the subject of discussion in Whitehall and the Commonwealth treasuries for months in advance.

Early in these proceedings Ministers agreed that the ultimate objective of our foreign economic policy must be "one world" — a multilateral trading system with convertibility and a minimum of discrimination, embracing the sterling area, Europe, Canada, the United States and the rest of the world. They ruled out as politically and economically impracticable Amery's suggestion for a major intensification of Imperial Preference with a view to making the Commonwealth more self-sufficient, and Robert Boothby's proposal to build up a non-dollar bloc consisting of the sterling area, which excluded Canada, and Western Europe. "This decision," Prof told the Prime Minister, "will, I fear, be unpopular with many Conservatives, but I am sure it is right."[1]

His real position in this matter was that, although he was strongly against convertibility, nondiscrimination and "one world" in 1952, he believed it to be the true ultimate objective, and his views were thus consistent with those he held during the war. He felt strongly that the country should not be rushed prematurely into the Robot solution, and that the pound should become convertible only when the balance of payments and reserves were strong enough and when the dollar shortage had been sufficiently alleviated.

It was, however, necessary, while avoiding premature convertibility, to show the Americans in particular that we were in earnest about our pledge, given in the Loan Agreement, to achieve convertibility and nondiscrimination. Moreover, the prevailing mood was such that a policy of simply carrying on and doing the best one could was dismissed with scorn as "the mixture as before." Clearly the time had come for bold and imaginative changes. The Treasury had theirs in the shape of

[1] Cherwell archives.

Robot. It was necessary to find an equally appealing counter-plan for the gradual approach.

By the beginning of August Prof had come to believe that an "Atlantic Payments Union" would serve this purpose. Essentially the suggestion was to bring the United States and Canada into the European Payments Union — which covered the continental countries, Britain, and, through sterling, the rest of the sterling area — in such a way that European currencies, including sterling, would in effect become gradually more and more convertible into dollars, and discrimination against the United States would be gradually relaxed, the speed depending on the pace at which the dollar shortage of Europe and the sterling area was relieved. There would also be a forum for the continuous discussion of all the economic problems facing Britain, the Commonwealth, Europe and the United States.

The favorable reception which this proposal at first encountered seemed to show the desire for some presentable scheme which was "one world" in character without being extremist or unilateral, but it eventually fell by the wayside. It was sufficiently persuasive, however, to force the Treasury off its Robot horse onto the far less dangerous steed of the "Collective Approach" to convertibility.

The Collective Approach was a proposal that emerged during August after much hard and bitter argument and maneuvering between officials of various Departments, the meetings often lasting until 3 A.M.; it was not accepted by Prof's officials. It was subsequently modified as a result of discussion by Ministers in early September.

The Approach was "Collective" in the sense that it was not unilateral. Unlike Robot, it was to be undertaken in agreement and conjunction with the United States and Canada and the principal European countries, instead of merely placing before them a painful *fait accompli*. It was a form of compromise between the views of the Robot "plungers" and of those who, like Prof, wished to wait until we were really strong enough before making sterling convertible. Under the proposal we should go convertible and let the pound float as soon as possible, but subject to certain safeguards, or preconditions. The main shields were that France, Belgium and Holland would go convertible at the same time, thus reducing to some extent the danger to Britain's reserves and trade of her having the only European currency convertible into dollars; that there should be trade rules to prevent other countries cutting imports from us in order to earn sterling which they could then convert into dollars; that the United States should provide a large loan, in some form, for the support of the operation and that she should pursue "good creditor" policies by cutting tariffs.

Prof was not satisfied with this proposal. He feared that the safeguards proposed would prove to be illusory, and continued to repeat his usual arguments against early convertibility and a floating rate. He was convinced that exchange restrictions and the inconvertibility of the pound for foreigners were symptoms of a disease. The disease was world dollar shortage and the failure to balance our trade. The disease could not be cured by repudiating the symptoms, and the first objective must be to solve the dollar problem, to achieve a good surplus in the balance of payments, and to build up the reserves to a much higher level. When that had been done he believed that all the rest would follow. It was fundamental to his argument that convertibility was a far less important objective than the expansion of production, the maintenance of employment, and the winning of the cold war, and, moreover, inconsistent with these objectives.

In spite of Prof's earnest appeal, it was decided to submit the Collective Approach as one possible policy to the preparatory meeting of Commonwealth officials on September 22nd. The Collective Approach received a rough handling, while Prof's suggestion of an Atlantic Payments Union was brought up only late in the day in a manner he regarded as unfair.

When considering afterward the objections of the Commonwealth officials to the Collective Approach he found evidence to show that most European countries, too, were alarmed at the prospect of convertibility and floating rates. This was based on reports of Governments to O.E.E.C., and strong criticism was also heard of the plan from United Kingdom officials abroad who were in touch with European opinion. He also believed that the United States would be most unlikely to support the scheme, and he concluded that we should scrap the Collective Approach, abandon, for the time being, all thought of early convertibility and a floating rate, and work out a new "gradual approach" to put before the Commonwealth Prime Ministers in November.

In spite of this spirited opposition, it was decided to follow the Collective Approach. Prof was naturally extremely disappointed but not unduly depressed. He wrote to the Prime Minister on October 31, 1952:

> I do not think the plan as disastrous as the so-called Robot plan which we rejected last February and again in June. For one thing it cannot be sprung on the world unannounced; for another I do not believe it will come to anything.[1]

In this he was proved right. But, as he said in that minute, he expected the Government to accept this new plan; and it was in fact adopted, some lingering apprehensions being allayed by the assurance that Britain would never be finally committed to it until the moment came for the pound to be made convertible. The other Commonwealth Governments were informed of the modifications to the original plan. They were told that the new proposals were put forward as a basis for discussion and that they implied no commitment on the timing of the convertibility operation itself.

It may seem that, at this stage, the Prof had lost. But in fact he had won, first by stopping a unilateral Robot operation in

[1] Cherwell archives.

February, and again in June; secondly by helping to ensure that, despite a good deal of backsliding, many hard conditions had to be fulfilled before sterling could be made convertible. These were confirmed by the Commonwealth Prime Ministers, and at the first hurdle — the negotiations with the United States — the plan came to a dead stop, exactly as the Prof had predicted.

When Butler and Eden went to Washington in early March 1953, the new Eisenhower Administration told them that they could not ask Congress for any large financial support for the good creditor policies. They also doubted whether our economy was yet strong or flexible enough to sustain the risks of a convertibility operation, and indicated that in their view the time was not yet opportune for putting the Collective Approach into effect, an attitude that retarded the plan for a long time.

We may sum up by saying that Prof regarded the preoccupation with convertibility that was forced upon Whitehall by the advocates of this plan as a deplorable waste of time and effort which could have been devoted far more profitably to other things. It was fundamental to his argument that measures should be taken to increase output, and the right kind of output, and that such exertions were infinitely more important than "financial jugglery." If we could achieve such production, convertibility and freedom from controls could safely follow.

He believed it essential to forget convertibility and floating rates until this country and the rest of the non-dollar world was stronger, and to concentrate on such basic matters as economic development of the Commonwealth, and increased production in Britain and the rest of Western Europe. He believed in financial incentive to enterprise and expansion, and disapproved of the special tax on profits that had to be imposed in the Budget of March 1952 to redeem a pledge made by Churchill before the election. He also felt that the time and trouble devoted to Robot during the February crisis might have been much more usefully spent devising a better excess-profits levy; this was to be found full of snags and difficulties which caused much trouble in the House of Commons.

He disliked controls but recognized that in certain circumstances they might be essential. In general he was not doctrinaire on economic policy. He liked to examine each problem on its merits, in a scientific and, if possible, quantitative manner. He quickly saw through shibboleths, and detested nostrums used as a substitute for clear thought or honest exposition.

By a curious irony Mr. Hugh Gaitskell, who had in the past made bitter attacks on Prof in the House of Commons, and was certainly no friend, felt bound to say in the debate on the economic situation on November 11, 1952:

I have just heard an interesting rumour on this subject — let me say at once that it did not reach me through the Civil Service or any Government supporter, but from another outside source — that the Cabinet very nearly reached a decision that there should be a return to convertibility, but that — and I must confess that I was surprised at this part of it — the noble Lord, Lord Cherwell, intervened very effectively, having, as we all know, the ear of the Prime Minister, and managed to get this policy stopped. In the light of things I have said in the past about the noble Lord, I feel now like withdrawing all of them. He has really done us a very good service if his relationship to the Prime Minister has enabled him to stop such a disastrous turn in our policy.

11

A Personal Triumph: The Birth
of the Atomic Energy Authority

WE HAVE IT on Sir John Cockcroft's authority[1] that Prof was skeptical about the feasibility of the atomic bomb and remained so for some time. Professor R. V. Jones was also convinced that neither Prof nor Tizard believed the atomic bomb to be possible. In March 1945, at Great George Street, Prof remarked to Jones: "There's many a slip 'twixt cup and lip, and what fools the Americans will look after spending so much money." Both these scientists inwardly shrank from the implications of the release of atomic energy, the most momentous event since primitive man discovered fire, and believed that only evil could come from this monstrous intrusion upon the strict reserves of nature. "Do you really think," Tizard asked Jones, "that the Universe was made for this?"

This chapter will describe the solitary struggle of one man to wrest the control of atomic energy from the hands of the Civil Service. During the course of this battle, he performed the greatest act of moral courage of his life, and in the end he triumphed.

"Lord Cherwell," said Sir John Cockcroft, "was also interested in the Atomic Energy Project which was directed by the MAUD Committee in 1940–41." This original British Atomic Energy Committee under Sir George Thomson derived its name from the fact that about the time it was holding its first meeting during the German invasion of Denmark a phys-

[1] Sir John Cockcroft to author.

icist in Britain received a cryptic telegram from the Danish physicist, Niels Bohr, who had been working on uranium fission. This referred to a certain Maud Ray Kent, and some quick mind deduced that the name formed an anagram for "radium taken," from which it was thought that the Germans had seized Bohr's radium and were working on the atomic bomb themselves. It was in gratitude for this secret message that the Committee was christened MAUD. When Bohr later reached England he explained that his brilliant anagram was not an anagram at all, but referred to his former governess, Maud Ray, who lived in Kent.

In July 1941 this Committee stated definitely that it would be possible to make an effective uranium bomb which would be equivalent in destruction to 1800 tons of TNT. The report was sent to a Special Defence panel of the Scientific Advisory Committee, which included Prof, who, immediately after the first meeting and before the panel's report, submitted a minute to the Prime Minister on August 28th, in which he described the possibilities, and recommended that a Minister of the War Cabinet should assume direct responsibility for the project. This led to Churchill's memorable minute that "Although personally I am quite content with existing explosives, I feel we must not stand in the path of improvement. . . ."

It was a crucial decision and it is impossible to tell what action might have been taken or how long it might have been delayed if the Committee's report had been left to take its normal course. The Prof saw that this might make the whole difference between winning or losing the war and that no time should be lost. His realization of this and his promptness in persuading the Prime Minister to take urgent action on it may well have had the result that the project got under way months before it would otherwise have done. It was Prof, too, who suggested to the Prime Minister that he should nominate Lord Waverley to take ministerial charge of it. Waverley, as a scientist by training, was particularly well qualified to undertake this duty, and he made it his business to see that the project received the priority which it deserved.

During the war Prof was impatient with the details of administration of the atomic energy project; his interest was devoted entirely to the scientific problems and to the broad question of what proportion of the effort in this development should be provided in wartime in and from the United Kingdom. The project was organized in a secret office known as the Directorate of Tube Alloys, a cover name suggested by Lord Waverley, within the framework of the Department of Scientific and Industrial Research. The Directorate was controlled by Sir Wallace Akers and Mr. Michael Perrin.

The Clarendon Laboratory team under Simon carried out important work in developing the gaseous diffusion method of separating U-235, and although this was not used in the war it provided the basis for the postwar Capenhurst diffusion plant.

When the explosion at Hiroshima opened a new era, the Conservatives were already out of office. There was, therefore, no occasion for Prof to consider how the project should be run once its first objective had been secured. Although Lord Waverley, who during the war had directed the administrative arrangements for the development of atomic energy, was retained by the Labour Government in a consultative capacity, he was given no opportunity to advise on its administrative control. It was, however, within the recollection of each of them that they discussed the future on one occasion, and in general agreed that it would be appropriate to set up some form of government undertaking outside the Civil Service.

At the end of the war the United States authorities soon made it brutally clear that the restricted co-operation that had existed between the United States and the United Kingdom in the atomic energy field was to come to an end, although it was not until 1946 that the MacMahon Act stopped co-operation entirely, except in the field of uranium procurement. It was Prof's close friendship with Admiral Strauss, Chairman of the United States Atomic Energy Commission, which enabled him to persuade the Americans to be less reticent about nuclear secrets in spite of the MacMahon Act, and the relaxations of that act were largely due to the same cause.

The Labour Government, in its first few months of office, decided that the United Kingdom should make its own atomic bomb. For this purpose great industrial undertakings were needed, and the Government decided to place the responsibility for atomic energy development in the hands of the Ministry of Supply from November 1, 1945. The Ministry of Supply was the natural department to be entrusted with all weapon manufacture. It had at that time spare resources of land, factories and skilled manpower, and few questioned the Government's decision. Certainly Prof did not.

Dissatisfaction with the administration of the Ministry of Supply did not begin until the autumn of 1949, when the first Russian atomic bomb was exploded. The capacity of the Soviet system to concentrate enormous technical resources upon a particular objective has since then been amply demonstrated. At that time, however, it was a great shock to all concerned: "During the war we worked hand in hand with the United States on atomic weapons," said Prof in 1951. "Despite their elaborate spying system, it is incredible that in 1945 the Russians should have known more about the production of atom bombs than we did. Could anything be more unsatisfactory?"

The many scientists employed in the project, and some outside, came to believe that the slow progress was entirely due to the attempt to treat the project as a normal departmental activity under the Ministry of Supply, and serious complaints began to be uttered about the lack of elasticity in the Civil Service procedure and salary scales. These complaints now led to two new but different proposals.

First, Prof saw Lord Addison, and afterward Attlee, and put forward proposals for a nationalized corporation, which were at first given a not unfavorable hearing. Addison was sufficiently impressed by the Prof's arguments to say that it seemed to him unthinkable that the Government would give anything but the highest priority to atomic development, and that he felt sure they would realize it was a matter of high policy and not one to be decided on technical service arguments even if these were sound.[1] Within the Ministry of Supply, Lord Portal, who had been Controller of Atomic Energy since early in 1946, was anxious for a change in the organization.

Treasury officials, unwilling to disturb the status quo, warned the Chancellor of the danger of entrusting the annual expenditure of many millions of pounds of public money to a body which would not be subject to day-to-day ministerial control, and the Minister of Supply and his senior officers naturally regarded the proposal to remove the project from their control as a reflection on their stewardship.

Various palliatives, falling short of transfer to a new corporation, were suggested; among them the so-called "ring-fence," under which it would have been recognized that persons employed in the project might be treated differently from the rest of the scientific and technical Civil Service where such differentiation was necessary in order to recruit or retain staff.

In April 1950, the Under-Secretary in charge of atomic energy administration in the Ministry of Supply, Mr. Friston How, wrote a memorandum in which he examined the "ring-fence" and "corporation" solutions. This document is of some permanent interest because the Waverley Committee, three years later, took as their starting point the outline of the organization of a possible corporation which it contained, and because the Atomic Energy Authority which emerged in 1954 differed little from that first sketch.

[1] Cherwell archives.

In 1950, however, the idea of a corporation could make no headway against the opposition of the Treasury and the Ministry of Supply, and all that was done was to set up a joint Treasury-Ministry of Supply Committee (on the lines of the wartime Treasury Inter-Service Committee) which was empowered to give quick decisions on cases where the application of Civil Service salary scales and other conditions of service were impeding the recruitment or retention of essential staff.

In February 1951 the Technical Committee, largely at the Prof's instigation, moved a resolution on the future of atomic energy. After the assurances of Addison, Attlee's attitude to this resolution came as a whiplash across the face of the advocates of change:

> The Prime Minister has decided that there is no case for reviewing the present organisation under which the Ministry of Supply is responsible for the atomic energy project unless and until —
>
> (*a*) concrete evidence is produced that the present arrangement is causing delay and inefficiency in developing and producing atomic weapons and in the application of atomic energy for peaceful purposes;
>
> or
> (*b*) conclusive evidence is given that an independent body under broad government control would be more efficient.

Prof replied to this bleak communication in a letter to Attlee on March 6, 1951:

> Lord Portal communicated to me the relevant paragraphs of your letter concerning the resolution which I moved at the Technical Committee and which we asked him to forward to you. I am afraid it does not carry us very much further since it would be impossible to provide "conclusive evidence" that another organisation would be better than the present one

without making the experiment. But the fact that the overwhelming majority of people who have really been concerned with the project, most of whom have considerable experience, take the view that such a change would reduce delays and improve efficiency would seem to create a very strong presumption that it would actually do so. Further than this it does not seem possible to go, any more than it is on any other occasion when a decision has to be made in advance — at least that is what my philosophical friends tell me.[1]

Prof then brought the matter before the Shadow Cabinet at a meeting at Chartwell in the spring of 1951. No record of the discussion appears to exist, but he understood that it was agreed to be Conservative policy to set up a nationalized corporation for atomic energy.

In this belief he introduced a motion in the House of Lords on July 5, 1951:

That this House regrets the slow progress made in this country in developing atomic energy for peaceful and for warlike purposes, and calls upon H.M.G., whilst retaining broad general control, to transfer work on this project from the Ministry of Supply to a separate organisation more flexible than the normal Civil Service system under the direct control of the head of the Government.

The draft of this motion was strengthened by Churchill himself. Prof moved it on the familiar lines of comparing our rate of progress with that of the Russians. He deduced that the fault lay in the Civil Service:

Only men used to tackling large industrial developments can successfully handle operations of this nature. . . . You cannot expect to win a tennis championship if you insist on using a niblick instead of a tennis racket.

[1] Cherwell archives.

He pointed to the need for urgent action now that the Controller, Portal, and the Scientific Adviser, Perrin, who had provided the whole central scientific focus for eight years, were both leaving convinced that no adequate progress could be made under the system of the Ministry of Supply. Prof was supported in this debate by Lords Halifax and Swinton, but Lord Alexander of Hillsborough took up the now entrenched Labour Government position that the Civil Service was as well adapted to this work as would be any other organization, and that so long as funds had to be provided by Parliament, this was the correct way to handle the project.

Prof accepted office in the Conservative Government that was returned in October 1951. This time he came back not only to be private adviser to Churchill on matters economic and scientific, but with the specific major objective of getting a bill through Parliament in the 1951–52 session, which would fulfill the House of Lords July resolution. Remote as always from the feelings of others, Prof imagined that this would be a short task and that he had the support of a united Cabinet and of all the technical leaders of the atomic energy project. It was a cruel shock to find that almost every hand was against him.

First, it would seem that Churchill had never realized until now that the production of the bomb was not something which went on in a few laboratories and which might thus be properly entrusted to an Oxford professor; but now involved a great industrial complex which was at last within sight of being able to produce fissile material for the explosion of the first United Kingdom bomb.

No doubt the fact that he appointed Prof's old antagonist Mr. Duncan Sandys as Minister of Supply led to these matters being impressed upon him more sharply than they might otherwise have been. It was inevitable that this ambitious man would quickly decide that the atomic energy project was one of the most important responsibilities of the Ministry of Supply, and adopt, without hesitation, the view of his Labour predecessor that there was no reason why that Ministry should be called upon to hand over control to some other body.

Secondly, the rest of the Cabinet, faced with the task of governing with a small parliamentary majority, had no desire whatever to add to their program an unnecessary and contentious bill. Thirdly, opposition in the Treasury was now solidly organized against a change which might prove extremely costly at a time of crisis in the national finances. Fourthly — and this was the unkindest cut of all to Prof — the technical heads of the project seemed now to have come to the conclusion that they did not really want a change.

It was one thing to carp interminably against the administrators of the Ministry of Supply; it was another thing to have it publicly alleged, as it had been in the House of Lords debate, that the whole project was proceeding at the tempo of a funeral march. It was one thing to suffer the frustrations of not being able to recruit a handful of men who would have been invaluable; it was another to have it seriously proposed that all the thousands of scientists and other workers would have to leave the Civil Service and face new and unknown conditions of employment under which, as they understood, security, which was the restriction they most disliked, was to be far tighter than before, and where safe tenure of employment, which was what they most valued, might be in jeopardy.

In his first month of office Prof discovered this disagreeable state of opinion in his tour of the northern atomic factories, and was much depressed by the defection of his fellow scientists. Only one of the half dozen men in technical charge spoke out in favor of a nationalized corporation. The remainder assured him that the change would be disastrous and would postpone the planned date for the bomb explosion in the autumn of 1952. At this time, indeed, only Perrin and Professor Skinner, both of whom had now left the project, continued to urge him on to proceed with his plans independently.

In these perplexing circumstances Prof was persuaded to accept the hostility of the majority of the civil servants in the project to a transfer and to put forward a hybrid scheme for the setting up of a body on the lines of the Medical Research Council, working on a grant-in-aid and composed of civil servants and others. The proposal was stillborn; it again encountered the unbending opposition of the Treasury, ostensibly on the ground that it would be difficult to have a staff of "sheep and goats" with different conditions of service. They suggested that if a change were required at all, transfer for responsibility for the project to another Minister — perhaps the Minister of Defence — might be considered.

While all this jockeying for position was taking place, Parliamentary Questions forced the Government to state who was responsible for atomic energy. Originally Prof had had no thought of assuming control of the project. His intentions were limited to the creation of the corporation; as soon as this was done an industrial-type board would take over the direction. The doubt and delay in setting up the corporation now raised the issue as to who was going to be in control of the project in the interim. Prof wanted this actual responsibility, and at first it seemed as though Churchill was prepared to concede it to him. This was naturally not a situation which the Minister, who had statutory responsibility for the project, or his Permanent Secretary, who was Accounting Officer, could accept. After a great deal of discussion, Churchill said on November 14th in the House of Commons:

> My noble friend, the Paymaster General, will be responsible for advising me on atomic energy questions. I am now considering what adjustments should be made to existing statutory responsibilities of the Ministry of Supply for these subjects.

The first month, therefore, ended with nothing more than an indication that legislation was being considered and a place booked in the legislative program, with no agreement at all as to what the bill should contain. The Treasury still argued, as they had been doing for the last two years, that a few changes in the Ministry of Supply could set everything to rights, and they offered to consider transfer of responsibility to the Ministry of Defence if it was unacceptable that the project should remain within the Ministry of Supply.

Thus the next stage of the campaign came to be a proposal to transfer responsibility to the Ministry of Defence by Order in Council, avoiding the need of a bill. Prof, in his hour of need, was unable to put the matter to Churchill until February, owing to the Washington Conference. He supposed that he could at least raise it during the voyage in the *Queen Mary*, but did not find the Prime Minister accessible.

Then, as throughout, he still regarded himself as only a private adviser to Churchill. He was urged at this stage to consider himself, as he was, a member of the Government, and to bring the matter, as a vital issue of policy, before the Cabinet. From this he recoiled on the ground that it would antagonize Churchill. Meanwhile, during Prof's absence at the Washington Conference, he was further embarrassed by discussion of the organizational dispute in the newspapers. An article by Professor Pryce in January, which was widely read, argued that opinion among scientists in the project was wholly against transfer. The difficulties of the civil servants concerned were at this period exacerbated by uncertainty as to where control of the project really rested.

On February 13, 1952, Churchill sent to the Treasury a directive drafted by Prof asking for the possibility of a transfer of responsibility to the Ministry of Defence to be examined. Churchill's marginal notes on Prof's draft showed that his sympathies were becoming alienated, and the Treasury's reply made clear that, having killed the corporation idea by suggesting a transfer to the Ministry of Defence, they now thought it safe to kill the Ministry of Defence proposal in turn.

Criticism was concentrated on the obvious weak point in the proposal: was the Minister of Defence to have actual or formal responsibility? If he had actual responsibility, there would be no room for Prof, and indeed the Ministry of Defence as a small co-ordinating body was wholly unsuited to handle the large industrial problems involved in running the project.

On March 9th, at Chequers, Churchill dictated, in Prof's presence, a minute approving transfer to the Ministry of Defence. Later in the day, however, he changed his mind and decided to leave the administration within the Ministry of Supply, although "Lord Cherwell is to be responsible directly under me." Prof was deeply disappointed, but in spite of another meeting at No. 10 on March 14th, Churchill refused to approve the idea of a transfer, and he finally declared at a meeting on March 20th his decision not to transfer the administration of the project.

At this meeting Prof was not able to direct the conversation to questions of organization. The talk turned mainly on whether he had been obstructed and what measures were necessary to give him effective power. At the end Churchill produced a document which left the administration exactly where it was but which contained a division of responsibility between Cherwell and Sandys, a sure bone of contention.

Prof now felt that he had either to accept the Prime Minister's document, with certain minor alterations, or to resign, but he soon realized that resignation was difficult. He was enmeshed in various Cabinet discussions and was deeply involved in preparations for the bomb test. He knew that in any case he had now made so many concessions on the organizational question that he had been maneuvered into a corner, and that he could give no good reason for resignation. Such a stand would now appear not as a result of the organization question but as a personal squabble about division of responsibility, which might harm Churchill.

The paper setting out the division of responsibilities between Prof and Sandys was circulated on April 10th. Prof was to preside over an Atomic Energy Board, comprising senior officers of the project, and was to take ministerial action on policy questions, and the Minister of Supply was to answer Parliamentary Questions in the House of Commons "other than those that the Prime Minister may decide to answer himself."

It was a strange method of depriving a Minister of powers conferred upon him by Act of Parliament, and the arrangement was to plague all the officials concerned for the next eighteen months. The decision to make no legislative changes "for the present" had been indicated by the Prime Minister in the House of Commons on March 24th, but it had added that Cherwell was "to exercise general supervision over work in this field." The decision to make no change was applauded by Mr. Strauss from the Opposition benches.

Prof had now achieved what he had originally not wanted: personal control of the project except for security and publicity. His control was exercised mainly through the Atomic Energy Board. This was not the first committee of the Ministry of Supply in which the heads of the various establishments concerned with the research and production of weapons had sat, but it was the first time that some uniform technical control was exercised.

The Board was thus the direct forerunner of the later Atomic Energy Executive and the Board of the Atomic Energy Authority. No one could claim that Prof used the Board in order to impose any scientific or technical direction of his own. He treated his chairmanship rather as a Minister than as a scientist, taking no particular side in the various scientific issues that presented themselves, but only concerned that the project should run harmoniously and at full speed.

The only issue on which he felt strongly was that of publicity, and the deep reticence of his character made him reluctant to publish anything, however desirable. This question alone caused disagreement, particularly with regard to the bomb test preparations, but in all other respects there was now a lull. All eyes were on Montebello. During this respite, the *Daily Express* published, on July 21st, an obituary on Prof's proposals: "The behind-the-scenes showdown between Mr. Duncan Sandys, Minister of Supply, and Lord Cherwell, the Prime Minister's Scientific Adviser, has ended in victory for Mr. Sandys."

Prof was convinced that he had been defeated. For a time he became disillusioned with the whole matter, and if, as he wished, he had gone back to Oxford that autumn, his proposal for an administrative change would have died. Even when Churchill had persuaded both Prof and the University of Oxford that he should stay on in Whitehall for a second year, he was reluctant to take up the cudgels again. His classical method of persuading Churchill to his way of thinking — the minute and the argument — no longer offered any hope of success. He had used it vainly in August, and again at Chequers, when he was brushed aside in a few moments.

Gradually his advisers won him round to the view that he must make a last effort to carry out his proposal; and that he must make this effort as a Minister, putting his case to the Cabinet. For a year the struggle had gone on by minute and counterminute, conclave after conclave, while Ministers had never once taken a collective view of the issue. With deep reluctance, and a strong sense of guilt, Prof began to work on a Cabinet paper.

In a vicious circle, he was torn cruelly between his loyalty and his beliefs. He convinced himself that this was almost an act of treachery to Churchill. To argue vigorously in private with the Prime Minister was one thing — he had done that throughout the war — but to challenge him in full council, to appeal to the Cabinet against the Prime Minister, was another. This was the act of high moral courage which must remain memorable as long as the atomic story is told.

Every instinct of affection, loyalty and gratitude conspired to make his decision odious. His long friendship with Churchill was one of his most precious possessions. He had cleaved to him when he was a voice crying in the wilderness, and their association had been unblemished by discord. It is to his lasting credit that at this moment he had the courage to place his convictions before his personal feelings, and to face whatever defunctive music might next fall upon his ears.

Two matters strengthened his hand. In August the first civil reactor program was approved. Thirteen months before, Prof had voiced the general opinion by saying in the House of Lords that the civil uses of atomic energy were still "decades away."

In spite of this, he was among the first to realize that a paper presented to the Atomic Energy Board in July 1952 showed that the development of a Pippa,[1] later famous under the name of Calder Hall, had real possibility of generating competitive electric power.

While to the end Prof remained far more conscious of the military importance of atomic energy and continued to base his claims for a change in the organization on military needs, he also realized that provision must be made for the industrial uses now and later on. In Sir John Cockcroft's words:

> For a long time he was sceptical about the possibility of economic civil power development. Nevertheless, he was tolerant and willing to be carried away by younger people's enthusiasm.[2]

---

[1] A pressurized industrial power-producing assembly which revealed that a natural uranium-fueled, graphite-moderated, carbon-dioxide-cooled reactor had real possibility of generating competitive electric power.

[2] Sir John Cockcroft to author.

The fact that industrial uses were at hand and not "decades away" necessarily strengthened his hand in arguing for an effective industrial organization. Secondly, there was at this time a further switch of opinion within the industrial side of the project in favor once more of a nationalized corporation: this followed one of the recurrent squabbles about salaries and recruitment within the Ministry of Supply.

Prof's Cabinet paper was timed to be circulated immediately after the Montebello bomb had been exploded, and it was actually sent round on September 30th. After describing the history and opening up of the exciting civil prospects and the decisive military importance of atomic energy, he wrote:

> Such an enterprise requires all the imagination and drive which we, as a nation, can furnish. It wants efficiency, elasticity and rapidity of decision: qualities of mind and outlook which we may hope to find in those who control large and growing industrial enterprises. We alone among the competing nations have chosen to put our atomic undertaking under the control of ordinary Government Departments. We have subjected it to the same rule as the collection of customs; it has the same pattern inside the Ministry of Supply as have the Royal Ordnance Factories whose job is the routine production of standardised weapons.
>
> We have indeed made the worst possible choice . . .

He therefore, sought

> the agreement of his colleagues to the setting-up of a national corporation . . . with a small executive board . . . financed by a grant-in-aid and its budget and investment programme . . . settled annually in advance in consultation with the Treasury. Within its approved budget and subject to direction which might at any time be given to it, the corporation would have complete freedom.
>
> Jealous as Parliament has shown itself of proposals for

grants-in-aid, I believe that an overwhelming case can be made in public for these proposals. . . . As interest shifts from weapons to power production it is essential that industry should be brought in — unless the Government wishes to monopolise the production and distribution of electricity. . . .

Indeed, it may be found that this aspect of the matter may even appeal to the Opposition, whose hostility to the change, such as I advocate, has only developed in the last year.

He proposed that there should be a bill in the 1953–54 session, but that a separate Ministry should be created forthwith by a short Act or Order in Council, charged with setting up an independent establishment which could be handed over to the Board.

In conclusion, I would beg my colleagues to face the requirements of the dawning age of nuclear power. The present makeshift arrangements should not be allowed to continue . . . If these proposals are rejected and the *status quo* maintained, the new industrial and military revolutions will pass us by. Quietly and imperceptibly we shall lose our place among the nations of the world.

A counterpaper was naturally circulated by the Minister of Supply. The only supporting paper was harmful to Prof's cause as it seemed merely to abuse the Civil Service. After three weeks the Cabinet had an inconclusive discussion of thirty minutes, and the whole matter was left in the air.

Prof was now desperate. He wrote privately to the Prime Minister as a prelude to resignation, and on October 24th received a cold reply:

MY DEAR PROF,
Thank you for your letter of October 24. I certainly cannot feel that I am pledged in this matter, which I frankly admit I have not mastered in all its variants, and still less that I made

a bargain with you about it when you took office. We all have
to try our best to deal with our problems as they come along.[1]

For the first time Prof stooped to lobbying, and approached
several other Ministers, who promised support.

At the resumed Cabinet a week later, the atmosphere was
different and more favorable. Some Ministers began to talk
of Prof's proposals as implementations of Party policy. He
said afterward that he thought that he had achieved more
at this Cabinet by silence under attack than he had by his
long and carefully briefed speech on the first occasion. In the
end a small Cabinet Committee was set up to examine the
matter. As the Committee contained a majority of Ministers
who had spoken in favor of Cherwell's proposals, there was
little doubt how it would report. In fifty minutes Cherwell
had, as a Minister, officially achieved all that he had failed to
carry as private adviser during the previous twelve months.

The Committee reported in January 1953. It found the old
arguments about salaries and security to be unconvincing, but
on the broad need for an organization competent to handle
the future industrial uses of atomic energy, the Committee
felt that there could be no question: "No novelty of organisation or difficulties of accounting should be allowed to stand in
the way of this." A Committee of experts under Lord Waverley should be appointed to prepare a detailed scheme for the
transfer of responsibility and for the setting-up of a satisfactory
form of organization. It was hoped that the change could be
carried through with the support of the Opposition.

The Waverley Committee was appointed in January

to devise a plan for transferring responsibility for atomic energy
from the Ministry of Supply to a non-departmental organisation
and to work out the most suitable form for the new organisa-

---

[1] Cherwell archives.

tion, due regard being paid to any constitutional and financial implications.

The Committee submitted an interim report on April 9th that "we are now satisfied that it is completely practicable to devise a plan which will include reasonable solutions to all these issues . . . but we are not in a position to commit ourselves in respect of the most suitable form for the new organisation . . . until we have been free to carry out our investigations upon the spot."

The Committee naturally wished to visit the highly secret atomic energy establishments before proceeding further with their investigation, and this could not be done without publicly disclosing the Committee's existence, which was up till then itself Top Secret.

The Cabinet's hand was forced by the journalist Chapman Pincher's announcement on April 4th that the Cabinet had decided that "Britain's atomic project should be taken away from the civil service and handed over to a separate organisation." His report mentioned "a panel of experts headed by Lord Waverley."

Some Ministers were in favor of announcing that the Committee had been set up, without disclosing that a decision in principle to establish a corporation had already been made. This strange compromise was embodied in the terms of the announcement made by the Prime Minister on April 28th. The Committee, he said, was indeed working out a plan, but no Government decision was stated and no reasons were put forward. But Mr. Strauss bluntly put it that "we gather that a decision has been taken in principle," and drew from the Prime Minister the definite statement that "we thought it was right to decide on the question of principle before appointing the Committee. . . ."

The Waverley Committee then visited the atomic energy

establishments and settled down to the detailed working-out of the scheme. Only two major questions of principle in which Prof was interested came before the Committee. The first and by far the most important question was whether the weapons development stations, principally Aldermaston, were to come under the new corporation, or whether they were to remain within the Ministry of Supply.

This discussion proceeded on the narrow point of control of weapons development. It did not touch the broader question of the political control of weapons, such as how many should be ordered or who should control them once they had been made. Nor did the discussion assume that in either case there would be any difference in the way in which service requirements were met. Up to this moment the discussions in Cabinet had assumed that the whole or none of the atomic energy project should be transferred from the Ministry of Supply.

Now the Ministry, accepting defeat on the main front, set out to try to keep control of the weapons establishments. This was the part of the organization where the commercial arguments were weakest and where the links with the Civil Service and the specific ordnance responsibilities were greatest. There was much to be said for the Ministry's case, but it was not one that Prof could possibly accept.

In his own mind the transfer of weapons development was the essence of his whole proposal, and he would regard it as completely emasculated if the control of weapons development were allowed to stay with the Ministry of Supply. His determination on this point was reinforced by all his memories of the dogged fights in the war to get the "conventional" weapon authority to concede a fair share of resources for the "unconventional" weapons of those days in M.D.1. A memorandum was, therefore, submitted to the Waverley Committee strongly attacking the Ministry of Supply's proposal. The memorandum argued that this would ignore the moral to be drawn from the gradual integration of the project during the last six years and would subordinate the manifold technical linkages of the weapons division with the production and research divisions to its superficial connections with the conventional weapons organization.

> If the new organisation was set up without weapons responsibility, it would concentrate on power production with disastrous results to the weapons programme.

The debate on this subject consumed more time before the Committee than anything else, but at last the Committee reached the conclusion that it would be "a grave blunder to set up a specialised organisation for atomic energy and not to make that organisation responsible for the military aspects — which will long remain a major, though not perhaps a dominant, part of the entire United Kingdom project."

The Committee had found little substance in the political arguments in favor of maintaining close government control over this particularly important weapon:

> There is really no political point in retaining the working-up of the fissile material into its final shape in departmental hands when all the previous stages are entrusted to others.

All aspects of atomic energy should in future be brought within the scope of one Minister who would not be swayed toward any one of the aspects of atomic energy by reason of the main duties of his department.

Prof's own evidence before the Committee had been largely taken up with this issue, but he also supported the proposal that the project should, as a first stage and while awaiting a new Act of Parliament to set up a corporation, be transferred to a separate government department. This proposal had been denounced by the Minister of Supply as "an interim receivership." The Committee accepted it as a necessary interim stage toward the setting-up of the corporation. They did not stop to reflect to what extent this earlier argument might not represent a final solution to many of the problems which had been raised. Prof's only other intervention before the Committee was to urge that salaries should in general be "on an industrial scale and so somewhat higher than those paid to civil servants holding similar posts."

The report of the Waverley Committee was signed on July 23rd. With the exception of the provision of the sections dealing with salaries and security, it was everything that Prof wanted. It was originally planned to present a White Paper before Parliament rose at the end of July, but such a rush would have appeared unseemly.

The report was considered by the Cabinet on August 10th. The Ministry of Supply made a final all-out effort to get the weapons organization taken away from the proposed corporation, and it was touch and go for a time whether the Cabinet would accept the report as it stood.

In the end, the Cabinet decided that they could not emasculate the Waverley proposals. They approved the report, therefore, as a whole, with certain minor qualifications insisted upon by the service departments. There was a final dispute between Prof and the Minister of Supply over the relations between the weapons division of the proposed corporation and the Ministry of Supply, but *detailed* arrangements were approved by the Cabinet on August 25th.

Work was now put in hand for the preparation of the White Paper announcing the setting-up of the corporation and the Order in Council providing for the interim transfer of the Ministry of Supply's atomic energy functions to a separate department of atomic energy. Prof took little interest in these matters of detail. Indeed, he was unable to follow them as he left for Australia on September 16th in order to discuss with the Commonwealth Government whether certain Australian uranium supplies could be developed and used for the proposed United Kingdom nuclear power program. He did not return until October 19th. On his return he found that administrative preparations had gone ahead so quickly that the transfer to a separate department could be fixed for January 1954. On October 27th he attended the last of the many Cabinets which had discussed the matter. The announcement in the Queen's Speech was finally approved, as were the terms of the accompanying White Paper.

On October 31st he resigned, happy in the knowledge that with the announcement of policy in the Queen's Speech a final and irretraceable step had been taken. A Department of Atomic Energy responsible to the Lord President of the Council thus came into being on January 1, 1954. The Atomic Energy Authority Bill was introduced into Parliament on February 11th and received the Queen's assent on June 4th. The Atomic Energy Authority came into being on July 19th and assumed responsibility for the project on August 1st, with Prof as one of the part-time members of the Authority. He continued to serve as a member until the day of his death.

Many measures have reached the Statute Book through the devotion which individuals have shown to causes in which they believe, but in most of these struggles the individual has had to engage in long public agitation to incline the temper of the people toward the measure he had at heart.

The establishment of the Atomic Energy Authority was won singlehanded by Cherwell. There was no aid from outside, and within relentless opposition. It must be regarded as his political monument. His chosen, well-proved instrument, the private minute to the Prime Minister, had broken in his hand; with much heart-searching he had appealed to the Cabinet, and by his dogged persistence and courage in the face of adversity he had won his victory. His name alone will be recognized by history as the true architect of the Atomic Energy Authority.

It is too early yet to cast the horoscope of its future, or to appraise the value to the country of the enormous priority which his achievement set upon the development of atomic energy in the middle fifties in the United Kingdom. The effect of his work was certainly not most obvious in the sphere in which he had set his heart: that the United Kingdom should diminish the lead which the Russians had established in atomic weapons. The impact of the Authority which he created was far more clearly seen in the swift development of the nuclear power program, which he thought of as a subsidiary effort, mainly to be welcomed because it strengthened the case for a change in control of weapons production. Intensely interested as he was when the early economic possibilities of nuclear power were first realized in the course of 1953, his interest was that of a scientist; it was not directly related to any view about coal shortage in the United Kingdom, nor with that of the energy gap in the economy of Western Europe, an issue which loomed immense in the next two years, and which at the time of Suez was to lead to such a great acceleration of the United Kingdom nuclear power program. It was then that the major implication of the Authority was realized; and the wisdom of the expansion of the program for which his efforts were so largely responsible and the value of his own achievement to the nation in this solitary effort will, at some time in the future, be calmly determined by history.

On October 19, 1953, Prof sent his formal resignation to the Prime Minister, together with a personal letter reverting to the suggestion recommending him for a C.H. (Companion of Honour):

You may remember that you suggested this ten years ago but I was not very enthusiastic. Now, nearing seventy, I would find it even harder to start acquiring letters after my name. The F.R.S. is different; it represents achievement as a physicist. And I think the list of my discoveries compares favourably with that of my more publicised colleagues. But the C.H. is a political award and I was only an amateur politician. Though I fully realise what an honour a C.H. is, I would therefore prefer to forego it. I hope you will not think me ungracious or worse, ungrateful. But I joined your Government purely because you said I could help you — and perhaps be of use to the country. I should hate to give cause to the suspicion, even if it be only in my own mind, that there might have been some other motive.[1]

Prof was genuine in his desire to forego this honor to which, according to his own peculiar processes of thought, he did not consider himself entitled. But once again he was overborne by a more forceful personality, and on October 29th the Queen's Private Secretary wrote saying that she would receive him on November 10th and take the opportunity of appointing him a member of the Companions of Honour.

[1] Cherwell archives.

12

1953–1957

As PROF SAT brooding over the future, he held ever more strongly to another old love which, in his opinion, was now becoming a matter of life and death, the immediate need of more technological education. He felt in his bones that the future of the world was passing into the hands of scientists and technicians, and that a fresh and intensive effort of technological education was required at once if England were not to sink within a generation to the position of Portugal. He had seen the splendid Massachusetts Institute of Technology; he knew the fervor with which the Russians were concentrating on technology, the immense appropriations on money that they were setting aside for it, and its absolute priority in their plans. He asked himself what, in modern times, money mattered when the stakes were so great.

For many years Prof had been advocating the establishment of a technological university on the lines of the Massachusetts Institute of Technology and such European establishments as that at Zürich. The policy was shortsightedly declined by the Conservative Government of 1951, but, during his period of office, the Government took major steps to expand facilities for technological education at Imperial College, London, and at other universities in the provinces.

The Government did not dispute the need for more and better technological education, but wide differences of opinion existed as to the manner in which this should be carried out.

337

It was the core of Prof's argument that the work could not be achieved by improving facilities at existing universities. He believed that to expand on the necessary scale would throw the life of a university such as Oxford or Edinburgh completely out of balance, and that it would be a prodigal waste of money and resources to provide an organization for less than a minimum of 1500 to 2000 students. He agreed that the only place where this might be done without distorting the balance was at Imperial College, London University.

A few discerning spirits like Lord Woolton, first as Lord President of the Council and afterward as Chancellor of the Duchy of Lancaster, and Lord Salisbury, both as Lord Privy Seal and as Lord President of the Council, strongly supported the need for technological universities. The Chancellor of the Exchequer, R. A. Butler, was in favor of building onto existing universities — Imperial College, Royal Technical College, Glasgow and the Manchester College of Technology. He did not think that at the time there was sufficient money to embark on a separate technological university, however strange it seems to a layman that such a vital project should be allowed to languish for want of funds, or be expected to operate on a shoestring.

Prof considered this view a shortsighted and evasive compromise. Butler's attitude was influenced by that of the University Grants Committee with which, as Chancellor of the Exchequer, he had a peculiar relationship. His position was cautious and to Prof unsatisfactory. To Lord Woolton, Butler wrote in March 1952:

> I think there is room for real doubt and divergence of view on the merits of the case, but none about what we can afford. I do not see how in present circumstances I could authorise the £6 million odd of capital expenditure, which would be needed to set the new university on its way. Therefore I feel that we must just put the idea on one side until better times.[1]

[1] Cherwell archives.

Prof was bitterly disappointed by this letter, on which he commented to Butler:

> I am most disappointed to read the copy of your letter to Woolton which you kindly sent me. It is, I think, undeniable that we have fallen behind the United States and many continental countries in industrial technique because they have produced first rate technologists in far greater numbers than we have here. Unless we can catch up with them, or, better still, overtake them, the future of our industry, especially in the export markets, is bleak.[1]

Prof thought that Butler was taking a shortsighted view on a fundamental problem, and that it was petty to a degree in an era of vast expansion to bilk at such a sum as £6 million in a matter which directly concerned the survival of the country. The idea of improving university schools of technology was merely trifling with the needs of the time. There were many branches of technology, and to train men properly an enormous amount of apparatus and a surprising number of professors and lecturers were demanded. He believed that a department of this size would swamp any of the existing universities, except perhaps Imperial College, London University. He argued that it would be far more economical to concentrate on at least one University of Technology. It would take several years to build it, and the £6 million, which so deterred Butler, would not amount to an exorbitant annual sum. It was fundamental that such a university, to attract desirable men, should enjoy the status and prestige of other universities.

He became restive and dissatisfied with the attitude of the University Grants Committee. He did not think that they had grasped the dilemma that to teach properly the main branches of technology required such a vast and expensive collection of apparatus and a faculty of at least forty professors on tech-

[1] Cherwell archives.

nological subjects, that the outlay could be justified only if it were used by 3000 to 4000 students.

In August 1952 he wrote to Butler:

> Thank you for your note enclosing the report of the U.G.C. on the development of higher technological education. Naturally I agree that the education of technologists should include a considerable proportion of ancillary non-technical and non-scientific subjects. But this does not mean that the technological university must, or should be a branch of another university. If the Imperial College develops in the way I hope it will, I suspect that in due course its reputation will outshine that of London and that its authorities will themselves ask for it to be made independent.[1]

Prof was opposed to an exclusively scientific education, and, in spite of his former jibes at humanists, it was with enthusiasm that he agreed to the inclusion of the arts and humanities in the curriculum. His desire was for a liberal education. He had a horror that a generation of young scientists would grow up perfectly equipped in their own subject, but in other respects almost completely uneducated. It was a prediction that was strikingly confirmed in the report by Sir Patrick Linstead and the British Association in January 1961, which stated that many of England's most able scientists were now so specialized that they could not be classed as "educated," and that some scientists had such a poor command of their own language that they were incapable of explaining their work to nonscientists, and that this deplorable state of affairs would continue until their curriculum in schools and colleges was widened.

Later, on March 26, 1954, Prof complained to the Prime Minister that, although the Cabinet had decided over a year ago that the Technical Colleges at Manchester and Glasgow should be raised to the level of self-contained units of univer-

[1] Cherwell archives.

sity status, nothing seemed to have happened, and he suggested that it might be better to set up an independent body, similar to the University Grants Committee, to deal specifically with technological universities.[1]

Advance was indeed proceeding at a snail's pace, and Lord Woolton, who had given great attention to this subject found it necessary to write to Butler:

> I must now place on record my view that the future of British industry is largely dependent on the development of technological education and training in the managerial classes in industry.
>
> I believe that if we are to retain anything like our present standard of living we shall have to improve the amount of wealth we can create from the labour and raw materials that are available to us in this country, and that the measure of this improvement will be the measure of the technological capacity of the higher executives in our various businesses. I hold these views so strongly that I hope you will understand the reasons why I not only wrote the paper for Cabinet, but have, on several occasions, asked for speed. I am sure that you won't take it amiss when I draw your attention to the fact that it is over twelve months since I raised the issue and that up to now, in spite of the Cabinet decision, we are still, little, if anything, further ahead.[2]

This letter expressed Prof's own views to a hair's breadth. By October 31st he had left the Government, but did not relax his efforts on behalf of technological education. He reminded Eden of the grim fact that the Russians had about 300,000 people working on five-year courses in technological universities; besides that, they had 1.6 million in technical colleges equal to our best:

[1] Cherwell archives.
[2] *Ibid.*

We simply must increase enormously our output of technologists if we are to keep pace with them. . . . I am sure the comparative neglect of technology is not because of ill-will anywhere, but simply because the immense difference between the two types of education is not realised. . . . What does not seem to be realised is that higher grade technology requires not only a sound knowledge of advanced physics and chemistry, but above all familiarity with advanced mathematics. . . . It is not the sort of thing a man can pick up at evening classes, however hard he works.[1]

Privately he told Charles: "If I were a Russian I should be polite to everyone and keep the peace. They are turning out twice as many technologists as America — more than all the rest of the world put together in fact — and with their immense population and unbounded mineral wealth they will dominate the world anyway in thirty or forty years if only they keep quiet. It may be that this has begun to dawn on them." On December 7, 1955, he spoke in the House of Lords on a motion by Lord Glyn on Higher Technological Education, in which he developed his theme.

In January 1956 he wrote again to Butler expressing anxiety at some of the speeches the Prime Minister had been delivering in the country on what the Government's intentions were in dealing with the shortage of technologists and scientists, and laying emphasis only on expanding and improving technical colleges:

I am absolutely convinced . . . that it is in the higher ranges of technology that we are so woefully short. Our technical colleges are quite good and are doing excellent work, but they cannot and do not educate men to the very high level which is vital if we are to hold our own in the modern world.

[1] Cherwell archives.

Prof felt that the difference between a technician and a technologist was still not sufficiently understood. It is, therefore, appropriate to give an expert's definition of these two words:

> The word "technician" is used to mean a man who has been trained to carry out established techniques which may be complex, and require a high degree of skill, or to work in a prescribed field under instruction; whereas by a "technologist" is meant a man who, as a result of broadly based studies and wide practical experience, has acquired a real understanding of scientific principles and can apply them to the development of industrial processes in diverse fields. It may sometimes be difficult to draw a sharp line of demarcation between the technician on one hand and the scientist or the technologist on the other, and nobody would like to see any barrier set up that might discourage the scientifically minded technician from becoming a scientist or technologist.[1]

Prof was the inspiration of John Colville's project to found a technological institute on the lines of the Massachusetts Institute of Technology, which he so much admired, out of funds to be raised from industrialists in this country, from America and from £25,000 given by the Churchill Birthday Trust. From the beginning of 1956 onward Prof took a keen interest in this project, which has at last provided at Cambridge University a technological institute of the type he had so long been urging — whose first Master is Sir John Cockcroft. Prof was a friend of Colville who had been private secretary to Churchill. Disturbed by the progress made by Russia he had bombarded Churchill with minutes, causing him in the end to regret that he had not been able to do more for technology. Churchill made a remark which appeared to Colville extraordinary in 1955: "One day we shall wake up and find the Russians ahead

[1] *Journal of the Royal Institute of Chemistry,* September 1954.

of us." The object of such a college was to produce men of the caliber of Penney and Cockcroft himself, not mere technicians with no knowledge outside their own subject, and although Prof would have preferred a self-contained institute as in Massachusetts, he was anxious that general culture should also be part of the curriculum. He had, of course, always favored the idea of a separate institute, but at that time it was still thought wiser to attach the new college to an existing university. Before he died Prof told Colville: "It is entirely right. Cambridge is the only place it could be. There is no engineering at Oxford." Churchill College might in some ways be regarded as a memorial to Cherwell rather than to Churchill.

His views on science and government are well summarized in an admirable sentence in a letter he wrote a few months before his death to F. A. Bishop, the Prime Minister's private secretary:

> What we want is that the people responsible for running the country should know something about science, not that scientists should run the country.

Prof was sometimes accused of aesthetic blindness, but he was in fact deeply interested in combining science with the humanities in the new technological institutes he hoped to see, and to provide a liberal rather than a narrow education. Another sign of his desire to enlist science in the aid of other forms of learning was his foundation at Oxford of the Research Laboratory for Archaeology and the History of Art. In founding this body he was attempting to exonerate scientists from the charge of being philistines by harnessing scientific research to the study of archaeology and history.

Two young scientists, Dr. Stuart Young and Dr. E. T. Hall, were chosen to conduct the laboratory by Prof and Professor Hawkes, Professor of European Archaeology. It was soon found that by conducting researches into the impurities of ancient bronzes it was often possible to determine their age and even where they were produced. Research on such impurities in coins made it possible to envisage the trade routes of the ancient world. It had also occurred to Prof that pottery and brick contained iron, which was sufficiently magnetic to be influenced by the earth's magnetic field, thus enabling geologists interested in the variations of the magnetic field to cooperate with historians seeking to establish the date of pottery.

Machines were provided for the analysis of coins by X-ray methods, and others for the examination of pigments in paintings, providing valuable information by analysis of the various layers of paint in the picture. It was in this laboratory that the Piltdown Skull was subjected to scientific tests by Hall, and its unauthentic character confirmed.

The terms of reference were to discover *new* methods, and the laboratory was brought into being as a recognized Oxford institution by Prof's personal influence, and the staff has since grown from two to twenty. Using his customary methods in obtaining support, he interested The Royal Society, the Nuffield Foundation, and D.S.I.R. (Directorate of Scientific Industrial Research), and new instruments were developed for detecting metal underground, for analysis of materials, and for establishing their date.

Prof, although much occupied with other affairs, became fascinated by this project, paying frequent visits to its premises at 6 Keble Road. He felt that archaeologists were working in the dark, and his instructions were that the staff should examine all physical phenomena with the object of assisting archaeology and history, one notable result being the establishment of the date of bones by radioactivity. Their methods of testing were safe, and won the confidence of the Ashmoleum Museum, who entrusted them with rare and fragile specimens.

It is interesting that although Prof, in his time, had enjoyed goading Oxford philosophers, this desire to associate science with other branches of learning led him to seek a closer union between physics and metaphysics. He had come to believe that the separation of these two branches of knowledge was wrong and that there should be integration, the physicists studying metaphysics, and the metaphysicians acquiring a knowledge of physics. He put forward these views in the first Robert Grosseteste Memorial Lecture, which he delivered on May 21, 1955, in the Chapter House of Lincoln Cathedral, saying in the course of his argument:

> But unfortunately the link between science and philosophy has been broken and these two aspects of knowledge have drifted so far apart that the protagonist of one — if I may use this word which has given rise recently to so much correspondence in the Press — often finds it hard to comprehend what the other is saying.
>
> The scientist is all too apt to fall into a rather superficial naïve realism and to think that the philosopher — or perhaps I should say metaphysician since it is in this branch of philosophy that the contact should be closest — is wasting his time fussing about definitions, foredoomed to failure since words can only be defined in words, so that argument in a vicious circle is inevitable.
>
> The metaphysician for his part is apt to think the scientist has lost all sense of the meaning of words, talking as he does of empty fields having a whole complex of curious properties and characteristics and a host of similar concepts embodying contradictions in terms.
>
> The scientist is much too busy to reconsider fundamentals, experimenting and theorising as he does on lines which have led to immense and, as we must now admit, appalling advances in man's mastery of nature. The metaphysician is all too apt to take the easy line that modern science requires so much mathematical apparatus that he cannot be expected to master it and

therefore unashamedly and often cheerfully proceeds to build up his description of the foundations of science on the basis of the views held by Galileo or perhaps by Newton.

Neither attitude is really justifiable. For a philosopher to refuse to consider modern science because the mathematics is too difficult is just as though a historian were to refuse to take account of a text because the handwriting was crabbed. On the other hand, the scientist — and when I say scientist I of course tend to think of my own subject, physics — could often profit by investigating with a critical eye some of the extraordinary fundamental ideas involved in many modern hypotheses. I cannot but feel that a synthesis of the two forms of thought is badly wanted. It would be a pity to erect the whole edifice of modern natural knowledge either on shifting sands or on foundations suffering from dry rot.

As the years passed the Prof carefully considered his position, and by the autumn of 1955 he began to put out cautious feelers about the question of his resignation as Dr. Lee's Professor of Experimental Philosophy. He was ready to go, and he can never have contemplated his occupancy of the Chair without a glow of pride. He could not be forced to resign as his professorship was a life appointment made before the statutes defined new rules for retirement. At this time, Harrod tells us:

. . . one or two valued members of the Laboratory took higher appointments elsewhere, in which they would have even greater scope. This was a severe blow, undermining as it did the Prof's arrangements. I told him he must replace these men. But he pointed out to me it was impossible. No first class physicist would be attracted to Oxford without some security of tenure of the position offered. The Prof was past the retiring age, and a new man would want an assurance about where he would stand under the Prof's successor. This was precisely what the

Prof himself could not give. For this reason, he explained, he could not continue to hold his own Chair for much longer.[1]

He was not upset by the prospect of resignation, but his mind was continually haunted by the fear that he might be compelled to leave his rooms, and in his old age be forced to pull out his roots and seek new lodgings in the bleak world outside. These rooms, which in his reticent soul he loved so deeply, had seen the brilliant dawn of his Oxford career. It was fitting that they should solace its twilight. He embarked on a long correspondence with the College and University authorities, and, in the end, by a unique decision, the Prof was allowed to keep his rooms after retirement, paying, at his own request, rent for them.

> When he finally retired, Christ Church paid him an unprecedented honour. The Senior Censor informed him that he could retain his rooms in College. This had never been done before within living memory. Even tutors, like Sidney Owen, who had devoted their whole lives to teaching Christ Church undergraduates and working in other ways for the College were compelled, when the fatal day to retire came, to pack up their books and leave. . . . None the less everyone greatly welcomed this concession to the Prof. How far off were the days when the normal seniority at High Table had only been granted him with great reluctance, and under the threat of legal action. Before he died machinery was set in motion for making him an Honorary Student. He knew this, but it proved too late to complete formal election.[2]

It is pleasant to know that once the rooms were his until death a feminine influence was set to work to soften their austerity. Shortly after leaving No. 11 Downing Street Prof had

[1] Sir Roy Harrod, *The Prof*, pages 267–268.
[2] *Ibid.*, page 268.

decided, by no means prematurely, that Harvey needed more help, although he disliked new faces around him. This resulted in the arrival of Mrs. Morton, a versatile and energetic young woman. The Prof had a strong distrust of ventilation in his rooms, and to Harvey's many other duties was added the new one of closing the windows when Mrs. Morton had opened them before the Prof's keen nose detected the intrusion of fresh air, and opening them again before Mrs. Morton discovered he had closed them.

She set to work on her gloomy task with tact, but firmly, and the frowsty rooms were transfigured. Flowers appeared for the first time; tennis prizes, which had for years lain tarnished in the dining room cabinet, were cleaned, and glittered as they were brought into use as ashtrays, decanters or vases. The dusty heaps of bygone scientific journals began to disappear, and the ugly rooms, in the last two and a half years of his life, took on an air at once civilized and gay.

He was filled with relief, and the world which, during the years of strife, had so often seemed hostile, now appeared in a conspiracy to lap him round with comfort and honor. It gave him another warm caress on May 9, 1956, when Sir Anthony Eden wrote asking if it would be agreeable to him if he submitted his name to the Queen for a Viscountcy.[1]

Prof was deeply moved that this generous proposal, so completely to Eden's credit, should have been made to someone who had retired before Eden became Prime Minister, and that he should have expressed such high regard:

> I value it [Prof wrote] especially as showing that you personally consider the small contribution I was able to make when we worked together was of some slight use. I am only sorry that I have not been able to be of any use to you since you took on your stupendous task. . . . You realise, I am

[1] Sir Anthony Eden had succeeded Sir Winston Churchill as Prime Minister in April 1955.

sure, how glad I would be to do anything at any time to make myself useful.

He was introduced to the House of Lords in his new degree on Wednesday, July 11, 1956, his sponsors being Lord Waverley and Lord Thurso. Prof, according to his nature, concealed his deep satisfaction in feeble jibes to Harrod about his honor. Its great merit, he thought, was that it put him a cut above some of his academic colleagues who had recently been ennobled.

At the end of October Prof was stricken by the death of his close friend and colleague Sir Francis Simon, his chosen successor to the Chair of Experimental Philosophy. Simon, as we have seen, had come to the Clarendon Laboratory with other German Jewish scientists in 1933. He had remained there ever since, become a naturalized British subject and been knighted. In Prof's opinion he was the greatest low-temperature physicist of his generation, and his death an irreparable loss both to physics in Oxford and to science in the world at large. "Not only was he supreme in experimental research; he had a clearer and more fundamental understanding of the basis of thermodynamics and its interrelation with statistical mechanics than any man since Einstein."[1] By his death the Clarendon Laboratory lost one of its finest ornaments and its new head. Now the succession was once more in confusion and doubt.

Hard on the heels of the Viscountcy followed, on November 1, 1956, the Hughes Medal of the Royal Society, arousing a flash of the old rancor. The Society had written informing Prof that the President and Council had awarded him the Hughes Medal "in recognition of your distinguished studies in many fields: the melting point formula and theory of specific heats; ionisation of stars; meteors and temperature inver-

---

[1] Letter from Lord Cherwell to the *Oxford Mail*, October 31, 1956.

sion in the stratosphere." Perhaps he thought the honor over-due, or perhaps he thought that the Royal Society should have conferred upon him a higher award, but his attitude was frigid, and he refused in the end to accept the medal in per-son, it being sent to him in December. He answered the con-gratulations of his scientific confreres in his usual deprecating manner, and in more than one letter there is a tinge of melan-choly and bitterness, referring to it as "the leaving present" and as a *"bene decessit."*

How much strife and how many disappointments as well as triumphs lay behind the bare recital of the great landmarks of his later career — Baron in 1941, Privy Counsellor in 1942, Paymaster General from 1942 to 1945 and from 1951 to 1953, Companion of Honour, November 1953, Viscount in 1956, and member of the United Kingdom Atomic Energy Authority from July 19, 1954, to July 2, 1957.

His speeches in the House of Lords from 1943 onward dealt with widely differing matters, such as scientific research, the Health Services, U.N.O., civil defense, food, economics, sci-ence and industry, roads, atomic energy, American aid and European payments, wireless telegraphy, radioactive sub-stances and many others, with the emphasis always on the economic state of the country, a subject on which he held strong views, considered by some to be unsound. These speeches may be read with enjoyment in Hansard, and even his opponents agreed that a mere half-dozen lessons in elocu-tion would have been sufficient to make him one of the most fascinating speakers in the House of Lords.

On the burning question of the day, the seizure of the Suez Canal in July 1956, his opinions were explosive. He had al-ways despised the Egyptians, and the conduct of Nasser was to him the ultimate humiliation of British power. It had al-ways been his conviction that civilized life rested upon the observance of obligations that had been accepted, and that if governments were allowed to repudiate treaties and contracts whenever it suited them, it would mean the end of civilized intercourse between nations.

"We simply cannot afford," he said, "to put ourselves at the mercy of someone who does not trouble to conceal his deep hostility to the West and especially to this country . . . If a tramp holds a knife at your throat, after abusing you for refusing to give him all the alms he has asked for, nobody in his senses would say — 'Well, after all, he has not yet assaulted you. As a peace-loving citizen you should wait until he has made an incision before taking any measures to prevent him cutting your throat.' To call such action 'gun boat diplomacy' — whatever that may mean — is an instance of pejorative language in place of logical argument."

He wrote afterward in confidence to Charles:

It is really appalling to think of the impudence of the Egyptians. Of course we ought never to have made them independent after we conquered the Middle East from the Turks in 1918. At that time nobody knew about the immense oil reserves in the Persian Gulf, but at the very least they ought to have preserved the Suez area as a colony . . .

I can't help feeling that our intervention was unhappily timed. It would have been better to let the Jews beat up Nasser. Now he has the alibi that if we had not come in he would have smashed the Jews comfortably.

The real fact of the matter is that U.N.O. is a snare and a delusion. It has never done any good except in Korea and that was only possible because Russia had walked out in a huff. Everybody must have realised that America would have intervened in Korea without U.N.O.'s sanction, but for this happy fluke.

It was his speech on "Some Defects of U.N.O." on December 11, 1956 which attained the greatest fame of all and proved what a wonderful analytical instrument his mind was when focused squarely upon a vulnerable subject. This memorable speech, which delighted those given to logical thought and enraged many who preferred to live by slogans and emotion, reminds us of the clinical probings of a surgeon laying bare a morbid physical condition.[1] His object was to show that the larger claims made on behalf of U.N.O. were fantastic, and that it was in fact a conglomeration of sovereign states, great and small, in which some were thousands of times more powerful and wealthy than others; some highly civilized, some almost illiterate. Yet they all had an equal vote, and in the Assembly 5 per cent of the world's population could carry the day against the other 95 per cent. In this remarkable speech, which should be read in full, we see his hatred of loose thinking and of those catch phrases, such as "Hand it over to U.N.O.," which appeared to him to be regarded by the weak-minded almost as an incantation.

Thus occupied, the Prof passed his time peacefully and with profit to his country. The old fires were rekindled by the proposal to build a road across Christ Church Meadow, which lay outside his windows, and they glowed no less fiercely when he found that its proponent was Mr. Duncan Sandys. He spoke of it in the House of Lords, begging Their Lordships to acquit him of selfishness in the matter, as he thought that his medical adviser would agree that he was unlikely to survive long enough to be disturbed by any surface traffic in Oxford, or, indeed, anywhere else.

His health at times depressed him acutely. Sometimes, in depression, he wondered, like Strafford, whether it was worth keeping up this "ruinous cottage," and, when suffering from conjunctivitis and toothache, wrote to his brother: "One wonders why one takes so much trouble to keep the other foot out."

[1] See Appendix V for full reproduction of this speech.

Since his days at Marsham Court at the end of the war he had suffered from a mild diabetic condition which was probably due to his peculiar diet and to an excessive consumption of oranges. His doctor, Frank, told him that there was too much sugar in orange juice, and Harvey worked out a weak form of it with saccharine. Potatoes, his great stand-by, were cut down, and this state of affairs continued for the last twelve years of his life. It made little difference to his health, and insulin was not required, but Prof, secretive as usual about his private affairs, gave instructions that if he were ever to be found unconscious away from home, the doctors were to be warned that he was diabetic. The diabetic condition had deteriorated by 1953, and in May of that year he confided to his brother:

> A day or two after you left I sent to Frank for the blood and urine tests. He rang up the next day and said I had severe diabetes and must at once go into a nursing home and be put on a strict diet cutting out all sugar, starch, bread, potatoes, rice etc. if I wanted to avoid leading the life of a chronic invalid on insulin. I said that this was "ausgeschlossen" but that I would work out my own diet and I think I have worked it. He has been on holiday but I hope to see him on Wednesday and return to more normal food. It is sickening just when sugar is to be derationed to be cut off.

His heart was a more serious anxiety, but did not appear to have reached a threatening condition, although Dr. Frank had diagnosed a slight tendency toward angina. He had complete confidence in Frank, a personal friend, and a brother-in-law of Professor Simon, who refused to send him bills. The Prof's indispositions were not noticeable except to those close to him. They had observed that he had given up serious golf, now only pottering about and practicing putting, becoming exasperated when he failed to sink a putt. At first he would discuss his health freely with Harvey, and carry out diabetic tests on himself, but in the end he became bored, and for the last two years of his life abandoned them.

In this last year Lord De L'Isle came upon Prof having tea in the House of Lords dining room. He sat down beside him and asked him how he was.

He replied as follows: "My dear Bill, you know the definition of the perfectly designed machine?" to which I replied that I didn't. "The perfectly designed machine," said the Prof, "is one in which all its working parts wear out simultaneously. I am that machine."

At the time I was amused, but I remembered the story a month later when I read that he had been found dead in his rooms at Oxford. It seems to me perfectly to represent his outlook and his humour.[1]

On July 2, 1957 there appeared nothing wrong with him until the evening. He evidently felt no foreboding, and had arranged to attend Wimbledon on July 4th with Mr. Robert Blake and his wife. He rose, as usual, rather late, and ordered his favorite lunch — mushroom soup, *oeufs en cocotte,* asparagus and hollandaise sauce. After lunch he watched tennis on the television. Miss Althea Gibson, the colored American champion, was trouncing Miss Christine Truman, who was not in her happiest vein. Prof, who had a strong and lamentable racial prejudice against the colored champion, kept up a peevish obbligato of waspish comment about Miss Truman's deficiencies. He had little opinion of women's tactical ability at the game and was fond of observing: "Let a woman pass you once down the tramlines, and she will go on trying to do it again for the rest of the match."

Later he went for a gentle stroll in the Meadow, while Harvey went out to buy food. He was caught on the telephone by the chauffeur, Roberts, with the news that Prof was ill. It

[1] Lord De L'Isle to author.

was a sultry and oppressive day. When Harvey reached the rooms in Meadow Buildings he found Prof lying on his bed, sweating profusely. Dr. Richards was sent for, and at about 6.45 Harvey helped him to undress Prof and put him to bed. Richards felt that a radio-cardiograph of his heart was necessary, and it was arranged for one to be done next day.

Charles Lindemann had been staying with Prof, but had left the week before. Harvey tried in vain to establish contact with him, for he was fishing in the wilds of Canada, and could not be reached. During his visit to Christ Church Charles and the Prof had agreed to alter their wills, but in no way on account of Prof's ill health. Prof had already made a will leaving the life interest of his estate to Charles, and Charles had left everything to Prof.

After discussion with his brother, and with the Treasurer of Christ Church, E. W. Gray, Prof agreed that this arrangement was foolish owing to the double death duties involved, and allowed himself to be persuaded by Gray to leave his money on discretionary trust to trustees, who could allocate any sum to Charles if he desired it, but which would otherwise be divided between Christ Church and Wadham. It is believed that his original intention was that the money should be divided equally between the two Colleges, but that he was so incensed by the Warden of Wadham's attitude toward the Christ Church Meadow road that he altered the proportions of the bequest to 60 per cent and 40 per cent in favor of Christ Church.

The new will was drawn up but not signed, and Prof's first thought after his attack was to get the will signed and witnessed at once. The Common Room butler, Little, and a Dr. Stewart were summoned to witness his signature, and this was fortunately done in time on July 2nd. He signed it in bed at 7 P.M., after receiving an injection between the shoulder blades, before the two witnesses who were not beneficiaries, after which the doctor left. The trustees were Mr. Robert Blake, the Christ Church tutor, whose brilliant brain and steadfast character Prof so admired and Mr. Patrick Davis from the solicitors, Gregory Rowcliffe, the son of H. W. C. Davis, the Oxford historian.

After this had been done Harvey was left alone with the Prof. He began to feel better, but could eat no dinner. From time to time Harvey looked in on the darkened bedroom. At 10.30 Prof was sick, and even in his weakness his fastidious mind rebelled at the necessity of Harvey having to look after him and deal with such a squalid business. He humbly apologized. A few moments before midnight he said: "I'll see if I can go to sleep now. If my light is out do not disturb me."

He had evidently no premonition of death and no fear. It was his usual practice to talk to Harvey for an hour or more at this time of the evening. Now he did not even say good night, indicating that he expected Harvey to remain, but that he had no thought of death. The light was turned off when Harvey left, and although he looked in several times, it was not switched on again. At 8.30 A.M., to Harvey's distress, the telephone bell stridently broke the silence. It was Dr. Richards, who told him to look in and see that all was well in the bedroom.

Harvey opened the door softly, apprehensive of waking him. He saw him dimly, but could hear no sound of breathing, and when he touched the hand it was cold. When Dr. Richards came on his summons, he switched on the light. Prof lay in exactly the same position as when Harvey had left him for the night, propped up in bed, his arms on the top of the bedclothes. On his face was a look of peace and, as one observer thought, of acceptance of his fate. The doctor said that he had been dead about seven hours, so that he must have died shortly after midnight on the morning of July 3rd. The sudden tragedy, sundering the two men who had been so close for thirty years, prostrated Harvey with grief and shock. He must have conferred with many people but had no recollection of any of them, nor of the passage of time. He could only remember the cat, the Tasmanian Devil, which each morning had jumped with friendly malice on the Prof's bed to tease him, skulking out of the rooms, warned of the smell of death by some strange animal telepathy. Brought back to Harvey, after one day it disappeared for ever.

Charles Lindemann was in Oxford two days later. Before his arrival it was left to Harvey to decide whether the body should be buried or cremated, and although the Prof had expressed a wish to be cremated in his will, he was buried in the ordinary way. Coronary thrombosis was the cause of death assigned on the death certificate.

The funeral service was held in Christ Church Cathedral. Among the mourners was the estranged sister to whom he had not spoken for forty years. When Winston Churchill entered, the congregation by a spontaneous impulse rose to their feet. Eighty-two years old and infirm, he had determined that day upon a last duty: "I must go to the grave," he repeated several times, and after the service he drove to the cemetery, two miles away.

> He walked in the procession up the cemetery path. He walked beyond the path, advancing over the difficult tufts of grass, with unfaltering, but ageing steps, onward to the graveside of his dear old friend.[1]

It has been said that "man inhabits, for his own convenience, a home-made universe within the greater alien world of external matter and his own irrationality. Out of the illimitable blackness of that world the light of his customary thinking scoops, as it were, a little illuminated cave — a tunnel of brightness, in which from the birth of consciousness to its death,

[1] Sir Roy Harrod, *The Prof*, page 276.

he lives, moves, and has his being." Cherwell was one of those men whose rich original endowment of mind allowed him to escape from such limitations, and from an eminence survey the nature of the Universe. Hence one more brick built into the temple of science was more important to him than all the fugitive triumphs of politics. Had it not been for his certainty of the wrath to come and his fears for air defense, he would never have presented himself as a Parliamentary candidate, for although his interest in politics and economics was strong he had no desire to be an actor in them. He played a notable part in great affairs, decisively influencing major issues, but he did so as a duty. He was never conscious of the excitement of politics, those dramatic moments that illuminate the dull contentions of the House of Commons at times of crisis, transforming it into a thrilling theater where a great play is enacted, and make Parliamentary life one that binds its devotees with hoops of steel.

Cherwell was singularly free from that failing so common to man, deplored by Pascal in the *Pensées,* of filling his leisure with meaningless distractions so as to preclude the necessity of thought, and Harrod is surely right in calling him "a thinking reed," an intellectual in the fullest sense whose mind — "that beautiful piece of mechanism" — was in constant movement. He wasted time only in the indulgence of talk — those midnight exchanges which lasted until the small hours of the morning, when the ball of conversation was tossed deftly to and fro.

No greater mistake could be made than to regard him as cold and diffident in emotion. Rather was he, under the sober mien he had assumed, a man alive and raw and quivering with authentic passions, nourishing love and hate with an intensity rare among men, revengeful in thought yet vulnerable to slights, warm and unchanging in friendship. It was the consciousness of these discordant elements that made him from the beginning determined to conceal them under a dry manner, and a strict observance of convention, but, unlike Dr. Jekyll, he could not "strip off these lendings and spring headlong into the sea of liberty." There came thus to be formed over the years a character in conflict, which did much to mask the fundamental simplicity of his nature.

Many great men when they die leave little behind them except the memory of their achievements. Cherwell left a void in the heart of his friends. How often have I mourned the fact that the door will never open again to admit that familiar figure, and reflected: "How much I wish Prof were here to explain all this." He had the faults inseparable from such a character. His vision was somewhat narrow and his obstinacy impervious to argument. He could, on many occasions, be safely accused of mental arrogance; but when we strike the final balance sheet, we know that there are also many who, remembering him, must sigh, as Storrs sighed over Lawrence, in Shakespeare's tremendous homage: "Would I were with him wheresoever he is."

APPENDIX I

Lord Cherwell's Scientific Publications

1910. (With W. Nernst and F. Koref.) Untersuchungen über die spezifische Wärme bei tiefen Temperaturen I. S.B. preuss. Akad. Wiss. p. 247.

1910. Über die Berschung molekularer Eigenfrequensen. Phys. Z. 11. 609–612.

1910. (With A. F. Lindemann.) A preliminary paper on some quantitative applications of radiation pressure to cosmic problems. Mon. Not. R. Astr. Soc. 71, No. 2.

1910. (With A. Magnus.) Über die Abhängigkeit der spezifischen Wärme Fester Körper Von Der Temperatur. Z. Elektrochem. No. 8.

1911. (With C. L. Lindemann.) Über ein neues für Röntgenstrahlen durchlässiges Glas. Z. Röntgen. 13.

1912. (With L. Chas.) Die Abhängigkeit des Durchdringungsvermögens der Röntgenstrahlen von Druck und Gasinhalt. Phys. Z. pp. 104–106.

1911. Some considerations on the forces acting between the atoms of solid bodies. In Nernst-Festschrift. Halle: Wilhelm Knapp.

1911. Untersuchungen über die spezifische Wärme bei tiefen Temperaturen. IV. S.B. preuss. Akad. Wiss. p. 316.

1911. (With W. Nernst.) Untersuchungen über die spezifische Wärme bei tiefen Temperaturen. V. S.B. preuss. Akad. Wiss. p. 494.

1911. (With W. Nernst.) Spezifische Wärme und Quantentheorie. Z. Elektrochem. No. 18.

1911. Über die Berechnung der Eigen frequenzen der Elektronen in selektiven Photoeffekt. Verhandl. ditsch. Phys. Ges. 13, 482.

1911. Über die Beziehungen zwischen chemischer Affinität und Elektronenfrequenzen. Verhandl. ditsch. Phys. Ges. 13, 1107.

1911. Über die Dulong-Petitsche Gesetz. (Inaugural Dissertation.)

1912. (With W. NERNST.) Untersuchungen über die spezifische Wärme. VI. Berechnung von Atomvärmen. S.B. preuss. Akad. Wiss. p. 1160.

1912. Some considerations on the forces acting between the atoms of solid bodies. Nernst-Festschrift. Halle: Wilhelm Knapp. p. 258.

1912. (With C. L. LINDEMANN.) Note on the tensile strength of materials at low temperatures. Nernst-Festschrift. Halle: Wilhelm Knapp. p. 264.

1913. (With F. SCHWERS.) Eine neue Methode zur Messung von wahren spezifischen Wärmen. Phys. Z. 14, 766.

1914. (With M. DE BROGLIE.) Einige Bemarkungen über Röntgenstrahlspektren. Verhandl. ditsch. Phys. Ges. 16. no. 4.

1914. Über die Grundlagen der Atommodelle. Verhandl. ditsch. Phys. Ges. 16. no. 6.

1915. Note on a number of dark stars. Mon. Not. R. Astr. Soc. 75. no. 3.

1915. Note on the theory of the metallic state. Phil. Mag. (6), 29, 127.

1915. Note on the relation between the life of radioactive substances and the range of the rays emitted. Phil. Mag. (6), 30, 560.

1916. (With A. F. LINDEMANN.) Daylight photography of stars as a means of testing the equivalence postulate in the theory of relativity. Mon. Not. R. Astr. Soc. 77, no. 2.

1917. Turn indicators for aeroplanes. Advisory Comm. for Aeronautics Reports and Memoranda no. 525 (H.M.S.O.).

1918. Note on the pulsation theory of copheid variable. Mon. Not. R. Astr. Soc. 78, no. 8.

1918. Notes on a geometrical construction for rectifying any arc of a circle. Phil. Mag. (6), 36, 472.

1919. (With A. F. LINDEMANN.) Preliminary note on the application of photo-electric photometry to astronomy. Mon. Not. R. Astr. Soc. 79, no. 5.

1919. (With F. W. ASTON.) The possibility of separating isotopes. Phil. Mag. (6), 37, 523.

1919. Note on the vapour pressure and affinity of isotopes. Phil. Mag. (6), 38, 173.

1919. The philosophical aspect of the theory of relativity. Mind, 29, no. 16.

1919. Note on the theory of magnetic storms. Phil. Mag. (6), 38, 669.

1920. Note on the significance of the chemical constant and its relation to the behaviour of gases at low temperatures. Phil. Mag. (6), 39, 21.

1920. Note on the theory of velocity of chemical reaction. Phil. Mag. (6), 40, 671.

1920. The philosophical aspect of the theory of relativity. (Symposium) Mind, 29, 437.

1922. Contribution to a discussion on "The radiation theory of chemical action." Trans. Faraday Soc. 17, 598.

1923. (With G. M. B. Dobson.) A theory of meteors, and the density of temperatures of the outer atmosphere to which it leads. Proc. Roy. Soc. A, 102, 411.

1923. (With G. M. B. Dobson.) Note on the photography of meteors. Mon. Not. R. Astr. Soc. 83, no. 3.

1923. (With G. M. B. Dobson.) A note on the temperature of the air at great heights. Proc. Roy. Soc. A, 103, 339.

1923. Note of the absorption of radiation inside a star. Mon. Not. R. Astr. Soc. 83, no. 5.

1923. Note on the constitution of the spiral nebulae. Mon. Not. R. Astr. Soc. 83, no. 6.

1923. Note on the theory of the specific heat of liquids. Phil. Mag. (6), 45, 1119.

1924. (With T. C. Keeley.) A new form of electrometer. Phil. Mag. (6), 47, 577.

1924. Note on the temperature coefficient of the mobility of ions in liquid. Z. Phys. Chem. 110, 394.

1924. The quantum theory (Symposium). Contribution to the Discussion of the Aristotelian Society and the Mind Association at University Coll., Reading, 11 to 14 July 1924.

1925. (With T. C. Keeley.) Photoelectric radiation pyrometer. Read at Oxford to the Physical Society of London.

1926. Spinning electrons (a letter). Nature. Lond. 117, 652.

1926. Meteors and the constitution of the upper air. Nature. Lond. 118, 195.

1926. The main points of divergence between electro-magnetic and quantum theory of light. Optical Convention, 1926, Part I.

1927. Note on the physical theory of meteors. Astrophys. J. 65, no. 2.

1931. Stellar structure. Nature. Lond. 127, 269.

1932. The Physical Significance of the Quantum Theory. The Clarendon Press.

1933. The place of mathematics in the interpretation of the universe. Philosophy, January.

1933. (With T. C. KEELEY.) Helium liquefaction plant at the Clarendon Laboratory, Oxford. Nature. Lond. 131, 191.

Date Unknown. Physics. Lecture. "Mind."

1933. The unique factorization of a positive integer. Quart. J. Math. (Oxford), 4, 319.

1936. Physical ultimates. Proc. Phys. Soc. 48, 815.

1926. The approach to the absolute zero. 2. The properties of matter at very low temperatures. Reprinted from the Science Museum Handbook Very Low Temperatures, Book III — Symposium of 7 Lectures.

1936. Research at the lowest temperatures and its importance to industry. (Public lecture delivered before the Institution in the Institution of Civil Engineers, 30 October.)

1939. Observations on the discussion on the constitution of the upper atmosphere. Quart. J. Roy. Met. Soc. Vol. LXV. No. 281, pp. 330–336.

1946. Note on the Distribution of the Intervals between Prime Numbers (Oxford). Reprinted from the Quarterly Journal of Mathematics Ox. series, Vol. 17, No. 65.

1948. Some metaphysical implications of Planck's quantum of action. Ann. Phys., Lpz. (6), 3, 49.

1949. (With F. V. ATKINSON.) The mean values of arithmetical functions. Quart. J. Math. (Oxford), 20, 65.

1955. Physics and Philosophy (Robert Grosseteste Memorial Lecture). Delivered on 12/5/55 in the Chapter House of Lincoln Cathedral. Oxford Univ. Press.

APPENDIX II

Sir George Thomson, F.R.S.:
Remarks on Lord Cherwell's Work
"The Physical Significance of the Quantum Theory"

CHERWELL'S STRENGTH as a physicist lay in two things: in his power of reducing a problem to its simplest form and in his wide knowledge of physics. His knowledge of mathematics was limited, but what he had he could use. He excelled at the flash of intuition, he was less successful at turning it into a steady flame. His most persistent attempt at an exhaustive study was of the quantum theory in its later form. His *Quantum theory* (1931), which was followed and preceded by a number of shorter and more popular expositions, was an attempt to expand the idea that one of two conjugate quantities, as position and momentum or time and energy, is meaningless without the other. He thought that the difficulty lay in the wrong things having been chosen as fundamental concepts — we ought to have used charge and action, not position and time — but he was not very successful in working this out, and a good deal of the book is just an expansion of Heisenberg's uncertainty principle. Cherwell was a true physicist in the sense that he demanded an intuitive theory, preferably one that could be visualized. He preferred statistical mechanics to thermodynamics in spite of his training with Nernst. It was natural for him to resent the purely mathematical formalism of orthodox wave mechanics, perhaps even he was right to do so, but he had nothing very effective to put in its place. The fact that he never worked on any one line, except on this impossibly difficult one for which his relative weakness in mathematics disqualified him, long enough to become wholly master of it, has reduced his reputation as a physicist, I think unfairly, but it was the defect of a quality which made him peculiarly well fitted for the two great achievements of his life, the work which he did in the war and afterwards as Churchill's scientific adviser, and the building up from almost nothing of the Clarendon school of physics.

APPENDIX III

Flying Bombs
Lord Cherwell's Predictions in December 1943,
and the Facts Revealed by the Raids in June 1944,

30th June 1944

Prime Minister

FLYING BOMBS

YOU ASKED me to look over my minute of the 18th December, 1943 and see how events and my present ideas fit in with it. I attach a table comparing where possible my forecasts with recent events.

These first figures were of course revised from time to time as fresh evidence came in showing gradual improvements in the new weapon. The revised estimates appeared as agreed figures in the C.O.S. reports, particularly C.O.S.(44) 46(o) and 276(o).

It must also be remembered that these original forecasts were made in a milieu in which 108,000 killed per month were being spoken of together with other improbable horrors (see the Home Secretary's minute to you of 4th August, 1943). Considering the difficulty of prophesying the details of an enemy secret weapon from a few aerial photos, some radar tracks and a certain amount of conflicting hearsay evidence, this preliminary note has proved much more accurate than I had any right to expect. It is of course much easier and safer to sit still and say nothing and then complain if others who tried to make some contribution were out in some degree.

P.S. Incidently in the first fortnight just over 700 flying bombs have entered the 700 square miles of the Greater London area, i.e. just about one per square mile. My guess that after the initial blitz about one bomb would explode within a half mile of the average Londoner once a fortnight has therefore not been very far out. Naturally some unlucky people have had a great many more whilst some have had a great many less.

Forecast — December 1943	*Actuality — June 1944*
1. There seems no reason to doubt that the ski sites are intended to store, assemble and launch jet-propelled aircraft travelling at about 400 miles an hour.	This, I think, was true. But the original ski sites were largely smothered by bombs and the actual attack has been delivered from a modified and less vulnerable type of site.
	Actual speeds have been 230–400 miles an hour.
2. I am inclined to believe that these are propelled not by some engine of the Whittle type but by some form of liquid fuel jet engine as used in the 293 glider bombs.	The engine actually used has been a totally novel intermittent jet type, most uneconomical in fuel but most ingenious in design.
3. If this view is right the useful load carried will be small, between one-third of a ton and one ton.	The actual weight of explosive carried is four-fifths of a ton.
(Page 4) If after all some form of (turbo-jet) engine is used, of course, the bomb-load might be greater, but it would certainly not exceed 4,000 pounds.	
4. The reliability of these aircraft at present seems to be low. There is good evidence that about one-third crash soon after launching, another third before they have gone three-quarters of the way and less than one-third go the whole 130 miles.	From December on there was a continuous slow improvement in the Baltic trials probably due to successive modifications, culminating in a loss of about one-eighth on launching. It seems probable that in operation today rather less than one-sixth crash

after launching. In the absence of defence measures, about two-fifths would crash on the way or around London and about two-fifths would fall within 10 miles of Charing Cross.

5. The average error is about 10 miles either way in the present experiments.

According to the Air Ministry Summary, the radius of the zone in which 80% of the flying bombs arriving in London have fallen has varied between 6 and 15 miles.

6. There are about 100 sites, so that unless they are interfered with, a salvo of 100 aircraft could be dispatched. It probably takes a good many hours to prepare each aircraft for launching but I should not exclude the possibility of two or three being got ready on each site and left standing in the open so as to have a good show on the opening day. Thereafter, if I were in the enemy's place, I should continue persistent harassing fire of say one aircraft on London every quarter of an hour. But unless the reliability of the weapon is much improved, less than one-quarter of these will get even within the 10 miles circle round the aiming point. We should have about 20 minutes warning of the salvo, but presumably there would be no point in having "warnings" and "all clears" for the harassing fire.

The Germans have attempted to build 88 ski sites and 57 modified sites. The maximum number of sites used has been about 40.

After the first 48 hours when 393 were fired, the average rate of fire from all sites has been one every 13 minutes. The enemy has however preferred to fire in small salvoes rather than in regular single shots and this has enabled the warning system to be retained.

As to accuracy, see para. 4 above.

7. If the warhead weighs one ton, the casualties to be expected will average 2–4 persons per aircraft reaching the London area.

It would have been better if in my December minute I had repeated the word *fatal* casualties which was obviously meant since notoriously one ton of bombs in a built-up area kills about three people.

This estimate of course corresponds to my remarks that broadly each aircraft fired would kill one person.

8. The storage capacity of each site would be at the most 20 aircraft. The complicated gyro-mechanism would probably limit large-scale production.

Nothing is yet known on these points.

9. From the state of the sites and because of the very unsatisfactory experiments in the Baltic I do not anticipate enemy action — certainly not full-scale — before March or April.

The attack began in June.

10. The destruction of these sites should not require an unmanageable bomber effort.

The destruction of a ski site on the average has required about 220 tons. (The more cunningly camouflaged modified sites have required more.)

A.D.G.B. countermeasures might conceivably destroy one-fifth of the flying bombs.

A.D.G.B. *claims* two-fifths of the number launched.

P.S. After the initial blitz I consider it will be unlikely that more than 3 aircraft per site will be dispatched per 24 hours.

Even after the initial blitz the rate per site per twenty-four hours has occasionally risen to five but the overall average has not been much more than three.

APPENDIX IV

Lord Cherwell and India

DURING THE SUMMER of 1943 the Prime Minister learned that our debt to India was rising at the rate of £1 million a day. He demanded an inquiry immediately and it was this that led to the appointment of the Committee on Indian Financial Questions of which Cherwell was a leading member. Indeed it was largely left to him to press for information and to try to inaugurate the kind of scrutiny that one normally regards as the role of the Treasury.

There was a surprising delay before the Treasury provided information about the headings under which the debt was accumulating and these headings were very broad ones. It was a reasonable inference that the Treasury was overburdened with work and Cherwell would not have been unsympathetic had it not also been so clear that effort was being wasted. About this time two Treasury officials arrived at Whitchurch in order to be able to assure the Chancellor that the services of the charwomen who cleaned the small officers' mess were paid by the officers themselves and not by the Ministry of Supply. Cherwell would have been just as outraged by this nonsense had it happened to any other research establishment. It was one instance, and not a solitary one, of the meticulous care with which the Treasury watched the expenditure of a few shillings a week in some directions while it was unable to give a reasonably detailed explanation of a rising indebtedness of £1 million a day.

The most startling fact unearthed by Cherwell himself at this time concerned the price of petrol. Under the Indian Financial Agreement, the U.K. reimbursed India for all expenditure on petrol, even if used for local defense, and the figure given under

371

this heading in one of the papers submitted to the Committee was £25 million for 1943–44. Cherwell's sharp eye spotted what everyone else had missed — that this implied a price of 2/5d. a gallon. His indignant query led to an inquiry in which it was first ascertained that, by mistake, the U.K. was being charged the Indian import duty; and the charge was then halved. Even at 1/5d. a gallon it was far too dear, and the second revelation was that the Treasury was being exploited by the oil companies who were charging f.o.b. Gulf of Mexico plus c.i.f. from there to India for petrol that came from Iran. An agreement had already been reached with the companies by which petrol was being supplied to the Middle East at about 7d. a gallon. Ultimately it transpired that the right figure was about £5 million, not £25 million, a saving for which Cherwell deserved, though he did not receive, the principal credit.

Apart from the debate about financial questions, Cherwell was deeply involved in the argument about India's need for imports of foodstuff. In 1943, the Government of India, strongly supported by Amery, the Secretary of State, was naturally very alarmed lest there should be a repetition of the Bengal famine. Unfortunately their request for half a million tons of grain would have had a very serious effect on the allied shipping program and would have affected military operations. Moreover, it could be held that if a real disaster were imminent even half a million tons would not avert it and it might be better to direct action against hoarding. The Government of India undoubtedly exaggerated probable requirements by assuming abnormally low crop yields. When normal yields were applied, prospects became more hopeful. The India Office, although very contemptuous about Cherwell's ability to forecast production, finally revised its own figures upward, and in the event his estimates proved to be nearer the truth. Some food was, of course, sent to India but not enough to disrupt the shipping program, and fortunately there was no repetition of the earlier disaster.

Cherwell was dissatisfied with the Indian financial arrangements for three reasons. First, he felt that the Agreement, drawn up on the assumption that Japan was neutral, had now become inappropriate and needed to be revised, a possibility contemplated in the Agreement itself. India was responsible for expenditure within India for local defense only; Britain met all expenditure beyond the Indian frontier, including the cost of Indian troops and all supplies obtained in India. All imported munitions, petrol and the like, were supplied free by Britain, including the supplies needed for local defense; Britain also contributed a large capital grant for the modernization of the Indian army. This sharing of the cost was less appropriate with Japan threatening India through Burma, and Cherwell felt that India should at least pay for all expenditure within her frontiers required for the South-East Asia Command. Even if it were thought unwise to propose a reallocation of expenditure already incurred, a revision of the Agreement would improve the position in the future.

The second reason for criticism was that the rupee was pegged at 1/6d. although inflation had been much more marked in India than in Britain. (The same point applied to Egyptian and to some other currencies.) Cherwell became involved in a prolonged debate about the proper value for a currency in which he showed a good deal more economic sophistication than his opponents.

Thirdly, he doubted whether contracting in India was satisfactory and pointed to profit margins twice as high on many items as in Britain. It proved extraordinarily difficult, however, to obtain the detailed information in London for a comprehensive report on contracts and his case could not be adequately supported.

What, in the end, did he achieve? The Financial Agreement was not changed and the debt continued to rise. As he foresaw, the sterling balances were a major source of trouble after the war. His warnings, like those of Keynes, had little effect. He may have been more successful to the extent that his inquisition caused the accounts to be more carefully scrutinized and contracting may also have been more closely watched. Here there is no direct evidence, but it seems likely that those once subjected to his searching inquiries would not wish to risk a repetition of the experience.

APPENDIX V

Some Defects of U.N.O.
(House of Lords, 11.12.56.)

WE ARE often told that U.N.O. is the only hope of the world for avoiding war, and, therefore, that we ought to believe that it must and will succeed in this laudable object. I wish I could see the logic of this. One might just as well say that if a man's only hope of avoiding bankruptcy is in winning a football pool, all right-thinking people ought to believe that he will do so. Somehow the proponents of U.N.O.'s infallibility have managed to persuade themselves that anyone who does not put his complete faith in the Organisation is not anxious to maintain peace — in fact is almost a warmonger. Some of them have reached a hysterical frame of mind in which merely to question whether U.N.O. will succeed in establishing peace in the world is considered wicked. No doubt I shall incur their severe displeasure, for what I intend to do is to analyse dispassionately the utility and value of this important — I said "important" not "impotent" — organisation.

First, what is this super-body to which we are to confide our fate? U.N.O. consists of some seventy-nine nations supposed to be sovereign and independent, though in some cases this is a somewhat dubious claim. They range from the giant powers, Soviet Russia and the United States, to tiny entities like Panama and Iceland. The population of the biggest is more than a thousand times greater than that of the smallest. The discrepancy in wealth and power is more than ten thousandfold. Yet in the Assembly, which is the ultimate governing body of U.N.O., each one has an equal vote. Thus barely 5 per cent of the world's population can carry the day against the other 95 per cent; and 10 per cent could claim a two-thirds majority in the Assembly. Or, to put

374

it another way, half the population of the world is represented by four delegates, and the other half by seventy-five delegates. What is more, these nations are represented in the Assembly by any group or body or individual which may succeed in seizing power.

There is, it is true, a so-called Credentials Committee. But it does not appear to be at all strict in making the delegates show that they represent the views of the majority or of any properly elected or selected Government. Anybody who has seized power — I believe, for instance, Mr. Kadar in Hungary — can, and does, send a delegate to vote on his behalf. In fact it is even worse than I have said, for these sovereign independent nations vary enormously in their standards of education and outlook. Some are the most highly civilised and educated countries on the planet. The inhabitants of others can scarcely read or write. Yet no attention is paid to this fact. Only recently there was a very close vote for the Vice-Presidency of the Assembly (I think it was between Italy and Liberia — Italy one of the oldest and most civilised cultures in history; Liberia, a small artificial State which has been in existence barely a hundred years, and very few of whose inhabitants have any conception of the outside world).

This is the Assembly, as I have said, the ultimate governing body of U.N.O. We were recently told that it is "the highest tribunal in the world," whose decisions all must obey without hesitation or question. As I have said, and, I hope, shown, the constitution of this body is utterly indefensible. If the vote of each nation were weighted in accordance with its population, there might be some semblance — though a very poor semblance — of logic in it. But this is not so, for the vote of 400 million Indians or 160 million Americans is equated to the vote of 4 million Bolivians or 100,000 Icelanders. Icelanders are admirable people, but I do not think the discrepancy between their culture and ours is as great as all that. And, of course, the 600 million inhabitants of Communist China have no vote at all. I do not suggest that weighting votes by populations would turn the Assembly into a tribunal. On the contrary, it would turn it into a sort of Volksgericht. The long and short of it is that justice cannot be found by counting the votes, however weighted, of interested parties.

This brings me to the word "tribunal," in the phrase "the highest tribunal in the world." Nothing could be more inept as a description of the Assembly. There is no pretence that it is a judicial body. No sworn evidence is taken or is obtainable; there is no judicial summing up, or any recognised body of law to which nations have an obligation to conform. The Assembly is split into a number of blocs. There are the Afro-Asian bloc, the South American bloc and the Iron Curtain bloc, the members of which tend to vote together on their likes and dislikes, in accordance with instructions from their home Government. No one pretends they are influenced by the evidence or the speeches. Practically always the repercussions it will have on the government's own position and interests decides which way a delegate votes: often votes are cast according to some bargain or arrangement; sometimes it is said they are to all intents and purposes peddled about. Judicial impartiality is the last thing that seems to matter. To describe a majority vote of such a body as "a decision of the highest tribunal in the world" is simply laughable. To pillory as criminal any nation which hestitates to comply with its decisions is monstrous. A judicial decision is one thing; a vote by a number of interested parties, without pretence of impartiality, without evidence or a body of laws to guide them is totally different.

Yet it is to this body that the Leader of the Opposition, only a few days ago, told us to say, "We obey you. We accept whatever you say." The absurdity of the constitution of the Assembly was, of course, recognised from the start by those framing the Charter of U.N.O. No nation could be expected to submit unquestioningly to such a body. Only if the great Powers were in agreement would there be any chance of its decisions being respected or enforced. If they were, it was hoped they could prevent small local wars among the minor Powers. If they were not, it was realised that it would be useless to expect the machine to operate.

To ensure this a sort of executive body, the Security Council, was instituted on which the five great Powers had permanent seats. Six more seats were allocated for two years at a time to other nations, selected by the Assembly. It is perhaps typical that, at the recent moment of crisis, apparently Siam presided over the meetings of the Security Council. According to the Charter, whilst the Assembly can recommend, only the Council can act. All the signatories of the Charter undertook to accept and carry out the decisions of the Council, but not those of the Assembly. Since what were at that time regarded as the five great Powers had a Veto in the Council, obviously action could never be taken against one of them, because no nation was under obligation to obey resolutions of the Assembly. This sensible intention appears now to have been cast aside.

When the Charter was concocted, the great Powers, with the exception of Germany, were allies, and it was hoped that their mutual good feeling and their common objectives would ensure that they would, in general, be in agreement. Unhappily, this idealistic hope was not fulfilled. Every time any controversial question arose, Russia interposed her Veto. Often she was alone, but usually any Iron Curtain country, which had managed to get elected to the Security Council by the Assembly, voting in the curious manner I have described, supported her. Russia applied her Veto, as I have said, on scores of occasions in the Security Council. No one seemed at all shocked. Our Left-Wingers regarded it as a more or less amiable idiosyncrasy, unfortunate but not to be taken amiss. England and France used the Veto on only one occasion, but the outcry, not only by the Fellow Travellers and Left-Wingers, but even by neutral ideologues, as Napoleon used to call them, has been deafening. There is a great deal that one could say about the special case that has caused so much stir but that would carry me too far.

In view of the persistent use of the Veto by Russia, a procedure was introduced which was not originally contained in the Charter of the United Nations. This consisted in convoking a special meeting of the Assembly and obtaining a recommendation in the desired sense by a two-thirds majority. Though no nation was, or is, under an obligation to obey such a resolution, this procedure could give a veneer of U.N.O. respectability to action which America or other nations desired to take against Russia's wishes. Now it has been invoked against us, and, of course, the considerable, and very vocal, body of people who always think England must be wrong have been howling about her delay in coming immediately to heel. Thousands of people have rushed into print, parading their alleged shame because we have failed instantly to obey a resolution passed by the Assembly — the world body voting on no known principle, actuated by the variegated principles which I have mentioned. They accuse us of breaking our word under the Charter. I do not suppose that 1 per cent of these people have read the Charter. If they had, they would have seen that we have never undertaken to obey the resolutions of the Assembly. I have not counted on how many occasions other nations have flouted Assembly resolutions. To do it seems to be the rule rather than the exception, and no one seems to worry very much. It is only when England fails to obey that the pack gives tongue.

*   *   *   *   *

I now turn to the question whether U.N.O. ever could work except if the Great Powers are unanimous in enforcing their will on the smaller nations. We are told that the intention is to substitute law for war; that that is, in essence, the whole object of the United Nations. It is another of those comfortable slogans expressing a desire felt by all of us in rhyming monosyllables, which seem to have an almost hypnotic effect. Of course, we all want the rule of law among nations; but what are the laws which we wish to rule? Evidently, it is not the laws accepted in principle for thousands of years — the fulfilment of contracts and the sanctity of treaties. Rather it seems to be commandments promulgated *ad hoc* by the Assembly whenever differences arise. That is submission to an arbitrary body. It is not law.

But even if this monstrous interpretation of the word "law" were taken, how is it to be enforced? As everybody knows, law is useless unless it is backed by a police force. It is no use magistrates finding a man guilty if they cannot compel him to make restitution or send him to prison if he refuses. Thus even if we accepted this weird U.N.O. body, with its odd form of voting, as the ultimate tribunal, it would be no good whatever unless it had some way of enforcing its decisions. We are told that in that case all we have to do is to endow U.N.O. with a police force. Indeed, my noble Leader seems to be greatly encouraged because a beginning has been made in doing this in the last few weeks. I think, on analysis, that this also is a case of wishful thinking.

A police force can operate because, on the whole, people are more or less equally strong, so that one policeman can arrest one man, and, again, because the proportion of criminals in the country is comparatively small, so that a police force of reasonable strength can cope with any gang it is likely to have to deal with. A U.N.O. police force would have a very different situation to confront. What sort of police force would be required to turn Russia out of Hungary, or America out of Formosa, should the Afro-Asian bloc, voting with the Latin-American or the Curtain countries, secure a vote to this effect in the Assembly?

We see how helpless U.N.O. is on the Suez Canal. Egypt, in flagrant breach of her Treaties, has blocked it from end to end. What has U.N.O. done about this? It has voted that Britain and France, who have troops available, should not intervene, and has sent a scratch selection of a few hundred soldiers from thirteen or fourteen different countries, speaking different languages, and without artillery or tanks, to preserve the peace. Even so, Colonel Nasser, who has refused again and again to obey U.N.O.'s behests, is allowed to dictate terms, to say what troops he will allow to form part of the police force and to decide when and where they should arrive and where they should be stationed. The so-called police force is merely a token which could be swept away by one brigade of Israelis and probably even by two or three divisions of Egyptians.

A police force, to be of any use, would have to be stronger than any nation or combination of nations. In fact, it would have to be more powerful than the Russian and American armies combined. How, otherwise, could it impose the will of U.N.O. in case those Powers happened to be on the same side? To contemplate such a huge force is, of course, simply absurd. It would cost at least £10,000 million a year to maintain; it would have to be backed by shipyards and factories capable of producing the fleets and aircraft, the arms and ammunitions, it required, which would cost thousands of millions more; and it would have to recruit many millions of men and train and officer them. On top of all this, nobody has explained where these gigantic armies, navies and air forces would be stationed, or how they would be transported. Once the facts are faced, I do not think anybody will seriously maintain that a police force capable of maintaining U.N.O.'s will on the Great Powers should they object, can be contemplated seriously. Nor, for my part, should I like to see it. For who would care to put an overwhelming military force at the disposal of an Assembly constituted and voting as I have described?

A new factor has come into the picture with the development of nuclear weapons. Any nation today which possesses hydrogen bombs can impose its will on any nation which has none. Though in the future there will be others, at present only two nations have a reasonable supply of these weapons, the United States and Russia. As long as they are on opposite sides, peace between them may be maintained, because each of them knows that a nuclear war would spell complete annihilation to one side or the other or, probably, to both. But if one of the two is uninterested or even lukewarm, the other can impose its will on any of the other nations of the world. For it is little use hoping that the opposing possessor of H-bombs, whatever his initial attitude, will come to the rescue in due course. There will not be any due course. In the last two world wars it was possible for America to waver for years before coming to a decision. Next time, the whole thing will be settled in a matter of days, perhaps even of hours.

Thus, all the nations, whatever they deem to be their status, must attach themselves to one or other of the H-bomb Powers. Unless they can get support from their protector, they will just have to give way. I do not think there is any means of escaping this painful conclusion. Nor is there any end in sight to this situation — nations glaring at one another and bluffing more or less successfully about their power and readiness to annihilate one another.

If force is ruled out, what about economic sanctions? The objection to these is that they can be applied only against some nations while others are immune. What is the use of enactments which can be enforced against one part of the community but not against the other? We, unhappily, are one of the nations most vulnerable to economic sanctions. But what would be the use of trying to impose them on Russia? Only nations which have built up an artificial economy, which depends upon the rule of law and upon the observance of the sanctity of treaties as it existed throughout the nineteenth century, are vulnerable to such sanctions. Autarchic systems are immune. Cutting off their imports or exports scarcely affects them. Napoleon discovered that 150 years ago.

Finally we are told that no nation can stand out against world opinion; that we can rely upon the moral forces of the Assembly's resolution. Surely this is more wishful thinking. What is more, it is flatly contradicted by experience. For several years now U.N.O. has condemned Egypt for refusing to allow the passage of Israel's ships through the Suez Canal in direct conflict with its obligations under the 1888 Treaty. Has the moral force of this condemnation had any effect on the Egyptians? None whatever. By a huge majority U.N.O. has called upon Russia to withdraw its troops from Hungary. Has the moral force of this resolution had any effect? Ask the Hungarians. If the Russians do not comply, we are told, they will be branded by the Assembly. The trouble is, that they have been branded already, and they do not seem to mind.

But, we are told, "Look at the great triumph of U.N.O. in stopping the North Koreans over-running the South Koreans." Nothing could be more misleading. America was able to obtain U.N.O.'s blessing for warlike action on that occasion simply owing to the fluke that the Russian delegate had retired from the Security Council in a sulk, so that he could not interpose his Veto in time. What would have happened if he had been present? The use of armed force would have been vetoed. Does anybody believe that the United States would simply have let events take their course and abandoned millions who had put their trust in them to be massacred? Of course not. With or without U.N.O.'s approval, they would have taken action; and quite right too. We should have thought less of them if they had flinched.

If all the nations in the world adopted Christian principles, of which there does not seem any immediate prospect, moral force might become effective. But this would happen only if nations had the feeling that they were being treated with justice. How can anyone talk of justice without sworn evidence and penalties for perjury, without the possibility of testing witnesses' statements by cross-examination? Even more important is that nations would have to be convinced that their case had been heard before an impartial tribunal and that the judges had given their verdict without fear or favour. Finally, it would be essential for the nations to be convinced that they were all equal before the law and that judgment would be enforced upon everybody, great or small. As I have explained, none of these vital conditions is fulfilled by U.N.O. in its present form, and I question whether, in the state of mind obtaining in nearly all the countries of the world today, with their inflamed ideas of national sovereignty and dignity, any system can be invented which would fulfil these essential conditions. My view is that it is nonsense to demand that nations should submit their vital interests to the decision of a body constituted in such an absurd manner as the General Assembly of U.N.O. Any Government which did so would be neglecting its duty. Civilisation is built up on the basis that contracts and treaties must be, and will be, observed. As I have said, the United Kingdom relies for its very existence on this principle.

We depend, unhappily, to a great extent upon imports of oil. We may have been foolish to allow our industries and national life generally to develop in this way, but it has happened. We cannot allow our people to go cold and hungry just because some people who claim to speak for world opinion have suddenly arbitrarily introduced some novel concept of national sovereignty which apparently permits the Government of any country, at its own sweet will, to repudiate its obligations and refuse to honour its promises. In the old days the victims of such maltreatment would have insisted upon its rights, if necessary by armed force. But this, we are told, is quite out of fashion. It would be "gunboat diplomacy." We must not use force: we must negotiate. You might as well say that, if someone snatches your watch in the

street, you must not resist, much less take it back. You must
negotiate with him. I suppose that, if you are lucky, you may
recover the chain. If I believed that the Socialist leaders, who
presumably one day will have charge of the nation's affairs — I
hope not for a long time — could not grasp this simple train of
reasoning, I should despair of the future of this country. Of
course it is no doubt tempting to snatch a Party advantage by
making sanctimonious speeches, and generally by taking what
purports to be the high moral line in these matters; but it really
shocked me that, when it was suggested in another place that the
Government spokesman had in mind the protection of our oil
supplies, he was greeted with boos and jeers. The Government
actually, it seems, were trying to safeguard the vital interests of
their country. What a terrible accusation!

It is easy for the Socialist Party, in Opposition, to take such a
line. They do not seem to mind very much whether we have two
or three million unemployed, and our people suffer from cold and
other distresses, so long as they can blame the Government. They
seem to think it quite all right that we should be at the mercy
of what the noble Viscount, Lord Bruce of Melbourne, called a
"tin-pot dictator"; that he should be free to impose petrol rationing
and other hardships on 200 million Europeans who have spent
centuries fighting for freedom from tyranny. They say that all
we should do is to chant in unison the magic syllables "U.N.O.,
U.N.O." although they know perfectly well that it never has availed,
and never will avail, to compel a nation protected by a powerful
friend, preferably with a Veto, to honour its obligations. As things
have developed, U.N.O. is used as a device behind whose gim-
crack façade a thief can shelter as long as he contents himself
with stealing from nations which can be prevented from retaliating
by one of the two great Powers.

To sum up, I do not think that U.N.O., at any rate in its present
form, can work. The governing body, the Assembly, consists of
a heterogeneous collection of so-called sovereign States, some of
which are thousands of times more numerous than others, and tens
of thousands of times more powerful and wealthy. Some of them
are highly civilised; others are all but illiterate. Yet they all have

an equal vote. Their decisions are given with no attempt at impartiality. They act on no known laws and have no rules of evidence. Their decisions can be enforced only if supported by at least one of the States with a store of H-bombs, provided that it is not faced with another State with an equally devastating store of weapons. Economic sanctions can be put into effect only by certain States against certain States. Others are immune. The moral force of public opinion has been proved to be utterly ineffective, even in cases of petty States like Egypt or Albania.

In these circumstances, nations, especially those dependent upon the sanctity of treaties and contracts for their survival, cannot be expected to entrust their fate unconditionally to U.N.O. It is an organisation which can be exploited by nations who wish to break the law, provided that they have powerful friends who will interpose on their behalf. It is a conception which we all wish could work, but it is plain to see that it cannot. It is high time that these facts should be stated plainly, unhappy as they are; otherwise, we may continue to be forced into a false sense of security and hope by the eloquent, ardent and often high-minded, but, I fear, misguided, advocates of this forlorn experiment in idealism.

What I have said will, I fear, arouse indignation in some quarters. That is always the way when comfortable emotional beliefs which cannot be sustained by evidence on logical grounds are challenged. The magic syllables "U.N.O." have acquired the status of an invocation, almost of a prayer. To cast doubt on the Organisation is considered akin to blasphemy. The role of the iconoclast is always hateful, but facts and logic cannot simply be brushed aside. I therefore think it my duty, as one not linked with the Government, and still less with the Opposition, to refuse to foster what I believe to be a dangerous delusion which is rapidly becoming a snare. Noble Lords are entitled to hear the facts. I only hope that they will ponder them dispassionately. For sooner or later we shall be compelled to face them.

APPENDIX VI

A Note on the Lindemann
Family Records

THE LINDEMANN FAMILY came from Alsace-Lorraine and F.A.'s father, Adolphus Frederick Lindemann, was born at Langenburg in the Palatinate on May 13, 1846. His grandfather was born at the castle of Jaegersburg on what was then French soil and so also was his grandfather's brother Chrétien Philippe Adolphe, Comte et Baron de Lindemann. He was born on November 30, 1811 and died in Paris, where he had lived nearly all his life, on May 2, 1886.

This enterprising uncle of F.A.'s father had migrated from the Palatinate to Paris when quite a young man and had married a wealthy Mademoiselle Fabre of the shipping line. She died in giving birth to a son, Charles Jules Adolphe, on November 17, 1847. This son remained unmarried and adopted F. A. Lindemann's elder brother, Charles Lionel Lindemann, who was his heir (*légataire universel*). He was head of the family and, when he died on April 18, 1929, left considerable property.

After the death of his first wife, Chrétien Philippe Adolphe married a Mademoiselle Flore Aimée Hermengilde Deleville (sometime de Leville, probably changed during the French Revolution), born on July 28, 1826, who died in Paris on April 30, 1905, at her house in the Champs Elysées. She owned a considerable property at Merignies in the north of France.

With his fortunes firmly established, Chrétien Philippe accepted some minor diplomatic post at the Court of Francis II, Roi des Deux Siciles, whom he would not abandon when he was besieged and had to capitulate at Gaeta on February 12, 1861. As he is supposed to be the only diplomat who remained with Francis II to the end he was fond of saying that he had been the Doyen of the Diplomatic Corps of the Royaume des Deux Siciles. One of Francis II's last actions before capitulating was, on February 6, 1861, to confer the hereditary title of "Conde" on Chrétien Philippe Adolphe. On February 11, 1875, he had a more substantial title conferred upon him by Ludwig II, King of Bavaria, namely the hereditary title of Baron and Freiherr (see *Almanac de Gotha Freiherrenbuch,* which also contains the title of "Conde"). Just ten years afterward the King of Bavaria became insane and drowned himself in the Starnberger Lake. When F. A. Lindemann became a peer these records were investigated by the College of Heralds and he chose the existing old family arms.

F.A.'s mother was beautiful, forceful and well-off. Her British-born father's name was Noble. He was a gifted and much-traveled engineer. Olga Noble was born in New London, Connecticut, on January 3, 1851 and died at Sidmouth, Devon, on January 11, 1927.

Her first marriage at the age of seventeen was to a Mr. Davidson, a wealthy banker, by whom she had two daughters and a son. After his death she married A. F. Lindemann, F.A.'s father, by whom she had three sons and a daughter. F.A. was the second son.

F.A.'s elder brother, Charles Lionel, was a keen experimental physicist who did a good deal of scientific work with him, but after his adoption by the head of the family, his father's first cousin, who had a lot of French property and lived in Paris, he was inevitably drawn into a more worldly orbit and married the beautiful Mademoiselle Marie Madeleine de Lagotellerie.

James, the third brother, known to the family as Sepi, was an endearing but hopeless spendthrift. His mother had thoroughly spoilt him in his early youth and his father could deny him nothing. He was often a sad trial to his brothers but had innumerable friends on the Riviera, where he was extremely popular in the bars and night clubs and had a lovely little Villa called "le Nid Bleu" overlooking Villefranche Harbor. He was an extraordinary linguist, which enabled him to play a very useful part during the Second World War.

F.A. grew up in an atmosphere of ease and affluence as his

parents' joint income amounted to fifteen or twenty thousand pounds, which was for those days considerable. His father had some part in the construction and laying of the early Atlantic cables, besides which he owned the waterworks of two towns in the Palatinate, which he had built after financing them in London. One supplied the capital, Speyer, and the other a sizable manufacturing town called Pirmasens.

F.A.'s father had emigrated to England from the Palatinate when a young man of about twenty and had settled there for the rest of his life and become naturalized.

Index